STUDIES IN CHANGE

A Book of the Short Story

PRENTICE-HALL INTRODUCTION TO LITERATURE SERIES

Maynard Mack, Editor

PRENTICE-HALL INTERNATIONAL, INC., *London*
PRENTICE-HALL OF AUSTRALIA, PTY., LTD., *Sydney*
PRENTICE-HALL OF CANADA, LTD., *Toronto*
PRENTICE-HALL OF INDIA (PRIVATE), LTD., *New Delhi*
PRENTICE-HALL OF JAPAN, INC., *Tokyo*

Hugh Kenner

Professor of English
University of California
Santa Barbara

STUDIES IN CHANGE

A Book of the Short Story

———

PRENTICE-HALL, INC.   ENGLEWOOD CLIFFS, N.J.

Second printing.........August, 1965

Library of Congress Catalog Card No.: 65-10148

Printed in the United States of America
[85844-C]

INTRODUCTION

— 1 —

Narrative, the recital of a chain of happenings, has held the Western imagination since Homer the Singer of Tales: it is the oldest creative use of language of which record remains. Five of us (says Odysseus) drove the smoking pole down into the Cyclops' eye; and as my weight bore it down they twisted it to and fro, as shipwrights drill a timber, till his eye's blood boiled up around the burning wood, and his eye-strings crackled in the heat. . . .—a sailor's tale, told in port. Or the hunter in the Grettir Saga tells how he knocked off balance the bear at the cliff edge, lopping one of its paws with his axe. A tale is a thing told; *tale* and *tell* are nearly the same word; there are marvels in the world, says the tale-teller, which, having known them, I can bring before your mind, if you will surrender yourself to my voice. My voice shall be your summons to belief. I shall relive the thing again in the telling, and shall talk as I relive it, and it shall be as if I were making the words up as I go along. I shall make you see what I see, and feel what I feel; we shall be astonished together, terrified together, valorous together. I shall submit myself again, for your enjoyment and my own, to dangers once already undergone (do not tax me with being a great liar), and no one, when we come past the crisis of the tale, shall see the Cyclops safely blinded, or the bear disabled, with more relief than I. Once upon a time. . . .

His art, in tavern or bivouac, by a small night fire or on the deck of a ship, wherever men have time to kill and attention to divert, is always the same: to unite our imaginations, instant by instant, with events made real. His art is at the core of the story-writer's art; but the short story is something different. *Story* is nearly the same word as *history*: a methodical record, something with system to it, very likely not told but written down; and the writing reread, and revised and improved. In it, happenings are related—but more than that, something is examined. Many a short story, but no tale, is a kind of case history. The genre as we understand it today was developed within a century or less, in a time of careful recording. Its authority is no longer the narrator's voice, but the relevance of a set of facts.

We can see its elements in Samuel Johnson's "Ned Druggett" (1758), which compresses two stories into a mere thousand words. The stories are told simultaneously. They comprise the same events, rotate about the same man, and are told, moreover, in the same words. One is the success story of a remnant dealer who by courtesy, diligence, and application—good mercantile virtues—rises unspoiled to prosperity and a country house. The other is a tale of mounting and pathetic illusion. Ned's friends in the old days would see him take his only recreation, which was "to stand at his own door and look into the street," for he was putting every penny into the business. And when he has grown rich enough to go some hours every week to his lodging in the country, knowing that "when a man advances in life he loves to entertain himself sometimes with his own thoughts," then to his old friends he recommends the pleasures of Meditation, for he has been "all the morning at the window, counting the carriages as they passed before him."

Ned has ended substantially where he began, only more prosperous and more deeply entoiled in illusion. This second story is one that can be told of him, but it is not one that he would be in a position to tell, for it never occurs to him to doubt that he is happy. Johnson, moreover, tells it in such a way that not a word of his account would offend or disillusion Ned. He does not hint or wink, however; he tells it, firmly and clearly, to anyone sensitive to the notation of his careful prose, from the moment when, informing us that in his penurious days Ned's only recreation was to look into the street, he places an enhancing capital letter on Recreation. A few lines later, we are told that Ned's reputation soon extended "from one end of the street to the other" in exactly the tone, and exactly the form of words, that would speak of fame spreading from China to Peru. Careful phrase by careful phrase the chronicle proceeds, rehearsing only facts, but balancing Ned's view of them against another view, until we are ready to respond to the rich tragicomedy of the climax. This climax is contained in eight deliberate words, epitome of a life forever managed, forever kept prudently free of impulse, ardor, rashness, joy: "But at last he resolved to be happy." Everything else in Ned's life it has been plausible, nay admirable, that he should make resolutions about, but not this. The resolved happiness occupies a single paragraph, pregnant with paradoxes Johnson is too scrupulous to underline—the fresh air, and the closed window; quiet and contemplation, and elevation to the highest dignities of a Shopkeeper; the pleasures of Meditation, and the counting of carriages; and not least, the pleasures of meditation, and Ned's need to convince invited guests that these pleasures are real, and that he really experiences them.

As in the tale, every sentence is made up of facts: things said, things done. But the Story invites us, indeed, unless we are going to find it pointless, *requires* us, to consider how differently people may value the same set of facts. This is perhaps the minimum formula for the short story, that it is concerned with how experiences are valued: not merely what was said and done, but what difference it made to someone. Men move through affairs they only partly understand, says the story-writer; I narrate this affair as carefully as I can, so that you can see why it matters: what someone learned or failed to learn, felt or did not feel, saw or failed to see; and you who read, if you read well, will at the end understand better than anyone; better even, perhaps, than I.

— 2 —

It follows that the short story has no set form, no set procedure. It may use a show of careful documentation, or it may not even tell us the principal character's name. It may start with setting, or with action, or with conversation. It may end when activity ends, or it may meditate after the ending of activity. The real action may commence in the reader's mind, after he has lifted up his eyes from the last words on the last page. The contract between reader and writer is simple and contains only two clauses. The writer will import no irrelevancies, the reader will give his undivided attention. These are, of course, complementary stipulations.

James Joyce, who wrote only fifteen short stories before he abandoned the form forever at twenty-five, pared off irrelevances by so heroic an effort that one could learn almost the whole discipline of responsive reading from the text of *Dubliners*. "The Boarding House" begins, "Mrs. Mooney was a butcher's daughter." She is the moral center of the story, yet we are to hear her speak only twelve words, learn only three details of her appearance, and never be told her first name at all. This means that for the purposes of the story she is a being with no first name; which means that no one ever speaks to her intimately; which means that she is the kind of woman she is. "She was a woman who was quite able to keep things to herself: a determined woman." That is the second sentence of the story, and it sets in motion just the two qualities of Mr. Mooney that will shape the story's course. "She had married her father's foreman and opened a butcher's shop near Spring Gardens." That is the third sentence, and we note that the subject of both verbs is "she," and that with formidable economy of effort she has found both husband and vocation near at hand. In another fifty crisp words we learn of her husband's wrecked life, and may surmise what drove him to drink. By the end of the first paragraph, in fact, we have the outline of one possible short story, a pathetic one, but not the one

Joyce is telling. He has sketched it in simply to place the fate of Bob Doran, with which our story deals, in a pattern of such fates. Mrs. Mooney is accustomed to dealing with men; men exist to be dealt with. Finding Polly a husband will take a little dealing.

Unlike her mother, Polly Mooney is shown to us:

> Polly was a slim girl of nineteen; she had light soft hair and a small full mouth. Her eyes, which were grey with a shade of green through them, had a habit of glancing upward when she spoke with anyone, which made her look like a little perverse madonna.

We are given this description of Polly midway through the story's survey of the boarding-house arrangements; that is the Polly anyone in the boarding house may see. Later in the story, when the trap has been firmly closed around Bob Doran, we are shown the Polly he remembers once seeing:

> It was her bath night. She wore a loose open combing jacket of printed flannel. Her white instep shone in the opening of her furry slippers and the blood glowed warmly behind her perfumed skin. From her hands and wrists too as she lit and steadied her candle a faint perfume arose.

It is delicate, vivid, suffused with the romance of propinquity; yet it is quite as brief as the earlier, the public description: as if Mr. Doran had really been granted no more than the boarders, merely granted it at less distance. The white instep, the perfume, the glow: these are his poor souvenirs of passion, now that his fate is being arranged downstairs. His future will consist of married intimacy with these details.

There is one more description of Polly:

> Then she dried her eyes and went over to the looking glass. She dipped the end of the towel in the water jug and refreshed her eyes with the cool water. She looked at herself in profile and readjusted a hairpin above her ear. Then she went back to the bed again and sat at the foot.

This is Polly as seen by herself, and she sees . . . next to nothing. "She looked at herself in profile and adjusted a hairpin above her ear." This is what we are shown of Mr. Doran's future; this is perhaps all there is to show: much self-communion, many profiles, many adjusted hairpins: and always, like the smell of a butcher shop, the suffusing presence of the bride's mother.

Fiction works in this way, including only what it has uses for. A television writer, by contrast, would have to cope with the fact that the camera sees everything that passes in front of it, sating our eyes with a blonde actress, grossly *there,* and so unable to render the selective romance, the poor brief sensual frugality, of Mr. Doran's remembered passion. Decisions about costumes, about furniture, about the faces of the accessory characters, about all the thousand things that would crowd into a visual presentation whether they were useful or not, would occupy the minds of everyone concerned with such a production, and the story would become a different story entirely. The mechanism by which Mr. Doran is trapped it could render very well. What it would not be able to render is the poverty of what he has to remember, and the aura of feminine mysteriousness, invading Bob Doran's virginal sensibility, to which that sketchiness of presentation corresponds.

Joyce does not delude his readers with that mysteriousness. He helps us understand how Mr. Doran apprehends it. Others clearly do not. Mrs. Mooney does not. The affair is presented from Mrs. Mooney's point of view in just fifteen words: ". . . she noticed that something was going on between Polly and one of the young men." It is told from Mr. Doran's at greater leisure, but he has pathetically little to cling to: that single vision in the hallway, a few hurried vignettes of considerateness, some kisses, and, for climax, "He remembered well her eyes, the touch of her hand, and his delirium. . . ." The dots are Joyce's. The next words are, "But delirium passes." That is all; it is with delicate, inarticulate feelings, stifled longings, indeterminable futures, that Mrs. Mooney is trafficking so blandly; and, setting down only the phrases that are necessary to contain this pathos, with its large margin of the unspeakable and the unspoken, Joyce can even specify the climate of the fateful day—

> It was a bright Sunday morning of early summer, promising heat, but with a fresh breeze blowing. . . .

—and have a use for the Sunday, the summer, the breeze, and the promise of heat. For Bob Doran, summoned before The Madam's gaze, heat will shortly be more than a promise.

— 3 —

If "The Boarding House" were a play, the climactic scene would be Mrs. Mooney's interview with hapless Bob. A playwright would be *forced* into writing such a scene: His medium demands confrontations and speeches. The story writer has a choice. Joyce chose to leave Mr. Doran at the foot of the stairs and wait out the interview with Polly above. The story ends,

> She waited on patiently, almost cheerfully, without alarm, her memories gradually giving place to hopes and visions of the future. Her hopes and visions were so intricate that she no longer saw the white pillows on which her gaze was fixed or remembered that she was waiting for anything.
> At last she heard her mother calling. She started to her feet and ran to the banisters.
> "Polly! Polly!"

"Yes, mamma?"
"Come down, dear. Mr. Doran wants to speak to you."
Then she remembered what she had been waiting for.

These are the last words of the story which began, "Mrs. Mooney was a butcher's daughter"; a story which commences with three hundred words on the purposeful maneuvers of the mother and ends by dwelling for two hundred words on the reveries of the daughter. The story is not "about" Bob Doran. Its movement, from the mother's youth to the daughter's, has simply defined itself by dealing with Bob Doran, almost in passing, as an undertow deals with a swimmer. It is with Polly, not with him, that we spend the last sentences. Her passivity balances her mother's purposefulness, the purposefulness from which she is now benefiting. And benefiting with how much insight into what is going on? With some, certainly; we have already been told that "in her wise innocence she had divined the intention behind her mother's tolerance." She assumes, apparently, that this is how the world runs; it is of such maneuvers that happiness is fabricated. Will she herself be so successful a mother? Probably not. Is she her mother's complaisant puppet? Not quite. She can lose herself in "hopes and visions of the future"; a little earlier, her arms about Bob's neck, she has spoken of putting an end to herself.

We may define Joyce's story, then, as just what is necessary to unlock the meaning contained in that final scene. It exists to explicate the meaning of "Hopes and visions of the future," or perhaps of "Then she remembered what she had been waiting for." Joyce was so conscious of building his stories toward such moments that he employed in his notebooks a technical term, *epiphany,* a showing-forth, in wry allusion to the eternal moment, annually celebrated in the Christian liturgy, when the First Cause of the world was shown in a stable to visitors from distant lands. Joyce had a programmatic interest in this notion. His stories build toward a static moment in part because Dublin is "the center of Irish paralysis," in which whatever happens merely underlines the harsh fact that nothing can happen. He was satisfying, however, structural needs as well. For we want a narrative to end because something in it has paused, resolved, changed, settled down, or declared its significance, rather than because the narrator has simply decided to stop. Aristotle spoke of plots requiring a beginning, a middle, and an end. Long ones may be allowed to stop of their own weight; but to end a brief narrative without suggesting that you are merely pausing before the next episode is a considerable imaginative feat. To arrange that a certain moment, or sentence, or scene, shall supply when we come to it the reason for the rest of the story's existence is one way to give the story a reason for ending where it does, and the reader's imagination a point of rest. It also helps clarify whatever inner logic has chosen all the rest of the things that went into the story: the sentences, glimpses, persons, encounters, sayings.

This center of gravity will not usually be found among the very last words; the story will generally run on a little past it, though with altered force of implication. It is often the moment when we find we have been attending not to a yarn but to a parable. "Ned Drugget" alters with "at last he resolved to be happy." William Carlos Williams' "The Use of Force" is transformed at the words "One goes on to the end," a consulting-room narrative having suddenly turned into a study of violence finding reasons for itself. Lawrence ends "The Shadow in the Rose Garden" not with the conventional shock of the mad lover, but with husband and wife glaring like wary animals. ("It would be violation to each of them to be brought into contact with the other.")

— 4 —

Or the story may turn on the moment when someone in the story arrives at insight. Miranda in Katherine Anne Porter's "The Grave" is obscurely disengaged from a nine-year-old's world of simple maxims, simple pleasures, by the sight of unborn rabbits: "Paul said cautiously, as if he were talking about something forbidden: 'They were just about ready to be born.'" And then Paul pledges her to secrecy.

> Miranda never told, she did not even wish to tell anybody. She thought about the whole worrisome affair with confused unhappiness for a few days. Then it sank quietly into her mind and was heaped over by accumulated thousands of impressions, for nearly twenty years. One day she was picking her path among the puddles and crushed refuse of a market street in a strange city of a strange country, when without warning, plain and clear in its true colors as if she looked through a frame upon a scene that had not stirred nor changed since the moment it happened, the episode of that far-off day leaped from its burial place before her mind's eye. . . .

"Its burial place"—deliberate phrase—recalls the vacant graves the children had explored just before the episode of the rabbit, and we are within a few sentences of a still more explicit recall. For she had not wholly obliterated that day in her memory: it was

> the day she had remembered always vaguely until now as the time she and her brother had found treasures in the opened graves.

They had moved then like innocent archaeologists in that humble Texas Mycenae, finding a gold ring and a dove-shaped coffin-screw in "the pit that had held her grandfather's bones." The past, her own family's past, its ardor, blood, and generation, has become, as old cities become, a pit holding a few incorruptible trinkets. In the same way now, in the strange city, the past she carries buried in her mind yields that indestructible, disturbing memory: the mysteries of birth springing inviolable from the loam of a metaphorical death. The whole story resembles a ritual which its participants enact without understanding what it means.

In the same way the children in Eudora Welty's "Moon Lake" enact a resurrection story, more explicitly the story of the musician Orpheus bringing Eurydice up from the shades, without any of them knowing that such a tale has been told for 3,000 years; and the protagonist of Hemingway's "After the Storm" struggles as though in a dream to enter a sunken world, while the dead lady's face looks up at him through underwater glass. He supposes that he is trying to scavenge a wreck, for money, as Miss Welty's children suppose that they are experiencing near-disaster at a summer camp; but the practical doings of each story are submerged in a ritual form, to move a reader toward wonder. Hemingway forces his story to spread about in our minds as a kind of dream by carefully withholding all comprehension from the protagonist. He has been outraged by his experience, but he is not haunted by it as we may be. "I found her and I never got a nickel out of her," he iterates; and he speculates on how so big a ship, "as big as the whole world," would have had to go down in such a gale, its captain not being free to "scud" like a lone scavenger in a little boat. The story's insight is ours, not his, and so is most of the wonder.

It is perhaps because the form, in its delicate economy, lends itself so readily to vignettes of people enacting more than they know, that so many short-story writers have chosen to write of children, outcasts, loners, provincial beings. The Irish storyteller Frank O'Connor has gone so far as to suggest that the proper province of the short story is some submerged population, and has accounted on this ground for the way it has flourished in locked-in cultures: Ireland, Czarist Russia, the American rural South. Perhaps more to the point, writers in such places have had a tradition of folk narrative available to them, as a structure to mimic: and one thing anthropologists have told us over and over about the folk tale is that it verges on the myth. The mythic dimension and the folk tale's narrative method perhaps come into the short story together. Faulkner's "Was" imitates the way stories get told by people who talk them out in a vast leisure to other people who already know, more or less, who all the protagonists are. He would be false to his method if he introduced characters quietly, one by one, with the kind of expert economy by which a magazine writer assists his readers' attention. We are plunged at once into the milieu of people listening to gossip about their neighbors or their neighbors' ancestors. And "Was," with its fox kept in the house for convenience of fox hunting, is an outrageous tall tale, and its card games expand before the mind into heroic encounters between men who are making all history—at any rate all the history that is relevant to them, estates, slaves, daughters in a world as vast as it needs to be, touching no other world—depend on the outcome of an ordeal or an encounter at arms, as in the tale of Troy or the legend of St. George.

— 5 —

For in so economical a form every sentence is apt to be immersed in time. "Then again he turned to survey the bedroom windows overlooking the garden," writes Lawrence after detaining us for two paragraphs with his "rather small young man." "He started, seeing a woman's figure; but it was only his wife." These words have been dipped in the bitter tensions of their marriage. Each sentence, in fact, in the opening paragraphs of "The Shadow in the Rose Garden" brings onto the page some psychic tension from a past of which we are told no more than we need to know.

> In a state of self-suppression, he went through into the garden. His jacket, however, did not look dejected. It was new, and had a smart and self-confident air, sitting upon a confident body.

He has just been surprised by the vigor of his own features in a mirror, as though he had some secret reason to doubt that vigor; and now the new jacket suggests a recent occasion for presenting a new front to the world. By this time the malaise of a man impatiently looking at his watch on a summer morning has made contact with some deeper malaise; he strolls with forced nonchalance, but a dozen small turns of phrase suggest his doubt as to his capacity to belong. We are to learn, later, many more details of his marriage: he is a laboring electrician from a coal mine, his wife feels superior to him, they are vacationing where (it turns out) she is drawn by the memory of a former lover. This sort of detail is folded casually into the conversations of one day, instead of taking its place in a chronological narrative that would begin with the wife's former amatory adventure. The result is not simply economy, but meaning. For the husband, as much as for us, the present is mysteriously saturated in significances his wife understands better than he; and the mixture of impatience and possessiveness that drives him to bully the tale out of her derives, within the story, much of its energy from the reader's own urge to know. We simultaneously want the information he wants, and are exacerbated by his tactics. In so enlisting the reader's normal curiosity, Lawrence has a knack of involving the reader with the meannesses in which Laurentian fiction specializes.

The events in Wyndham Lewis' "Time the Tiger" are also saturated in a past, but a *public* past: A time of shirt buttons that stayed on, scissors that cut, telephones that worked, tokens of comfort remembered out of a postwar shabbiness. Long though the story dwells among such irritations, it is occupied not with them but with two people. Its first concern is to establish the texture of lives saturated with the motifs of political argument, in a great modern state whose day-to-day operations have grown sufficiently inefficient to invade everyone's consciousness. Politics, Lewis implies, is to modern man as water to fish; and fish grow aware of water only when it is polluted. One man, Mark, regards the ambient shabbiness as the birth-time of a brave new world; the other man, Charles, as the doing of a crew of rascally planners. The two, being old friends, can keep their disagreement upon a plane of amicable discussion (partly because Mark, the socialist, cannot deny that the irritations are there), until a final scene which Lewis, in defiance of every textbook on narrative economy, delays until he has deployed enough documentation for a young novel. When the explosion occurs three lives are ruined: public affairs have suddenly invaded not merely the sphere of personal comfort but the citadel of personal happiness. For the story is *about* the power mundane detail, and the rationalizations to which, in a modern state, it gives rise, can exert over human lives.

A form that can support such diverse manifestations as "Ned Drugget," "Time the Tiger," "The Grave," "The Shadow in the Rose Garden"; that can manage its affairs as complexly as Henry James' "The Tone of Time" or as sparsely as Samuel Beckett's "Stones," will not submit to tidy definition. There is clearly no such thing as an ideal short story to which the patterns of these stories and a hundred others imperfectly approximate. It is too young a form to have been submitted to the great critical codifiers of the seventeenth and eighteenth centuries, who have left us with certain notions of normal poems and normal dramas, from which the *avant garde* may be more or less successfully, if not very usefully, distinguished. Perhaps this much can be said: the short story is a study of change. Something, at its end, is irrevocably other. Perhaps this otherness is explicit: Bob Doran forever caught, The Pupil forever dead; perhaps it is latent, as when the narrator of "Stones" gives himself to the frenzies of System but quickly loses interest in System's deliverances; perhaps it is only a change we undergo ourselves. To be learning something, said Aristotle, is the chief human pleasure; and when a short story works as the best stories can, we learn more, irrevocably more, of what men and women can do and suffer, and of what their doing and suffering can mean.

HUGH KENNER

A NOTE ON THE SELECTIONS

These are not offered as the twenty-five Best Short Stories, but as twenty-five stories sufficiently varied to display the extensiveness both of the genre and of the modes of mastery it can accommodate.

Nor are the stories necessarily "typical" of their authors. Some prolific writers—Lawrence and Faulkner especially—project through their fictions a world on which any single story affords only a misleadingly partial view. In such cases I have sought neither the best nor the quintessential story, but one which is reasonably self-contained.

Numerous European masters, for instance Chekhov and Turgenev, are not represented because only extensive reading can help the foreign student intuit effects the available translations muffle and disperse.

The arrangement of the book is meant to permit profitable comparison of any two adjacent stories. Of course, many other comparisons are possible. The headnotes are meant not to control the reader's attention but to nudge it, often by supplying information.

CONTENTS

STUDIES IN CHANGE

A Book of the Short Story

Samuel Johnson (1709–1784)

NED DRUGGET

Drugget *is a coarse woolen cloth used for floor coverings; a* Comfit *is a piece of candied fruit. As these names imply, Johnson, to whose generation the term "short story" was unknown, conceived himself to be working in the very old tradition of the* exemplum, *or moral tale; but the author's good nature, and the techniques of careful documentation in which his age was schooling itself, enabled him to withhold the explicit moral and fashion instead a small gem of ironic narrative. How early are you sure that you are not reading an uncomplicated success story? Does this knowledge come as a surprise?*

I paid a visit yesterday to my old friend *Ned Drugget*, at his country-lodgings. *Ned* began trade with a very small fortune; he took a small house in an obscure street, and for some years dealt only in remnants. Knowing that *light gains make a heavy purse,* he was content with moderate profit; having observed or heard the effects of civility, he bowed down to the counter edge at the entrance and departure of every customer, listened, without impatience, to the objections of the ignorant, and refused, without resentment, the offers of the penurious. His only Recreation was to stand at his own door and look into the street. His dinner was sent him from a neighbouring Alehouse, and he opened and shut the shop at a certain hour with his own hands.

His reputation soon extended from one end of the street to the other, and Mr. *Drugget*'s exemplary conduct was recommended by every master to his apprentice, and by every father to his son. *Ned* was not only considered as a thriving trader, but as a man of Elegance and Politeness, for he was remarkably neat in his dress, and would wear his coat threadbare without spotting it; his hat was always brushed, his shoes glossy, his wig nicely curled, and his stockings without a wrinkle. With such qualifications it was not very difficult for him to gain the heart of Miss *Comfit*, the only daughter of Mr. *Comfit* the confectioner.

Ned is one of those whose happiness marriage has increased. His wife

From *The Idler* (July 29, 1758).

1

had the same disposition with himself, and his method of life was very little changed, except that he dismissed the lodgers from the first floor, and took the whole house into his own hands.

He had already, by his parsimony, accumulated a considerable sum, to which the fortune of his wife was now added. From this time he began to grasp at greater acquisitions, and was always ready, with money in his hand, to pick up the refuse of a Sale, or to buy the Stock of a Trader who retired from business. He soon added his parlor to his shop, and was obliged, a few months afterwards, to hire a warehouse.

He had now a Shop splendidly and copiously furnished with every thing that time had injured, or fashion had degraded, with fragments of tissues, odd yards of brocade, vast bales of faded silk, and innumerable boxes of antiquated ribbons. His shop was soon celebrated through all quarters of the town, and frequented by every form of ostentatious Poverty. Every maid, whose misfortune it was to be taller than her Lady, matched her gown at Mr. *Drugget's,* and many a maiden who had passed a winter with her aunt in *London,* dazzled the Rustics, at her return, with cheap finery which *Drugget* had supplied. His shop was often visited in a morning by Ladies, who left their coaches in the next street, and crept through the Alley in linen gowns. *Drugget* knows the rank of his customers by their bashfulness, and when he finds them unwilling to be seen, invites them up stairs, or retires with them to the back window.

I rejoiced at the increasing prosperity of my friend, and imagined that as he grew rich, he was growing happy. His mind has partaken the enlargement of his fortune. When I stepped in for the first five years, I was welcomed only with a shake of the hand; in the next period of his life, he beckoned across the way for a pot of beer; but, for six years past, he invites me to dinner; and, if he bespeaks me the day before, never fails to regale me with a fillet of veal.

His riches neither made him uncivil nor negligent: He rose at the same hour, attended with the same assiduity, and bowed with the same gentleness. But for some years he has been much inclined to talk of the fatigues of business, and the confinement of a shop, and to wish that he had been so happy as to have renewed his uncle's lease of a farm, that he might have lived without noise and hurry, in a pure air, in the artless society of honest Villagers, and the contemplation of the works of nature.

I soon discovered the cause of my friend's Philosophy. He thought himself grown rich enough to have a lodging in the country, like the mercers on *Ludgate-hill,* and was resolved to enjoy himself in the decline of life. This was a revolution not to be made suddenly. He talked three years of the pleasures of the country, but passed every night over his own shop. But at last he resolved to be happy, and hired a lodging in the Country, that he may steal some hours in the week from business;

for, says he, *when a man advances in life he loves to entertain himself sometimes with his own thoughts.*

I was invited to this seat of quiet and contemplation among those whom Mr. *Drugget* considers as his most reputable friends, and desires to make the first witnesses of his elevation to the highest dignities of a Shopkeeper. I found him at *Islington,* in a room which overlooked the high road, amusing himself with looking through the window, which the clouds of dust would not suffer him to open. He embraced me, told me I was welcome into the Country, and asked me, If I did not feel myself refreshed. He then desired that dinner might be hastened, for fresh air always sharpened his appetite, and ordered me a toast and a glass of wine after my walk. He told me much of the pleasures he found in retirement, and wondered what had kept him so long out of the Country. After dinner company came in, and Mr. *Drugget* again repeated the praises of the Country, recommended the pleasures of Meditation, and told them, that he had been all the morning at the window, counting the carriages as they passed before him.

James Joyce (1882–1941)

THE BOARDING HOUSE

Mrs. Mooney running over her arguments ("outraged mother"; "taken advantage of youth and inexperience"; "the girl has to bear the brunt") provides a checklist of stage melodrama clichés, but in Joyce's Dublin, cliché invades people's lives. Each sentence in this story registers with precision something the people in it think important. The fifteen stories in Dubliners *(written 1904–1907) employ with unprecedented scrupulousness the technique of meaningful documentation.*

To what clichés is Bob Doran's happiness sacrificed? Polly's? Does Mrs. Mooney believe in her maxims or just use them? Is the story told from her point of view? Bob's? Polly's? Whose?

Mrs. Mooney was a butcher's daughter. She was a woman who was quite able to keep things to herself: a determined woman. She had married her father's foreman and opened a butcher's shop near Spring Gardens. But as soon as his father-in-law was dead Mr. Mooney began to go to the devil. He drank, plundered the till, ran headlong into debt. It was no use making him take the pledge: he was sure to break out again a few days after. By fighting his wife in the presence of customers and by buying bad meat he ruined his business. One night he went for his wife with the cleaver and she had to sleep in a neighbor's house.

After that they lived apart. She went to the priest and got a separation from him with care of the children. She would give him neither money nor food nor house-room; and so he was obliged to enlist himself as a sheriff's man. He was a shabby stooped little drunkard with a white face and a white mustache and white eyebrows, penciled above his little eyes, which were pink-veined and raw; and all day long he sat in the bailiff's room, waiting to be put on a job. Mrs. Mooney, who had taken what remained of her money out of the butcher business and set up a boarding house in Hardwicke Street, was a big imposing woman. Her house

From *Dubliners*. Originally published by B. W. Huebsch in 1916. Reprinted by permission of The Viking Press, Inc.

had a floating population made up of tourists from Liverpool and the Isle of Man and, occasionally, *artistes* from the music halls. Its resident population was made up of clerks from the city. She governed the house cunningly and firmly, knew when to give credit, when to be stern and when to let things pass. All the resident young men spoke of her as *The Madam*.

Mrs. Mooney's young men paid fifteen shillings a week for board and lodgings (beer or stout at dinner excluded). They shared in common tastes and occupations and for this reason they were very chummy with one another. They discussed with one another the chances of favorites and outsiders. Jack Mooney, the Madam's son, who was clerk to a commission agent in Fleet Street, had the reputation of being a hard case. He was fond of using soldiers' obscenities: usually he came home in the small hours. When he met his friends he had always a good one to tell them and he was always sure to be on to a good thing—that is to say, a likely horse or a likely *artiste*. He was also handy with the mits and sang comic songs. On Sunday nights there would often be a reunion in Mrs. Mooney's front drawing room. The music-hall *artistes* would oblige; and Sheridan played waltzes and polkas and vamped accompaniments. Polly Mooney, the Madam's daughter, would also sing. She sang:

> *"I'm a . . . naughty girl.*
> *You needn't sham:*
> *You know I am."*

Polly was a slim girl of nineteen; she had light soft hair and a small full mouth. Her eyes, which were gray with a shade of green through them, had a habit of glancing upward when she spoke with anyone, which made her look like a little perverse madonna. Mrs. Mooney had first sent her daughter to be a typist in a corn-factor's office but, as a disreputable sheriff's man used to come every other day to the office, asking to be allowed to say a word to his daughter, she had taken her daughter home again and sent her to do housework. As Polly was very lively the intention was to give her the run of the young men. Besides, young men like to feel that there is a young woman not very far away. Polly, of course, flirted with the young men but Mrs. Mooney, who was a shrewd judge, knew that the young men were only passing the time away: none of them meant business. Things went on so for a long time and Mrs. Mooney began to think of sending Polly back to typewriting when she noticed that something was going on between Polly and one of the young men. She watched the pair and kept her own counsel.

Polly knew that she was being watched, but still her mother's persistent silence could not be misunderstood. There had been no open complicity between mother and daughter, no open understanding but, though people in the house began to talk of the affair, still Mrs. Mooney did not intervene. Polly began to grow a little strange in her manner and the young man was evidently perturbed. At last, when she judged it to be the right moment, Mrs. Mooney intervened. She dealt with moral problems as a cleaver deals with meat: and in this case she had made up her mind.

It was a bright Sunday morning of early summer, promising heat, but with a fresh breeze blowing. All the windows of the boarding house were open and the lace curtains ballooned gently toward the street beneath the raised sashes. The belfry of George's Church sent out constant peals and worshipers, singly or in groups, traversed the little circus before the church, revealing their purpose by their self-contained demeanor no less than by the little volumes in their gloved hands. Breakfast was over in the boarding house and the table of the breakfast room was covered with plates on which lay yellow streaks of eggs with morsels of bacon fat and bacon rind. Mrs. Mooney sat in the straw armchair and watched the servant Mary remove the breakfast things. She made Mary collect the crusts and pieces of broken bread to help to make Tuesday's bread pudding. When the table was cleared, the broken bread collected, the sugar and butter safe under lock and key, she began to reconstruct the interview which she had had the night before with Polly. Things were as she had suspected: she had been frank in her questions and Polly had been frank in her answers. Both had been somewhat awkward, of course. She had been made awkward by her not wishing to receive the news in too cavalier a fashion or to seem to have connived and Polly had been made awkward not merely because allusions of that kind always made her awkward but also because she did not wish it to be thought that in her wise innocence she had divined the intention behind her mother's tolerance.

Mrs. Mooney glanced instinctively at the little gilt clock on the mantelpiece as soon as she had become aware through her revery that the bells of George's Church had stopped ringing. It was seventeen minutes past eleven: she would have lots of time to have the matter out with Mr. Doran and then catch short twelve at Marlborough Street. She was sure she would win. To begin with she had all the weight of social opinion on her side: she was an outraged mother. She had allowed him to live beneath her roof, assuming that he was a man of honor, and he had simply abused her hospitality. He was thirty-four or thirty-five years of age, so that youth could not be pleaded as his excuse; nor could ignorance be his excuse since he was a man who had seen something of the world. He had simply taken advantage of Polly's youth and inexperience: that was evident. The question was: What reparation would he make?

There must be reparation made in such case. It is all very well for the man: he can go his ways as if nothing had happened, having had his moment of pleasure, but the girl has to bear the brunt. Some mothers would be content to patch up such an affair for a sum of money; she had known cases of it. But she would not do so. For her only one reparation could make up for the loss of her daughter's honor: marriage.

She counted all her cards again before sending Mary up to Mr. Doran's room to say that she wished to speak with him. She felt sure she would win. He was a serious young man, not rakish or loud-voiced like the others. If it had been Mr. Sheridan or Mr. Meade or Bantam Lyons her task would have been much harder. She did not think he would face publicity. All the lodgers in the house knew something of the affair; details had been invented by some. Besides, he had been employed for thirteen years in a great Catholic wine-merchant's office and publicity would mean for him, perhaps, the loss of his job. Whereas if he agreed all might be well. She knew he had a good screw for one thing and she suspected he had a bit of stuff put by.

Nearly the half-hour! She stood up and surveyed herself in the pier glass. The decisive expression of her great florid face satisfied her and she thought of some mothers she knew who could not get their daughters off their hands.

Mr. Doran was very anxious indeed this Sunday morning. He had made two attempts to shave but his hand had been so unsteady that he had been obliged to desist. Three days' reddish beard fringed his jaws and every two or three minutes a mist gathered on his glasses so that he had to take them off and polish them with his pocket handkerchief. The recollection of his confession of the night before was a cause of acute pain to him; the priest had drawn out every ridiculous detail of the affair and in the end had so magnified his sin that he was almost thankful at being afforded a loophole of reparation. The harm was done. What could he do now but marry her or run away? He could not brazen it out. The affair would be sure to be talked of and his employer would be certain to hear of it. Dublin is such a small city: everyone knows everyone else's business. He felt his heart leap warmly in his throat as he heard in his excited imagination old Mr. Leonard calling out in his rasping voice: "Send Mr. Doran here, please."

All his long years of service gone for nothing! All his industry and diligence thrown away! As a young man he had sown his wild oats, of course; he had boasted of his free-thinking and denied the existence of God to his companions in public houses. But that was all passed and done with . . . nearly. He still bought a copy of *Reynolds's Newspaper* every week but he attended to his religious duties and for nine-tenths of the year lived a regular life. He had money enough to settle down on; it was not that. But the family would look down on her. First of all there was her disreputable father and then her mother's boarding house was beginning to get a certain fame. He had a notion that he was being had. He could imagine his friends talking of the affair and laughing. She *was* a little vulgar; some times she said "I seen" and "If I had've known." But what would grammar matter if he really loved her? He could not make up his mind whether to like her or despise her for what she had done. Of course he had done it too. His instinct urged him to remain free, not to marry. Once you are married you are done for, it said.

While he was sitting helplessly on the side of the bed in shirt and trousers she tapped lightly at his door and entered. She told him all, that she had made a clean breast of it to her mother and that her mother would speak with him that morning. She cried and threw her arms round his neck, saying:

"O Bob! Bob! What am I to do? What am I to do at all?"

She would put an end to herself, she said.

He comforted her feebly, telling her not to cry, that it would be all right, never fear. He felt against his shirt the agitation of her bosom.

It was not altogether his fault that it had happened. He remembered well, with the curious patient memory of the celibate, the first casual caresses her dress, her breath, her fingers had given him. Then late one night as he was undressing for bed she had tapped at his door, timidly. She wanted to relight her candle at his for hers had been blown out by a gust. It was her bath night. She wore a loose open combing jacket of printed flannel. Her white instep shone in the opening of her furry slippers and the blood glowed warmly behind her perfumed skin. From her hands and wrists too as she lit and steadied her candle a faint perfume arose.

On nights when he came in very late it was she who warmed up his dinner. He scarcely knew what he was eating feeling her beside him alone, at night, in the sleeping house. And her thoughtfulness! If the night was anyway cold or wet or windy there was sure to be a little tumbler of punch ready for him. Perhaps they could be happy together. . . .

They used to go upstairs together on tiptoe, each with a candle, and on the third landing exchange reluctant good nights. They used to kiss. He remembered well her eyes, the touch of her hand and his delirium. . . .

But delirium passes. He echoed her phrase, applying it to himself: *"What am I to do?"* The instinct of the celibate warned him to hold back. But the sin was there; even his sense of honor told him that reparation must be made for such a sin.

While he was sitting with her on the side of the bed Mary came to the door and said that the missus wanted to see him in the parlor. He stood up to put on his coat and waistcoat, more helpless than ever. When he was dressed he went over to her to comfort her. It would be all right, never fear. He left her crying on the bed and moaning softly: "O *my God!*"

Going down the stairs his glasses became so dimmed with moisture that he had to take them off and polish them. He longed to ascend through the roof and fly away to another country where he would never hear again of his trouble, and yet a force pushed him downstairs step by step. The implacable faces of his employer and of the Madam stared upon his discomfiture. On the last flight of stairs he passed Jack Mooney who was coming up from the pantry nursing two bottles of *Bass.* They saluted coldly; and the lover's eyes rested for a second or two on a thick bulldog face and a pair of thick short arms. When he reached the foot of the staircase he glanced up and saw Jack regarding him from the door of the return room.

Suddenly he remembered the night when one of the music-hall *artistes,* a little blond Londoner, had made a rather free allusion to Polly. The reunion had been almost broken up on account of Jack's violence. Everyone tried to quiet him. The music-hall *artiste,* a little paler than usual, kept smiling and saying that there was no harm meant: but Jack kept shouting at him that if any fellow tried that sort of a game on with his sister he'd bloody well put his teeth down his throat, so he would.

Polly sat for a little time on the side of the bed, crying. Then she dried her eyes and went over to the looking glass. She dipped the end of the towel in the water jug and refreshed her eyes with the cool water. She looked at herself in profile and readjusted a hairpin above her ear. Then she went back to the bed again and sat at the foot. She regarded the pillows for a long time and the sight of them awakened in her mind secret, amiable memories. She rested the nape of her neck against the cool iron bedrail and fell into a revery. There was no longer any perturbation visible on her face.

She waited on patiently, almost cheerfully, without alarm, her memories gradually giving place to hopes and visions of the future. Her hopes and visions were so intricate that she no longer saw the white pillows on which her gaze was fixed or remembered that she was waiting for anything.

At last she heard her mother calling. She started to her feet and ran to the banisters.

"Polly! Polly!"

"Yes, mamma?"

"Come down, dear. Mr. Doran wants to speak to you."

Then she remembered what she had been waiting for.

Robert McAlmon (1896–1956)

THE JACK RABBIT DRIVE

This story should be compared to "The Boarding House" for its management of the sentence and to "The Grave" for its management of its theme. What comes through McAlmon's prose is the intensity of an experience remembered from a South Dakota boyhood, and he would have said that he refused to give it a shape or significance it didn't have at the time. Sincerity is easier to invoke than to define.

If the sentences in "The Boarding House" register things the characters think important, what do the sentences in this story register? (Remember that no writer will bother to construct a sentence to which he attaches no importance whatever.)

Why does the jack rabbit drive cling to McAlmon's memory; in short, what is the story's theme? At what point in the story do you discover what it is? Does the boy discover what it is, or just the reader?

It was agreed upon by members of the community that the thousands of jack rabbits throughout the countryside must be exterminated, in part at least. Their burrowings and nibblings destroyed too much grain and property. So for two weeks the day set for a drive was given wide publicity.

Horace slipped out of the house through the kitchen, stopping there to sneak cookies from under Linda's eyes. At the moment, however, she was feeling in good humor, and her black face, already gleaming with perspiration, gleamed more with a tender smiling at his six-year-old guile, and she gave him six cookies, whereupon he went joyfully into the back yard to look hopefully about. Maybe Freddie was around to be played with. He didn't like Freddie much but he was better than nobody. Horace felt uncomfortable because his mother had put a new suit on him, and made him wear an overcoat, and if Billie Anderson saw him with his yellow hair slicked back Billie might call him "mamma's boy"

From *McAlmon and the Lost Generation*, edited by Robert E. Knoll. Reprinted by permission of the University of Nebraska Press and Miss Victoria McAlmon.

and that would mean another fight, because he and Billie were supposed to have a great scrap someday to show which was the best fighter in town of their age.

It was somewhat sheepishly that he began to play with Sally Porter a few minutes later. She was more fun to be with than Freddie, if she only weren't a girl. She dared do anything, and wasn't nearly so scared of going blocks from home if she could without her mother seeing and calling her back to play on the Porters' front lawn. Horace didn't want to play there because every boy in the neighborhood could see, and Sally might want to play doll house, which Horace didn't mind if Billie Anderson wasn't apt to know about it. The Porter horse, that was to run in the County Fair races, was picketed on the lawn too, and he'd stepped on Horace's bare foot one day when Horace was petting him. That was no fun, you can bet. The horse didn't mean to maybe, but Horace didn't want that to happen again.

As playing on the lawn was no fun at all Horace and Sally were out in back of the barn, almost without thinking to get there. It was the alley they were supposed not to play in too, because the nigger washerwoman's kids played there, since their ma's shack sat on top of the alley. Mrs. Darian told Horace there wasn't any harm in his playing with the colored children, but Mrs. Porter wouldn't let Sally. They had not been there long, however, before Horace got scared, remembering that he'd killed one of those niggers' chickens by hitting it on the head with a stone he'd thrown; except he hadn't really killed it. He had only stunned it, because when he and the nigger kids, all scared of what their mas would say, buried the rooster in the manure pile, it began to flop and finally got up and ran away, dizzy in the head. Maybe Mrs. Lincoln, the nigger woman, wasn't mad at him though, because she had sent him an egg no bigger than a robin's that one of her hens had laid, but he didn't know. Maybe she'd just sent it to please his mother for whom she did washing.

"We gotta go somewhere else and play because I'm not going to have them darkie kids butting in on us. I have an idea anyway. Billie Anderson says you can get a cent a bottle for beer bottles from the bartender at the saloon."

"Why you awful boy, Horace. If we did that we'd just get the hide licked off us and you know it," Sally said, pretending great horror. "Why mamma is always giving it to papa because he goes in there and if she heard I did that! And she would because someone would tell her."

"Aw rats, don't be a fraidy cat."

"You know I ain't no fraidy cat."

"Maybe you ain't, but Freddie is. I ast him yesterday to look for beer bottles with me and he wouldn't, and he cried and ran home and we scrapped, and he was going to tell on me, but I didn't care. I told him

'Tattle-tale, tattle-tale,
Hanging to the bull's tail—'"

"You are the naughtiest boy," Sally said with triumphant righteousness, and so daring Horace, encouraged him to the scandalous conclusion of the ditty. Sally believed it her duty to act shocked and refuse to speak to Horace for a few seconds, but the strain of that soon told on her, and being sure that no older person had heard Horace, she relaxed to curiosity.

"Where do you suppose we can find some beer bottles?" she asked. "We could hide them and collect a lot and then maybe get in the back door of the saloon and Mr. Murphy wouldn't tell on us."

After an hour's search in the alleys Sally had found one bottle that might be a beer bottle, or even a whiskey bottle, and Horace had found three bottles that he was sure were beer bottles, as he was sure Sally's was only a pop bottle. So the two went around to the alley behind the main street until they came to the backshed entrance to the saloon. They were afraid to go in, but after a consultation decided they'd better go in together and both get lickings if they were caught.

"The men will take it more like a joke if you're there," Horace sagely informed Sally. "They always think girls don't know nothing."

Sidling up to the bar inside Sally looked discreetly wide-eyed and innocent as she piped up, "I'se got some beer bottles, Mr. Man. P'ease give me some pennies for them." Horace was too scared to notice much that Sally was putting on baby accents.

"Well, I'll be—" Murphy, the bartender, started to say, but checked his profanity. "You kids will get paddled if your families hear you're coming in here. You'd better beat it quick. You'll get me in trouble too if they hear I let you in."

"We want candy." Horace broke in, feeling more at ease as he sensed that Murphy was a companion in guilt. "Just this once, buy these bottles." His heart was going at a terrific pace and he felt uncomfortable because of many strange men about the bar who had laughed raucously at him and Sally.

"Here's a nickel. Now quick and beat it, kiddies," Murphy said and handed Horace the money.

"Don't I get none too?" lisped Sally.

"Divide that, you two kids. You'll founder yourself on all day suckers or cheap chocolates if I give you more," Murphy explained good naturedly, leaning over to pat Sally's tow head, and to tweak at one of her braids. He relented, however, and slipped her a nickel too, so she and Horace went happily out of the saloon, in their glee carelessly going through the front door, when they quickly remembered and were scared.

"O golly, Sally. I'll bet yer pa can see us because his office is right across the street."

"It ain't papa I care about knowing. He wouldn't lick me and he wouldn't dare tell mamma on me either, because she'd say that was his blood coming out in me. That's what she always says when she licks me."

The children now felt completely involved in guilt and decided it wasn't any use resisting temptation any more that afternoon, so they bought some all day suckers, and gum, and chocolates. They walked down the main street and soon came to the edge of the town where Daly's pasture was. It was a warm autumn afternoon, but too chilly to sit on the bank of the pond long, and few minnows were to be seen in the muddy water. A few cows were grazing on the dry grass in the pasture, but the children saw that they didn't come too near.

"I wonder which gives the most milk, the papa or the mamma cow," Horace queried, remembering the cow his father had sold because she went dry.

"It ought to be the papa cow because that's how cows support themselves, and the papa ought to always support the family, but mamma says it ain't so with us, cause papa drinks up everything he makes. I like pap better though. He isn't cranky every minute of the day."

This problem did not interest Horace much. He was full of candy, and drowsy in the sun except that it was cold on his pants when he sat on the ground. As his mind wandered he remembered that his brother Ralph had spoken of a jack rabbit drive at the breakfast table. That had excited Horace, but his mother told him of course he couldn't watch anything so brutal.

"I tell you, Sally," Horace said, "there's a jack rabbit drive to end up at the corner down the road. Let's run down there and see if there's any sign of it."

Since ten o'clock in the morning groups of men and boys had been occupied with the jack rabbit drive. On every side for miles from town, farmers, farm boys, and all the countless dogs of the countryside had been scouring the land to scare up rabbits. The clamor of guns firing, dogs barking, men shouting and beating with clubs, and horses trampling about was calculated to terrify all the rabbits who came within the range of the two semicircles of inclosing rabbit hunters.

It was by now four o'clock in the afternoon and evening chill was coming into the air. Going to the corner fence Horace knew of, Sally and he soon began to discern noises of the drive off in the distance. Now and then there was an echo or re-echo of a gunshot. Faintly, as though imagined, the resonance of a shot would sound, though neither Sally nor Horace could verify any one report as the noises were becoming more clear and decisive, or their expectant senses made them alert.

"I saw Dingo, pa's half-breed hunter dog, tear up a rabbit's burrow once, and he just ripped that rabbit all to pieces," Sally said. "That made pa mad because it showed that Dingo was no good as a hunter to tear game to pieces. That rabbit squealed once when Dingo grabbed it but it just squealed once."

"Ralph said he bet all the rabbit burrows in the country would be dug open, there are so many dogs," Horace volunteered. "I've never seen a jack rabbit. Only them pet rabbits I had when I was a baby two years ago. Gosh, I was mad at mamma for making me wear skirts a whole year after Billie had been wearing pants, but it wasn't as bad as Freddie having to wear long hair up till just last month. His mamma wants to make a girlboy out of him."

Fifteen minutes passed, with sounds of the drive coming clearly to them, and again seeming to grow dimmer, until finally the resonance of noises became continually louder. The distinguishable bark of dogs could be heard: the baying of hounds, the yipe of fox terriers, the excited joyful bark of mongrels, and the general hysteria of all the dogs' excitement. It was infrequently that a gun was fired.

Suddenly there was a rush of men from across the fields on every side, and they were shouting at each other.

"Here you are, boys; here you are." "Get in on every side." "Get your clubs ready. Knock them out as fast as they come hurtling against the fence." "They'll be here in thousands inside of three minutes." "Kill 'em at one blow."

From the village, men, women, and children, too, had begun to arrive for the end-up of the drive, the sounds of which had echoed through the town for the last half-hour. A share of even the women from the village carried clubs, or limbs of trees, and all the men and boys in the drive were so armed. The hullabaloo grew greater, with cursings, leaping about, and rabbit-threatening gesticulations in mock display of what they'd do to the rabbits.

The rabbits began coming. Tearing along, panic-struck huge white jack rabbits catapulted across the prairie towards the fence corner. Men on horses, men on foot, and dogs with lapping slobbery tongues circled in on them. The rabbits hurled themselves on at leaps of twenty, thirty, or even forty feet in the case of the huge-sized jacks. Shrilly, above the pandemonium a shriek of rabbit pain sounded now and then as some dog captured a jack and ripped it to bits.

Horace and Sally, standing near the front of the spectators, watched feverishly. Rabbits smashed into the impenetrable fence to be beaten on the head by men or boys jumping about. Before struck, terror was making the rabbits squeal. A continuous ripping, tearing sound, punctuated by the thump, thump, thump of clubs against the light-boned heads of the rabbits, went on.

At one moment Horace saw a rabbit caught by a great lean greyhound. Within a second another dog had caught the same rabbit by another portion of its body. Horace heard the squeal of that rabbit, saw the look of rodent terror in its eyes, and—dizzy within himself—heard the rip of the body. A stunned feeling held him, watching as though hypnotized. He was biting his lips and twitching his face nervously, unaware of himself or of his reactions to what he was seeing. It didn't seem that what he was seeing was actual. The jack rabbits looked so powerful and electric as they came across the prairie, and so limp, like damp besmudged cotton, as they lay torn upon the ground with the yellow of their hides, and the red of their interiors, showing.

Shortly the thing was done with. Heaped in piles against the fence were more than a thousand rabbit bodies. Their dull, glazed, half-open eyes, Horace noticed. He lingered, half wondering if they might not move again. Surely something more was going to happen after all this excitement.

"What happens to rabbits when they're dead?" Horace wondered, dazedly curious, to Sally, having heard of death before, but never having realized what it might mean.

"Huh, listen to the kid. Say sonny, them jacks is dead, and dead they'll stay and not be destroying crops on us farmers," a heavy-set man said with rough good nature to Horace, who shrank within himself from the obscenity, to him, of the man's manner. Yet his wonder made him speak in mechanical bewilderment.

"But they were alive just a few minutes ago."

"Sure kid, but they ain't now. We saw to that."

Horace didn't know how to think, and maybe he was afraid but not in a way he could cry about, or that he could ask his mother about. What if something began chasing people like the rabbits had been chased?

Sally was ready to go home, though she was still looking fascinatedly at the pile of rabbits. Horace had a moment of aversion to her because she leaned over and touched one, and didn't seem to feel sorry for it. A farm boy picked up a little mutilated rabbit and handed it to her. "Here, girlie," he told her, patting her head, "take this home to your mamma and have her cook it for you. It's nicer than chicken."

Sally took the rabbit and started to follow Horace, who had walked ahead of her. She caught up to him.

"You aren't going to take that rabbit home, are you? You couldn't eat it, could you?"

"Why not? Mamma feeds us rabbits lots of times."

"But it's dead," Horace explained.

"Every meat you eat is. That's what happens to all the cows that get shipped out of the stock yard every week."

Horace's mind was stalled. He couldn't think. He changed the topic.

"I'll bet them rabbits were stronger than you or me. I'll bet we couldn't have held one without its kicking away because a man I saw grab a live one could hardly hold it."

Sally, becoming conscious that Horace walked away from her because she was carrying the rabbit, threw it aside with a quick gesture and said, "Nasty dead thing."

"It isn't its fault it's nasty," Horace said.

"I think it's awful. The poor rabbits."

"I don't know whether it's awful or not. People said it was a good thing to get rid of them."

When Horace and Sally got back to their houses they separated. Horace went through the kitchen, not even noticing Linda. In the sitting room he avoided speaking to his mother and, taking up a picture book, buried himself in the big easy chair. There was much he wanted to know but he didn't want his mother to know he had seen the jack rabbit drive.

Continually his mind reverted to the rabbits, how their white furry flesh had been torn, their squeals, the fear in their eyes. As he sat trying to think his mind was filled, not with definite pictures of rabbits, but with a flood of nervous images of rabbit carnage that made him shudder and want to shut the thought out. But he didn't try to look at his book. He even felt impatient with his mother when she began talking to him and so prevented him from thinking about the rabbits. He liked to think that as he shuddered he was trying to shut out the white ripping and squealing image.

Through dinnertime Horace was very quiet, and his mother asked him if he didn't feel very well.

"Rats, sick," his brother Ralph said. "Don't baby him. He's probably been up to something and keeps quiet not to give himself away."

"Nonsense, Ralph," his mother answered. "I can see that the boy is pale, and his eyes have a feverish look. Don't think I don't know children better than my own son knows them. Think of your wanting to let him see the rabbit drive. At his age what would you have thought? He's been hearing about that brutal affair I'm sure."

Soon after dinner Horace was sent up to bed, where, after saying his prayers, he was left, and ducked his head under the covers as soon as his mother was out of the room and he was alone in darkness. He began to tell himself a long story about a rabbit drive, except that the rabbit drive would come later on in the story. He kept delaying it, wanting a very exciting situation to work up to. Gradually, however, sleep overtook him, in spite of his fear in the dark, out of which anything might come. Suppose a great jack rabbit leaped right on him through the open window. He wouldn't know what to do then. He lay still, except that at imagined sounds he peeked from under the covers. At one moment he was sure there was something standing at the foot of his bed, but he knew he'd get scolded and teased if he called out, or ran downstairs, and he would have to say of course he didn't believe in boogie mans. He wondered if Sally was scared in the dark too, if she really was, but maybe she wouldn't say so any more than he would.

He was standing way out in the dark fields, and everywhere rabbits were nibbling about him, so many that he could not walk without stepping on them. They nibbled at his feet too, trying to eat him up. And one came running terrifically to leap at him; and after him many others came, running straight at him to knock him down and cover his face and body with their cottony bodies. They would smother him like the two princes smothered by their uncle. He couldn't move and they kept coming. Awaking, he moaned, and then, knowing it was a dream, kept quiet with his fear. Looking out from under his covers he saw the moon shining through the window, so that he could see there was no one, only his coat, at the foot of his bed. Half of his room was almost in day lightness, but back there in the corner, or in the closet—

He wanted to cry, almost, but nobody he wanted would hear him, and if there was somebody back in the corner and they heard him they'd know he was afraid. He must not cry, so as to be able to speak if they came over to get him. He must tell them that they dare not touch him; that he wasn't scared.

At last he went to sleep again.

Katherine Anne Porter (1894–   )

THE GRAVE

"Miranda leaped into the pit that had held her grandfather's bones":
the author of "The Jack Rabbit Drive" would have protested that this
is not Miranda's perception but the author's. The carefully written
final paragraph shapes the story as nothing in the preceding story is
shaped. Though one suspects an autobiographical basis, Miss Porter's
attention is on the internal economy of a brief work of art.

Remembering what you have learned from "The Jack Rabbit
Drive," try to state the theme of this story and to identify the point
at which it becomes explicit. Does Miranda come to know the mean-
ing of her experience? Do you think Miranda is the author in dis-
guise? Why or why not?

THE Grandfather, dead for more than thirty years, had been twice disturbed in his long repose by the constancy and possessiveness of his
widow. She removed his bones first to Louisiana and then to Texas as
if she had set out to find her own burial place, knowing well she would
never return to the places she had left. In Texas she set up a small cemetery in a corner of her first farm, and as the family connection grew, and
oddments of relations came over from Kentucky to settle, it contained at
last about twenty graves. After the Grandmother's death, part of her
land was to be sold for the benefit of certain of her children, and the
cemetery happened to lie in the part set aside for sale. It was necessary
to take up the bodies and bury them again in the family plot in the big
new public cemetery, where the Grandmother had been buried. At last
her husband was to lie beside her for eternity, as she had planned.

The family cemetery had been a pleasant small neglected garden of
tangled rose bushes and ragged cedar trees and cypress, the simple flat
stones rising out of uncropped sweet-smelling wild grass. The graves
were lying open and empty one burning day when Miranda and her
brother Paul, who often went together to hunt rabbits and doves,

propped their twenty-two Winchester rifles carefully against the rail
fence, climbed over and explored among the graves. She was nine years
old and he was twelve.

They peered into the pits all shaped alike with such purposeful ac-
curacy, and looking at each other with pleased adventurous eyes, they
said in solemn tones: "These were graves!" trying by words to shape a
special, suitable emotion in their minds, but they felt nothing except an
agreeable thrill of wonder: they were seeing a new sight, doing something they had not done before. In them both there was also a small disappointment at the entire commonplaceness of the actual spectacle. Even
if it had once contained a coffin for years upon years, when the coffin was
gone a grave was just a hole in the ground. Miranda leaped into the pit
that had held her grandfather's bones. Scratching around aimlessly and
pleasurably as any young animal, she scooped up a lump of earth and
weighed it in her palm. It had a pleasantly sweet, corrupt smell, being
mixed with cedar needles and small leaves, and as the crumbs fell apart,
she saw a silver dove no larger than a hazel nut, with spread wings and
a neat fan-shaped tail. The breast had a deep round hollow in it. Turning it up to the fierce sunlight, she saw that the inside of the hollow
was cut in little whorls. She scrambled out, over the pile of loose earth
that had fallen back into one end of the grave, calling to Paul that she
had found something, he must guess what. . . . His head appeared
smiling over the rim of another grave. He waved a closed hand at her.
"I've got something too!" They ran to compare treasures, making a game
of it, so many guesses each, all wrong, and a final showdown with
opened palms. Paul had found a thin wide gold ring carved with intricate flowers and leaves. Miranda was smitten at sight of the ring and
wished to have it. Paul seemed more impressed by the dove. They made
a trade, with some little bickering. After he had got the dove in his hand,
Paul said, "Don't you know what this is? This is a screw head for a
coffin! . . . . I'll bet nobody else in the world has one like this!"

Miranda glanced at it without covetousness. She had the gold ring
on her thumb; it fitted perfectly. "Maybe we ought to go now," she
said, "maybe one of the niggers'll see us and tell somebody." They knew
the land had been sold, the cemetery was no longer theirs, and they felt
like trespassers. They climbed back over the fence, slung their rifles
loosely under their arms—they had been shooting at targets with various
kinds of firearms since they were seven years old—and set out to look for
the rabbits and doves or whatever small game might happen along. On
these expeditions Miranda always followed at Paul's heels along the
path, obeying instructions about handling her gun when going through
fences; learning how to stand it up properly so it would not slip and
fire unexpectedly; how to wait her time for a shot and not just bang
away in the air without looking, spoiling shots for Paul, who really

could hit things if given a chance. Now and then, in her excitement at
seeing birds whizz up suddenly before her face, or a rabbit leap across
her very toes, she lost her head, and almost without sighting she flung
her rifle up and pulled the trigger. She hardly ever hit any sort of mark.
She had no proper sense of hunting at all. Her brother would be often
completely disgusted with her. "You don't care whether you get your
bird or not," he said. "That's no way to hunt." Miranda could not understand his indignation. She had seen him smash his hat and yell with
fury when he had missed his aim. "What I like about shooting," said
Miranda, with exasperating inconsequence, "is pulling the trigger and
hearing the noise."

"Then, by golly," said Paul, "whyn't you go back to the range and
shoot at bulls-eyes?"

"I'd just as soon," said Miranda, "only like this, we walk around
more."

"Well, you just stay behind and stop spoiling my shots," said Paul,
who, when he made a kill, wanted to be certain he had made it. Miranda, who alone brought down a bird once in twenty rounds, always
claimed as her own any game they got when they fired at the same
moment. It was tiresome and unfair and her brother was sick of it.

"Now, the first dove we see, or the first rabbit, is mine," he told her.
"And the next will be yours. Remember that and don't get smarty."

"What about snakes?" asked Miranda idly. "Can I have the first
snake?"

Waving her thumb gently and watching her gold ring glitter, Miranda lost interest in shooting. She was wearing her summer roughing
outfit: dark blue overalls, a light blue shirt, a hired-man's straw hat, and
thick brown sandals. Her brother had the same outfit except his was a
sober hickory-nut color. Ordinarily Miranda preferred her overalls to any
other dress, though it was making rather a scandal in the countryside,
for the year was 1903, and in the back country the law of female decorum
had teeth in it. Her father had been criticized for letting his girls dress
like boys and go careering around astride barebacked horses. Big sister
Maria, the really independent and fearless one, in spite of her rather
affected ways, rode at a dead run with only a rope knotted around her
horse's nose. It was said the motherless family was running down, with
the Grandmother no longer there to hold it together. It was known that
she had discriminated against her son Harry in her will, and that he was
in straits about money. Some of his old neighbors reflected with vicious
satisfaction that now he would probably not be so stiffnecked, nor have
any more high-stepping horses either. Miranda knew this, though she
could not say how. She had met along the road old women of the kind
who smoked corncob pipes, who had treated her grandmother with most
sincere respect. They slanted their gummy old eyes sideways at the

granddaughter and said, "Ain't you ashamed of yoself, Missy? It's aginst the Scriptures to dress like that. Whut yo Pappy thinkin about?" Miranda, with her powerful social sense, which was like a fine set of antennae radiating from every pore of her skin, would feel ashamed because she knew well it was rude and ill-bred to shock anybody, even bad-tempered old crones, though she had faith in her father's judgment and was perfectly comfortable in the clothes. Her father had said, "They're just what you need, and they'll save your dresses for school. . . ." This sounded quite simple and natural to her. She had been brought up in rigorous economy. Wastefulness was vulgar. It was also a sin. These were truths; she had heard them repeated many times and never once disputed.

Now the ring, shining with the serene purity of fine gold on her rather grubby thumb, turned her feelings against her overalls and sockless feet, toes sticking through the thick brown leather straps. She wanted to go back to the farmhouse, take a good cold bath, dust herself with plenty of Maria's violet talcum powder—provided Maria was not present to object, of course—put on the thinnest, most becoming dress she owned, with a big sash, and sit in a wicker chair under the trees. . . . These things were not all she wanted, of course; she had vague stirrings of desire for luxury and a grand way of living which could not take precise form in her imagination but were founded on family legend of past wealth and leisure. These immediate comforts were what she could have, and she wanted them at once. She lagged rather far behind Paul, and once she thought of just turning back without a word and going home. She stopped, thinking that Paul would never do that to her, and so she would have to tell him. When a rabbit leaped, she let Paul have it without dispute. He killed it with one shot.

When she came up with him, he was already kneeling, examining the wound, the rabbit trailing from his hands. "Right through the head," he said complacently, as if he had aimed for it. He took out his sharp, competent bowie knife and started to skin the body. He did it very cleanly and quickly. Uncle Jimbilly knew how to prepare the skins so that Miranda always had fur coats for her dolls, for though she never cared much for her dolls she liked seeing them in fur coats. The children knelt facing each other over the dead animal. Miranda watched admiringly while her brother stripped the skin away as if he were taking off a glove. The flayed flesh emerged dark scarlet, sleek, firm; Miranda with thumb and finger felt the long fine muscles with the silvery flat strips binding them to the joints. Brother lifted the oddly bloated belly. "Look," he said, in a low amazed voice. "It was going to have young ones."

Very carefully he slit the thin flesh from the center ribs to the flanks, and a scarlet bag appeared. He slit again and pulled the bag open, and there lay a bundle of tiny rabbits, each wrapped in a thin scarlet veil. The brother pulled these off and there they were, dark gray, their sleek wet down lying in minute even ripples, like a baby's head just washed, their unbelievably small delicate ears folded close, their little blind faces almost featureless.

Miranda said, "Oh, I want to *see*," under her breath. She looked and looked—excited but not frightened, for she was accustomed to the sight of animals killed in hunting—filled with pity and astonishment and a kind of shocked delight in the wonderful little creatures for their own sakes, they were so pretty. She touched one of them ever so carefully. "Ah, there's blood running over them," she said and began to tremble without knowing why. Yet she wanted most deeply to see and to know. Having seen, she felt at once as if she had known all along. The very memory of her former ignorance faded, she had always known just this. No one had ever told her anything outright, she had been rather unobservant of the animal life around her because she was so accustomed to animals. They seemed simply disorderly and unaccountably rude in their habits, but altogether natural and not very interesting. Her brother had spoken as if he had known about everything all along. He may have seen all this before. He had never said a word to her, but she knew now a part at least of what he knew. She understood a little of the secret, formless intuitions in her own mind and body, which had been clearing up, taking form, so gradually and so steadily she had not realized that she was learning what she had to know. Paul said cautiously, as if he were talking about something forbidden: "They were just about ready to be born." His voice dropped on the last word. "I know," said Miranda, "like kittens. I know, like babies." She was quietly and terribly agitated, standing again with her rifle under her arm, looking down at the bloody heap. "I don't want the skin," she said, "I won't have it." Paul buried the young rabbits again in their mother's body, wrapped the skin around her, carried her to a clump of sage bushes, and hid her away. He came out again at once and said to Miranda, with an eager friendliness, a confidential tone quite unusual in him, as if he were taking her into an important secret on equal terms: "Listen now. Now you listen to me, and don't ever forget. Don't you ever tell a living soul that you saw this. Don't tell a soul. Don't tell Dad because I'll get into trouble. He'll say I'm leading you into things you ought not to do. He's always saying that. So now don't you go and forget and blab out sometime the way you're always doing. . . . Now, that's a secret. Don't you tell."

Miranda never told, she did not even wish to tell anybody. She thought about the whole worrisome affair with confused unhappiness for a few days. Then it sank quietly into her mind and was heaped over by accumulated thousands of impressions, for nearly twenty years. One day she was picking her path among the puddles and crushed refuse of

a market street in a strange city of a strange country, when without warning, plain and clear in its true colors as if she looked through a frame
upon a scene that had not stirred nor changed since the moment it happened, the episode of that far-off day leaped from its burial place before
her mind's eye. She was so reasonlessly horrified she halted suddenly
staring, the scene before her eyes dimmed by the vision back of them. An
Indian vendor had held up before her a tray of dyed sugar sweets, in the
shapes of all kinds of small creatures: birds, baby chicks, baby rabbits,
lambs, baby pigs. They were in gay colors and smelled of vanilla, maybe.
. . . It was a very hot day and the smell in the market, with its piles of
raw flesh and wilting flowers, was like the mingled sweetness and cor-
ruption she had smelled that other day in the empty cemetery at home:
the day she had remembered always until now vaguely as the time she
and her brother had found treasure in the opened graves. Instantly upon
this thought the dreadful vision faded, and she saw clearly her brother,
whose childhood face she had forgotten, standing again in the blazing
sunshine, again twelve years old, a pleased sober smile in his eyes, turning the silver dove over and over in his hands.

Eudora Welty (1909–   )

MOON LAKE

One need not have identified the guiding presence of the myth of Orpheus to sense the dreamlike otherworldliness of setting and sensibility that unifies this story. It arises not from ornamental writing— the writing deals matter-of-factly with data and impressions alike —but from the way children's wonder is made to interact with the facts presented. A child's viewpoint is one of the short story writer's most serviceable gambits.

How do we know the viewpoint is a child's, even though a child isn't telling the story?

"A girl nearly drowned but a boy revived her": How does the viewpoint keep this from being an adequate summary of the story?

— *1* —

From the beginning his martyred presence seriously affected them. They had a disquieting familiarity with it, hearing the spit of his despising that went into his bugle. At times they could hardly recognize what he thought he was playing. Loch Morrison, Boy Scout and Life Saver, was under the ordeal of a week's camp on Moon Lake with girls.

Half the girls were county orphans, wished on them by Mr. Nesbitt and the Men's Bible Class after Billy Sunday's visit to town; but all girls, orphans and Morgana girls alike, were the same thing to Loch; maybe he threw in the two councilors too. He was hating every day of the seven. He hardly spoke; he never spoke first. Sometimes he swung in the trees; Nina Carmichael in particular would hear him crashing in the foliage somewhere when she was lying rigid in siesta.

While they were in the lake, for the dip or the five-o'clock swimming period in the afternoon, he stood against a tree with his arms folded, jacked up one-legged, sitting on his heel, as absolutely tolerant as an old fellow waiting for the store to open, being held up by the wall. Waiting for the girls to get out, he gazed upon some undisturbed part of the water. He despised their predicaments, most of all their not being able to swim. Sometimes he would take aim and from his right cheek shoot an imaginary gun at something far out, where they never were. Then he resumed his pose. He had been roped into this by his mother.

At the hours too hot for girls he used Moon Lake. He dived high off the crosspiece nailed up in the big oak, where the American Legion dived. He went through the air rocking and jerking like an engine, splashed in, climbed out, spat, climbed up again, dived off. He wore a long bathing suit which stretched longer from Monday to Tuesday and from Tuesday to Wednesday and so on, yawning at the armholes toward infinity, and it looked black and formal as a minstrel suit as he stood skinny against the clouds as on a stage.

He came and got his food and turned his back and ate it all alone like a dog and lived in a tent by himself, apart like a nigger, and dived alone when the lake was clear of girls. That way, he seemed able to bear it; that would be his life. In early evening, in moonlight sings, the Boy Scout and Life Saver kept far away. They would sing "When all the little ships come sailing home," and he would be roaming off; they could tell about where he was. He played taps for them, invisibly then, and so beautifully they wept together, whole tentfuls some nights. Off with the whippoorwills and the coons and the owls and the little bobwhites—down where it all sloped away, he had pitched his tent, and slept there. Then at reveille, how he would spit into that cornet.

Reveille was his. He harangued the woods when the little minnows were trembling and running wizardlike in the water's edge. And how lovely and altered the trees were then, weighted with dew, leaning on one another's shoulders and smelling like big wet flowers. He blew his horn into their presence—trees' and girls'—and then watched the Dip.

"Good morning, Mr. Dip, Dip, Dip, with your water just as cold as ice!" sang Mrs. Gruenwald hoarsely. She took them for the dip, for Miss Moody said she couldn't, simply couldn't.

The orphans usually hung to the rear, and every other moment stood swayback with knees locked, the shoulders of their wash dresses ironed flat and stuck in peaks, and stared. For swimming they owned no bathing suits and went in in their underbodies. Even in the water they would stand swayback, each with a fist in front of her over the rope, looking over the flat surface as over the top of a tall mountain none of them could ever get over. Even at this hour of the day, they seemed to be expecting little tasks, something more immediate—little tasks that were never given out.

Mrs. Gruenwald was from the North and said "dup." "Good morning, Mr. Dup, Dup, Dup, with your water just as cold as ice!" sang Mrs. Gruenwald, fatly capering and leading them all in a singing, peter-ing-out string down to the lake. She did a sort of little rocking dance in her exhortation, broad in her bathrobe. From the tail end of the line she looked like a Shredded Wheat Biscuit box rocking on its corners.

Nina Carmichael thought, There is nobody and nothing named Mr. Dip, it is not a good morning until you have had coffee, and the water is the temperature of a just-cooling biscuit, thank Goodness. I hate this little parade of us girls, Nina thought, trotting fiercely in the center of it. It ruins the woods, all right. "Gee, we think you're mighty nice," they sang to Mr. Dip, while the Boy Scout, waiting at the lake, watched them go in.

"Watch out for mosquitoes," they called to one another, lyrically because warning wasn't any use anyway, as they walked out of their kimonos and dropped them like the petals of one big scattered flower on the bank behind them, and exposing themselves felt in a hundred places at once the little pangs. The orphans ripped their dresses off over their heads and stood in their underbodies. Busily they hung and piled their dresses on a cedar branch, obeying one of their own number, like a whole flock of ferocious little birds with pale topknots building themselves a nest. The orphan named Easter appeared in charge. She handed her dress wrong-side-out to a friend, who turned it and hung it up for her, and waited standing very still, her little fingers locked.

"Let's let the orphans go in the water first and get the snakes stirred up, Mrs. Gruenwald," Jinny Love Stark suggested first off, in the cheerful voice she adopted toward grown people. "Then they'll be chased away by the time *we* go in."

That made the orphans scatter in their pantie-waists, outwards from Easter; the little gauzes of gnats they ran through made them beat their hands at the air. They ran back together again, to Easter, and stood excitedly, almost hopping.

"I think we'll all go in in one big bunch," Mrs. Gruenwald said. Jinny Love lamented and beat against Mrs. Gruenwald, Mrs. Gruenwald's solid, rope-draped stomach all but returning her blows. "All take hands —march! Into the water! *Don't* let the stobs and cypress roots break your legs! *Do* your best! Kick! Stay on top if you can and hold the rope if necessary!"

Mrs. Gruenwald abruptly walked away from Jinny Love, out of the bathrobe, and entered the lake with a vast displacing. She left them on the bank with her Yankee advice.

The Morgana girls might never have gone in if the orphans hadn't balked. Easter came to a dead stop at Moon Lake and looked at it squinting as though it floated really on the Moon. And mightn't it be on the Moon?—it was a strange place, Nina thought, unlikely—and three miles from Morgana, Mississippi, all the time. The Morgana girls pulled the orphans' hands and dragged them in, or pushed suddenly from behind, and finally the orphans took hold of one another and waded forward in a body, singing "Good Morning" with their stiff, chiplike lips. None of them could or would swim, ever, and they just stood waist-deep and waited for the dip to be over. A few of them reached out and caught the struggling Morgana girls by the legs as they splashed from one barky post to another, to see how hard it really was to stay up.

"Mrs. Gruenwald, look, they want to drown us."

But Mrs. Gruenwald all this time was rising and sinking like a whale, she was in a sea of her own waves and perhaps of self-generated cold, out in the middle of the lake. She cared little that Morgana girls who learned to swim were getting a dollar from home. She had deserted them, no, she had never really been with them. Not only orphans had she deserted. In the water she kept so much to the profile that her single pushing-out eyeball looked like a little bottle of something. It was said she believed in evolution.

While the Boy Scout in the rosy light under the green trees twirled his horn so that it glittered and ran a puzzle in the sun, and emptied the spit out of it, he yawned, snappingly—as if he would bite the day, as quickly as Easter had bitten Deacon Nesbitt's hand on Opening Day.

"Gee, we think you're mighty nice," they sang to Mr. Dip, gasping, pounding their legs in him. If they let their feet go down, the invisible bottom of the lake felt like soft, knee-deep fur. The sharp hard knobs came up where least expected. The Morgana girls of course wore bathing slippers, and the mud loved to suck them off. The alligators had been beaten out of this lake, but it was said that water snakes—pilots— were swimming here and there; they would bite you but not kill you; and one cottonmouth moccasin was still getting away from the niggers— if the niggers were still going after him; he would kill you. These were the chances of getting sucked under, of being bitten, and of dying three miles away from home.

The brown water cutting her off at the chest, Easter looked directly before her, wide awake, unsmiling. Before she could hold a stare like that, she would have had to swallow something big—so Nina felt. It would have been something so big that it didn't matter to her what the inside of a snake's mouth was lined with. At the other end of her gaze the life saver grew almost insignificant. Her gaze moved like a little switch or wand, and the life saver scratched himself with his bugle, raked himself, as if that eased him. Yet the flick of a blue-bottle fly made Easter jump.

They swam and held to the rope, hungry and waiting. But they had to keep waiting till Loch Morrison blew his horn before they could come out of Moon Lake. Mrs. Gruenwald, who capered before breakfast, believed in evolution, and put her face in the water, was quarter of a mile out. If she said anything, they couldn't hear her for the frogs.

— 2 —

Nina and Jinny Love, with the soles of their feet shocked from the walk, found Easter ahead of them down at the spring.

For the orphans, from the first, sniffed out the way to the spring by themselves, and they could get there without stops to hold up their feet and pull out thorns and stickers, and could run through the sandy bottoms and never look down where they were going, and could grab hold with their toes on the sharp rutted path up the pine ridge and down. They clearly could never get enough of skimming over the silk-slick needles and setting prints of their feet in the bed of the spring to see them dissolve away under their eyes. What was it to them if the spring was muddied by the time Jinny Love Stark got there?

The one named Easter could fall flat as a boy, elbows cocked, and drink from the cup of her hand with her face in the spring. Jinny Love prodded Nina, and while they looked on Easter's drawers, Nina was opening the drinking cup she had brought with her, then collapsing it, feeling like a lady with a fan. That way, she was going over a thought, a fact: Half the people out here with me are orphans. Orphans. She yearned for her heart to twist. But it didn't, not in time. Easter was through drinking—wiping her mouth and flinging her hand as if to break the bones, to get rid of the drops, and it was Nina's turn with her drinking cup.

Nina stood and bent over from the waist. Calmly, she held her cup in the spring and watched it fill. They could all see how it spangled like a cold star in the curling water. The water tasted the silver cool of the rim it went over running to her lips, and at moments the cup gave her teeth a pang. Nina heard her own throat swallowing. She paused and threw a smile about her. After she had drunk she wiped the cup on her tie and collapsed it, and put the little top on, and its ring over her finger. With that, Easter, one arm tilted, charged against the green bank and mounted it. Nina felt her surveying the spring and all from above. Jinny Love was down drinking like a chicken, kissing the water only.

Easter was dominant among the orphans. It was not that she was so bad. The one called Geneva stole, for example, but Easter was dominant for what she was in herself—for the way she held still, sometimes. All orphans were at once wondering and stoic—at one moment loving everything too much, the next folding back from it, tightly as hard green buds growing in the wrong direction, closing as they go. But it was as if Easter signaled them. Now she just stood up there, watching the spring, with the name Easter—tacky name, as Jinny Love Stark was the first to say. She was medium size, but her hair seemed to fly up at the

temples, being cropped and wiry, and this crest made her nearly as tall
as Jinny Love Stark. The rest of the orphans had hair paler than their
tanned foreheads—straight and tow, the greenish yellow of cornsilk that
dimmed black at the roots and shadows, with burnt-out-looking bangs
like young boys' and old men's hair; that was from picking in the fields.
Easter's hair was a withstanding gold. Around the back of her neck beneath the hair was a dark band on her skin like the mark a gold
bracelet leaves on the arm. It came to the Morgana girls with a feeling
of elation: the ring was pure dirt. They liked to look at it, or to remember, too late, what it was—as now, when Easter had already lain down
for a drink and left the spring. They liked to walk behind her and see
her back, which seemed spectacular from crested gold head to hard,
tough heel. Mr. Nesbitt, from the Bible Class, took Easter by the wrist
and turned her around to him and looked just as hard at her front. She
had started her breasts. What Easter did was to bite his right hand, his
collection hand. It was wonderful to have with them someone dangerous
but not, so far, or provenly, bad. When Nina's little lead-mold umbrella,
the size of a clover, a Crackerjack prize, was stolen the first night of
camp, that was Geneva, Easter's friend.

Jinny Love, after wiping her face with a handmade handkerchief,
pulled out a deck of cards she had secretly brought in her middy pocket.
She dropped them down, bright blue, on a sandy place by the spring.
"Let's play cassino. Do they call you *Easter?*"

Down Easter jumped, from the height of the bank. She came back
to them. "Cassino, what's that?"

"All right, what do *you* want to play?"

"All right, I'll play you mumblety-peg."

"I don't know how you play that!" cried Nina.

"Who would ever want to know?" asked Jinny Love, closing the circle.

Easter flipped out a jackknife and with her sawed fingernail shot out
three blades.

"Do you carry that in the orphan asylum?" Jinny Love asked with
some respect.

Easter dropped to her scarred and coral-colored knees. They saw the
dirt. "Get down if you want to play me mumblety-peg," was all she said,
"and watch out for your hands and faces."

They huddled down on the piney sand. The vivid, hurrying ants
were everywhere. To the squinted eye they looked like angry, orange
ponies as they rode the pine needles. There was Geneva, skirting behind
a tree, but she never came close or tried to get in the game. She pretended to be catching doodlebugs. The knife leaped and quivered in the
sandy arena smoothed by Easter's hand.

"I may not know how to play, but I bet I win," Jinny Love said.

Easter's eyes, lifting up, were neither brown nor green nor cat; they

had something of metal, flat ancient metal, so that you could not see
into them. Nina's grandfather had possessed a box of coins from Greece
and Rome. Easter's eyes could have come from Greece or Rome that
day. Jinny Love stopped short of apprehending this, and only took care
to watch herself when Easter pitched the knife. The color in Easter's
eyes could have been found somewhere, away—away, under lost leaves—
strange as the painted color of the ants. Instead of round black holes in
the center of her eyes, there might have been women's heads, ancient.

Easter, who had played so often, won. She nodded and accepted
Jinny Love's barrette and from Nina a blue jay feather which she transferred to her own ear.

"I wouldn't be surprised if you cheated, and don't know what you
had to lose if you lost," said Jinny Love thoughtfully but with an admiration almost fantastic in her.

Victory with a remark attached did not crush Easter at all, or she
scarcely listened. Her indifference made Nina fall back and listen to
the spring running with an endless sound and see how the July light
like purple and yellow birds kept flickering under the trees when the
wind blew. Easter turned her head and the new feather on her head
shone changeably. A black funnel of bees passed through the air, throw-
ing a funneled shadow, like a visitor from nowhere, another planet.

"We have to play again to see whose the drinking cup will be,"
Easter said, swaying forward on her knees.

Nina jumped to her feet and did a cartwheel. Against the spinning
green and blue her heart pounded as heavily as she touched lightly.

"You ruined the game," Jinny Love informed Easter. "You don't know
Nina." She gathered up her cards. "You'd think it was made of fourteen-
carat gold, and didn't come out of the pocket of an old suitcase, that
cup."

"I'm sorry," said Nina sincerely.

As the three were winding around the lake, a bird flying above the
opposite shore kept uttering a cry and then diving deep, plunging into
the trees there, and soaring to cry again.

"Hear him?" one of the niggers said, fishing on the bank; it was Elberta's sister Twosie, who spoke as if a long, long conversation had been
going on, into which she would intrude only the mildest words. "Know
why? Know why, in de sky, he say 'Spirit? Spirit?' And den he dive
boom and say 'GHOST'?"

"Why does he?" said Jinny Love, in a voice of objection.

"Yawl knows. *I* don't know," said Twosie, in her little high, helpless
voice, and she shut her eyes. They couldn't seem to get on by her. On
fine days there is danger of some sad meeting, the positive danger of it.
"*I* don't know what he say dat for." Twosie spoke pitifully, as though

accused. She sighed. "Yawl sho ain't got yo' eyes opem good, yawl. Yawl
don't know what's out here in woods wid you."

"Well, what?"

"Yawl walk right by mans wid great big gun, could jump out at yawl.
Yawl don't eem smellim."

"You mean Mr. Holifield? That's a flashlight he's got." Nina looked
at Jinny Love for confirmation. Mr. Holifield was their handy man, or
rather simply "the man to be sure and have around the camp." He
could be found by beating for a long time on the porch of the American
Legion boat house—he slept heavily. "He hasn't got a gun to jump out
with."

"I know who you mean. I hear those boys. Just some big boys, like
the MacLain twins or somebody, and who cares about them?" Jinny
Love, with her switch indented the thick mat of hair on Twosie's head
and prodded and stirred it gently. She pretended to fish in Twosie's
woolly head. "Why ain't *you* scared, then?"

"I is."

Twosie's eyelids fluttered. Already she seemed to be fishing in her
night's sleep. While they gazed at her crouched, devoted figure, from
which the long pole hung, so steady and beggarlike and ordained an
appendage, all their passions flew home again and went huddled and
soft to roost.

Back at the camp, Jinny Love told Miss Moody about the great big
jackknife. Easter gave it up.

"I didn't mean you couldn't *drink* out of my cup," Nina said, waiting
for her. "Only you have to hold it carefully, it leaks. It's engraved."

Easter wouldn't even try it, though Nina dangled it on its ring right
under her eyes. She didn't say anything, not even "It's pretty." Was she
even thinking of it? Or if not, what did she think about?

"Sometimes orphans act like deaf-and-dumbs," said Jinny Love.

— 3 —

"Nina!" Jinny Love whispered across the tent, during siesta. "What do
you think you're reading?"

Nina closed *The Re-Creation of Brian Kent*. Jinny Love was already
coming directly across the almost-touching cots to Nina's, walking on her
knees and bearing down over Gertrude, Etoile, and now Geneva.

With Jinny Love upon her, Geneva sighed. Her sleeping face looked
as if she didn't want to. She slept as she swam, in her pantie-waist, she
was in running position and her ribs went up and down frantically—a
little box in her chest that expanded and shut without a second's rest

between. Her cheek was pearly with afternoon moisture and her kitten-like teeth pearlier still. As Jinny Love hid her and went over, Nina seemed to see her still; even her vaccination mark looked too big for her.

Nobody woke up from being walked over, but after Jinny Love had fallen in bed with Nina, Easter gave a belated, dreaming sound. She had not even been in the line of march; she slept on the cot by the door, curved shell-like, both arms forward over her head. It was an inward sound she gave—now it came again—of such wholehearted and fateful concurrence with the thing dreamed, that Nina and Jinny Love took hands and made wry faces at each other.

Beyond Easter's cot the corona of afternoon flared and lifted in an intensity that came through the eyelids. There was nothing but light out there. True, the black Negroes inhabited it. Elberta moved slowly through it, as if she rocked a baby with her hips, carrying a bucket of scraps to throw in the lake—to get hail Columbia for it later. Her straw hat spiraled rings of orange and violet, like a top. Far, far down a vista of intolerable light, a tiny daub of black cotton, Twosie had stationed herself at the edge of things, and slept and fished.

Eventually there was Exum wandering with his fish pole—he could dance on a dime, Elberta said, he used to work for a blind man. Exum was smart for twelve years old; too smart. He found that hat he wore—not a sign of the owner. He had a hat like new, filled out a little with peanut shells inside the band to correct the size, and he like a little black peanut in it. It stood up and away from his head all around, and seemed only following him—on runners, perhaps, like those cartridges for change in Spights' store.

Easter's sighs and her prolonged or half-uttered words now filled the tent, just as the heat filled it. Her words fell in threes, Nina observed, like the mourning-dove's call in the woods.

Nina and Jinny Love lay speechless, doubling for themselves the already strong odor of Sweet Dreams Mosquito Oil, in a trance of endurance through the hour's siesta. Entwined, they stared—orphanlike themselves—past Easter's cot and through the tent opening as down a long telescope turned on an incandescent star, and saw the spiral of Elberta's hat return, and saw Exum jump over a stick and on the other side do a little dance in a puff of dust. They could hear the intermittent crash, splash of Loch Morrison using their lake, and Easter's voice calling again in her sleep, her unintelligible words.

But however Nina and Jinny Love made faces at they knew not what, Easter concurred; she thoroughly agreed.

The bugle blew for swimming. Geneva jumped so hard she fell off her cot. Nina and Jinny Love were indented with each other, like pressed leaves, and jumped free. When Easter, who had to be shaken, sat up drugged and stupid on her cot, Nina ran over to her.

"Listen. Wake up. Look, you can go in in my bathing shoes today."

She felt her eyes glaze with this plan of kindness as she stretched out her limp red shoes that hung down like bananas under Easter's gaze. But Easter dropped back on the cot and stretched her legs.

"Never mind your shoes. I don't have to go in the lake if I don't want to."

"You do. I never heard of that. Who picked you out? You do," they said, all gathering.

"You make me."

Easter yawned. She fluttered her eyes and rolled them back—she loved doing that. Miss Moody passed by and beamed in at them hovered around Easter's passive and mutinous form. All along she'd been afraid of some challenge to her counselorship, from the way she hurried by now, almost too daintily.

"Well, *I* know," Jinny Love said, sidling up. "I know as much as you know, Easter." She made a chant, which drove her hopping around the tent pole in an Indian step. "You don't have to go, if you don't want to go. And if it ain't so, you still don't have to go, if you don't want to go." She kissed her hand to them.

Easter was silent—but if she groaned when she waked, she'd only be imitating herself.

Jinny Love pulled on her bathing cap, which gave way and came down over her eyes. Even in blindness, she cried, "So you needn't think you're the only one, Easter, not always. What do you say to that?"

"I should worry, I should cry," said Easter, lying still, spread-eagled.

"Let's us run away from basket weaving," Jinny Love said in Nina's ear, a little later in the week.

"Just as soon."

"Grand. They'll think we're drowned."

They went out the back end of the tent, barefooted; their feet were as tough as anybody's by this time. Down in the hammock, Miss Moody was reading *The Re-Creation of Brian Kent* now. (Nobody knew whose book that was, it had been found here, the covers curled up like side combs. Perhaps anybody at Moon Lake who tried to read it felt cheated by the title, as applying to camp life, as Nina did, and laid it down for the next person.) Cat, the niggers' cat, was sunning on a post and when they approached jumped to the ground like something poured out of a bottle, and went with them, in front.

They trudged down the slope past Loch Morrison's tent and took the track into the swamp. There they moved single file between two walls; by lifting their arms they could have touched one or the other pressing side of the swamp. Their toes exploded the dust that felt like the powder clerks pump into new kid gloves, as Jinny Love said twice. They were eye to eye with the finger-shaped leaves of the castor bean plants, put out like those gypsy hands that part the curtains at the back of rolling wagons, and wrinkled and coated over like the fortuneteller's face.

Mosquitoes struck at them; Sweet Dreams didn't last. The whining lifted like a voice, saying "I don't want. . . ." At the girls' shoulders Queen Anne's lace and elderberry and blackberry thickets, loaded heavily with flower and fruit and smelling with the melony smell of snake, overhung the ditch to touch them. The ditches had dried green or blue bottoms, cracked and glazed—like a dropped vase. "I hope we don't meet any nigger men," Jinny Love said cheerfully.

Sweet bay and cypress and sweetgum and live oak and swamp maple closing tight made the wall dense, and yet there was somewhere still for the other wall of vine; it gathered itself on the ground and stacked and tilted itself in the trees; and like a table in the tree the mistletoe hung up there black in the zenith. Buzzards floated from one side of the swamp to the other, as if choice existed for them—raggedly crossing the sky and shadowing the track, and shouldering one another on the solitary limb of a moon-white sycamore. Closer to the ear than lips could begin words came the swamp sounds—closer to the ear and nearer to the dreaming mind. They were a song of hilarity to Jinny Love, who began to skip. Periods of silence seemed hoarse, or the suffering from hoarseness, otherwise inexplicable, as though the world could stop. Cat was stalking something at the black edge of the ditch. The briars didn't trouble Cat at all, it was they that seemed to give way beneath that long, boatlike belly.

The track serpentined again, and walking ahead was Easter. Geneva and Etoile were playing at her side, edging each other out of her shadow, but when they saw who was coming up behind them, they turned and ran tearing back towards camp, running at angles, like pullets, leaving a cloud of dust as they passed by.

"Wouldn't you know!" said Jinny Love.

Easter was going unconcernedly on, her dress stained green behind; she ate something out of her hand as she went.

"We'll soon catch up—don't hurry."

The reason orphans were the way they were lay first in nobody's watching them, Nina thought, for she felt obscurely like a trespasser. They, they were not answerable. Even on being watched, Easter remained not answerable to a soul on earth. Nobody cared! And so, in this beatific state, something came out of *her*.

"Where are you going?"

"Can we go with you, Easter?"

Easter, her lips stained with blackberries, replied, "It ain't my road."

They walked along, one on each side of her. Though they automatically stuck their tongues out at her, they ran their arms around her waist. She tolerated the closeness for a little while; she smelled of orphan-starch, but she had a strange pure smell of sweat, like a sleeping baby, and in her temple, so close then to their eyes, the skin was transparent enough for a little vein to be seen pounding under it. She seemed very tender and very small in the waist to be trudging along so doggedly, when they had her like that.

Vines, a magnificent and steamy green, covered more and more of the trees, played over them like fountains. There were stretches of water below them, blue-black, netted over with half-closed waterlilies. The horizontal limbs of cypresses grew a short, pale green scruff like bird feathers.

They came to a tiny farm down here, the last one possible before the muck sucked it in—a patch of cotton in flower, a house whitewashed in front, a cleanswept yard with a little iron pump standing in the middle of it like a black rooster. These were white people—an old woman in a sunbonnet came out of the house with a galvanized bucket, and pumped it full in the dooryard. That was an excuse to see people go by.

Easter, easing out of the others' clasp, lifted her arm halfway and turning for an instant, gave two waves of the hand. But the old woman was prouder than she.

Jinny Love said, "How would you all like to live there?"

Cat edged the woods onward, and at moments vanished into a tunnel in the briars. Emerging from other tunnels, he—or she—glanced up at them with a face more masklike than ever.

"There's a short-cut to the lake." Easter, breaking and darting ahead, suddenly went down on her knees and slid under a certain place in the barbed wire fence. Rising, she took a step inward, sinking down as she went. Nina untwined her arm from Jinny Love's and went after her.

"I might have known you'd want us to go through a barbed wire fence." Jinny Love sat down where she was, on the side of the ditch, just as she would take her seat on a needlepoint stool. She jumped up once, and sat back. "Fools, fools!" she called. "Now I think you've made me turn my ankle. Even if I wanted to track through the mud, I couldn't!"

Nina and Easter, dipping under a second, unexpected fence, went on, swaying and feeling their feet pulled down, reaching to the trees. Jinny Love was left behind in the heartless way people and incidents alike are thrown off in the course of a dream, like the gratuitous flowers scattered from a float—rather in celebration. The swamp was now all-enveloping, dark and at the same time vivid, alarming—it was like being inside the chest of something that breathed and might turn over.

Then there was Moon Lake, a different aspect altogether. Easter climbed the slight rise ahead and reached the pink, grassy rim and the innocent open. Here it was quiet, until, fatefully, there was one soft splash.

"You see the snake drop off in the water?" asked Easter.

"Snake?"

"Out of that tree."

"You can have him."

"There he is: coming up!" Easter pointed.

"That's probably a different one," Nina objected in the voice of Jinny Love.

Easter looked both ways, chose, and walked on the pink sandy rim with its purpled lip, her blue shadow lolling over it. She went around a bend, and straight to an old gray boat. Did she know it would be there? It was in some reeds, looking mysterious to come upon and yet in place, as an old boat will. Easter stepped into it and hopped to the far seat that was over the water, and dropping to it lay back with her toes hooked up. She looked falling over backwards. One arm lifted, curved over her head, and hung till her finger touched the water.

The shadows of the willow leaves moved gently on the sand, deep blue and narrow, long crescents. The water was quiet, the color of pewter, marked with purple stobs, although where the sun shone right on it the lake seemed to be in violent agitation, almost boiling. Surely a little chip would turn around and around in it. Nina dropped down on the flecked sandbar. She fluttered her eyelids, half closed them, and the world looked struck by moonlight.

"Here I come," came Jinny Love's voice. It hadn't been long. She came twitching over their tracks along the sandbar, her long soft hair blowing up like a skirt in a play of the breeze in the open. "But I don't choose to sit myself in a leaky boat," she was calling ahead. "I choose the land."

She took her seat on the very place where Nina was writing her name. Nina moved her finger away, drawing a long arrow to a new place. The sand was coarse like beads and full of minute shells, some shaped exactly like bugles.

"Want to hear about my ankle?" Jinny Love asked. "It wasn't as bad as I thought. I must say you picked a queer place, I saw an *owl*. It smells like the school basement to me—peepee and old erasers." Then she stopped with her mouth a little open, and was quiet, as though something had been turned off inside her. Her eyes were soft, her gaze stretched to Easter, to the boat, the lake—her long oval face went vacant.

Easter was lying rocked in the gentle motion of the boat, her head turned on its cheek. She had not said hello to Jinny Love anew. Did she see the drop of water clinging to her lifted finger? Did it make a rainbow? Not to Easter: her eyes were rolled back, Nina felt. Her own hand was writing in the sand. Nina, Nina, Nina. Writing, she could dream that her self might get away from her—that here in this faraway place she could tell her self, by name, to go or to stay. Jinny Love had begun building a sand castle over her foot. In the sky clouds moved no more perceptibly than grazing animals. Yet with a passing breeze, the boat gave a knock, lifted and fell. Easter sat up.

"Why aren't we out in the boat?" Nina, taking a strange and heady initiative, rose to her feet. "Out there!" A picture in her mind, as if already furnished from an eventual and appreciative distance, showed the boat floating where she pointed, far out in Moon Lake with three girls sitting in the three spaces. "We're coming, Easter!"

"Just as I make a castle. I'm not coming," said Jinny Love. "Anyway, there's stobs in the lake. We'd be upset, ha ha."

"What do I care, I can swim!" Nina cried at the water's edge.

"You can just swim from the first post to the second post. And that's in front of camp, not here."

Firming her feet in the sucking, minowy mud, Nina put her weight against the boat. Soon her legs were half hidden, the mud like some awful kiss pulled at her toes, and all over she tautened and felt the sweat start out of her body. Roots laced her feet, knotty and streaming. Under water, the boat was caught too, but Nina was determined to free it. She saw that there was muddy water in the boat too, which Easter's legs, now bright pink, were straddling. Suddenly all seemed easy.

"It's coming loose!"

At the last minute, Jinny Love, who had extracted her foot from the castle with success, hurried over and climbed to the middle seat of the boat, screaming. Easter sat up swaying with the dip of the boat; the energy seemed all to have gone out of her. Her lolling head looked pale and featureless as a pear beyond the laughing face of Jinny Love. She had not said whether she wanted to go or not—yet surely she did; she had been in the boat all along, she had discovered the boat.

For a moment, with her powerful hands, Nina held the boat back. Again she thought of a pear—not the everyday gritty kind that hung on the tree in the backyard, but the fine kind sold on trains and at high prices, each pear with a paper cone wrapping it alone—beautiful, symmetrical, clean pears with thin skins, with snow-white flesh so juicy and tender that to eat one baptized the whole face, and so delicate that while you urgently ate the first half, the second half was already beginning to turn brown. To all fruits, and especially to those fine pears, something happened—the process was so swift, you were never in time for them. It's not the flowers that are fleeting, Nina thought, it's the fruits—it's the time when things are ready that they don't stay. She even went through the rhyme, "Pear tree by the garden gate, How much longer must I wait?"—thinking it was the pears that asked it, not the picker.

Then she climbed in herself, and they were rocking out sideways on the water.

"Now what?" said Jinny Love.

"This is all right for me," said Nina.

"Without oars?—Ha ha."

"Why didn't you tell me, then!—But I don't care now."

"You never are as smart as you think."

"Wait till you find out where we get to."

"I guess you know Easter can't swim. She won't even touch water with her foot."

"What do you think a *boat's* for?"

But a soft tug had already stopped their drifting. Nina with a dark frown turned and looked down.

"A chain! An old mean chain!"

"That's how smart you are."

Nina pulled the boat in again—of course nobody helped her!—burning her hands on the chain, and kneeling outward tried to free the other end. She could see now through the reeds that it was wound around and around an old stump, which had almost grown over it in places. The boat had been chained to the bank since maybe last summer.

"No use hitting it," said Jinny Love.

A dragonfly flew about their heads. Easter only waited in her end of the boat, not seeming to care about the disappointment either. If this was their ship, she was their figurehead, turned on its back, sky-facing. She wouldn't be their passenger.

"You thought we'd all be out in the middle of Moon Lake by now, didn't you?" Jinny Love said, from her lady's seat. "Well, look where we are."

"Oh, Easter! Easter! I wish you still had your knife!"

"—But let's don't go back yet," Jinny Love said on shore. "I don't think they've missed us." She started a sand castle over her other foot.

"You make me sick," said Easter suddenly.

"Nina, let's pretend Easter's not with us."

"But that's what *she* was pretending."

Nina dug into the sand with a little stick, printing "Nina" and then "Easter."

Jinny Love seemed stunned, she let sand run out of both fists. "But how could you ever know what Easter was pretending?"

Easter's hand came down and wiped her name clean; she also wiped out "Nina." She took the stick out of Nina's hand and with a formal gesture, as if she would otherwise seem to reveal too much, wrote for herself. In clear, high-waisted letters the word "Esther" cut into the sand. Then she jumped up.

"Who's that?" Nina asked.

Easter laid her thumb between her breasts, and walked about.

"Why, I call that 'Esther.'"

"Call it 'Esther' if you want to, I call it 'Easter.'"

"Well, sit down. . . ."

"And I named myself."

"How could you? Who let you?"

"I let myself name myself."

"Easter, I believe you," said Nina. "But I just want you to spell it right. Look—E–A–S—"

"I should worry, I should cry."

Jinny Love leaned her chin on the roof of her castle to say, "I was named for my maternal grandmother, so my name's Jinny Love. It couldn't be anything else. Or anything better. You see? Easter's just not a real name. It doesn't matter how she spells it, Nina, nobody ever had it. Not around here." She rested on her chin.

"I have it."

"Just see how it looks spelled right." Nina lifted the stick from Easter's fingers and began to print, but had to throw herself bodily over the name to keep Easter from it. "Spell it right and it's real!" she cried.

"But right or wrong, it's tacky," said Jinny Love. "You can't get me mad over it. All I can concentrate on out here is missing the figs at home."

"'Easter' is real beautiful!" Nina said distractedly. She suddenly threw the stick into the lake, before Easter could grab it, and it trotted up and down in a crucible of sun-filled water. "I thought it was the day you were found on a doorstep," she said sullenly—even distrustfully.

Easter sat down at last and with slow, careful movements of her palms rubbed down the old bites on her legs. Her crest of hair dipped downward and she rocked a little, up and down, side to side, in a rhythm. Easter never did intend to explain anything unless she had to—or to force your explanations. She just had hopes. She hoped never to be sorry. Or did she?

"I haven't got no father. I never had, he ran away. I've got a mother. When I could walk, then my mother took me by the hand and turned me in, and I remember it. I'm going to be a singer."

It was Jinny Love, starting to clear her throat, who released Nina. It was Jinny Love, escaping, burrowing her finger into her castle, who was now kind, pretending Easter had never spoken. Nina banged Jinny Love on the head with her fist. How good and hot her hair was! Like hot glass. She broke the castle from her tender foot. She wondered if Jinny Love's head would break. Not at all. You couldn't learn anything through the head.

"Ha, ha, ha!" yelled Jinny Love, hitting back.

They were fighting and hitting for a moment. Then they lay quiet, tilted together against the crumbled hill of sand, stretched out and looking at the sky where now a white tower of cloud was climbing.

Someone moved; Easter lifted to her lips a piece of cross-vine cut back in the days of her good knife. She brought up a kitchen match from her pocket, lighted up, and smoked.

They sat up and gazed at her.

"If you count much on being a singer, that's not a very good way to start," said Jinny Love. "Even boys, it stunts their growth."

Easter once more looked the same as asleep in the dancing shadows, except for what came out of her mouth, more mysterious, almost, than words.

"Have some?" she asked, and they accepted. But theirs went out.

Jinny Love's gaze was fastened on Easter, and she dreamed and dreamed of telling on her for smoking, while the sun, even through leaves, was burning her pale skin pink, and she looked the most beautiful of all: she felt temptation. But what she said was, "Even after all this is over, Easter, I'll always remember you."

Off in the thick of the woods came a fairy sound, followed by a tremulous silence, a holding apart of the air.

"What's that?" cried Easter sharply. Her throat quivered, the little vein in her temple jumped.

"That's Mister Loch Morrison. Didn't you know he had a horn?"

There was another fairy sound, and the pried-apart, gentle silence. The woods seemed to be moving after it, running—the world pellmell. Nina could see the boy in the distance, too, and the golden horn tilted up. A few minutes back her gaze had fled the present and this scene; now she put the horn blower into his visionary place.

"Don't blow that!" Jinny Love cried out this time, jumping to her feet and stopping up her ears, stamping on the shore of Moon Lake. "You shut up! We can hear!—Come on," she added prosaically to the other two. "It's time to go. I reckon they've worried enough." She smiled. "Here comes Cat."

Cat always caught something; something was in his—or her—mouth, a couple of little feet or claws bouncing under the lifted whiskers. Cat didn't look especially triumphant; just through with it.

They marched on away from their little boat.

— 4 —

One clear night the campers built a fire up above the spring, cooked supper on sticks around it, and after stunts, a recitation of "How They

Brought the Good News from Ghent to Aix" by Gertrude Bowles, and the ghost story about the bone, they stood up on the ridge and poured a last song into the woods—"Little Sir Echo."

The fire was put out and there was no bright point to look into, no circle. The presence of night was beside them—a beast in gossamer, with no shine of outline, only of ornament—rings, earrings. . . .

"March!" cried Mrs. Gruenwald, and stamped down the trail for them to follow. They went single file on the still-warm pine needles, soundlessly now. Not far away there were crackings of twigs, small, regretted crashes; Loch Morrison, supperless for all they knew, was wandering around by himself, sulking, alone.

Nobody needed light. The night sky was pale as a green grape, transparent like grape flesh over each tree. Every girl saw moths—the beautiful ones like ladies, with long legs that were wings—and the little ones, mere bits of bark. And once against the night, just before Little Sister Spights' eyes, making her cry out, hung suspended a spider—a body no less mysterious than the grape of the air, different only a little.

All around swam the fireflies. Clouds of them, trees of them, islands of them floating, a lower order of brightness—one could even get into a tent by mistake. The stars barely showed their places in the pale sky—small and far from this bright world. And the world would be bright as long as these girls held awake, and could keep their eyes from closing. And the moon itself shone—taken for granted.

Moon Lake came in like a flood below the ridge; they trailed downward. Out there Miss Moody would sometimes go in a boat; sometimes she had a late date from town, "Rudy" Spights or "Rudy" Loomis, and then they could be seen drifting there after the moon was up, far out on the smooth bright surface. ("And she lets him hug her out there," Jinny Love had instructed them. "Like this." She had seized, of all people, Etoile, whose name rhymed with tinfoil. "Hands off," said Etoile.) Twice Nina had herself seen the silhouette of the canoe on the bright water, with the figures at each end, like a dark butterfly with wings spread open and still. Not tonight!

Tonight, it was only the niggers, fishing. But their boat must be full of silver fish! Nina wondered if it was the slowness and near-fixity of boats out on the water that made them so magical. Their little boat in the reeds that day had not been far from this one's wonder, after all. The turning of water and sky, of the moon, or the sun, always proceeded, and there was this magical hesitation in their midst, of a boat. And in the boat, it was not so much that they drifted, as that in the presence of a boat the world drifted, forgot. The dreamed-about changed places with the dreamer.

Home from the wild moonlit woods, the file of little girls wormed into the tents, which were hot as cloth pockets. The candles were lighted by Miss Moody, dateless tonight, on whose shelf in the flare of nightly revelation stood her toothbrush in the glass, her hand-painted celluloid powder box, her Honey and Almond cream, her rouge and eyebrow tweezers, and at the end of the line the bottle of Compound, containing true and false unicorn and the life root plant.

Miss Moody, with a fervent frown which precluded interruption, sang in soft tremolo as she rubbed the lined-up children with "Sweet Dreams."

> "Forgive me
> O please forgive me
> I didn't mean to make
> You cry!
> I love you and I need you—"

They crooked and bent themselves and lifted nightgowns to her silently while she sang. Then when she faced them to her they could look into the deep tangled rats of her puffed hair and at her eyebrows which seemed fixed forever in that elevated line of adult pleading.

> "Do anything but don't say good-bye!"

And automatically they almost said, "Good-bye!" Her hands rubbed and cuffed them while she sang, pulling to her girls all just alike, as if girl-hood itself were not an infinity, but a commodity. ("I'm ticklish," Jinny Love informed her every night.) Her look of pleading seemed infinitely perilous to them. Her voice had the sway of an aerialist crossing the high wire, even while she sang out of the nightgown coming down over her head.

There were kisses, prayers. Easter, as though she could be cold tonight, got into bed with Geneva. Geneva like a little June bug hooked onto her back. The candles were blown. Miss Moody ostentatiously went right to sleep. Jinny Love cried into her pillow for her mother, or perhaps for the figs. Just outside their tent, Citronella burned in a saucer in the weeds—Citronella, like a girl's name.

Luminous, of course, but hidden from them, Moon Lake streamed out in the night. By moonlight sometimes it seemed to run like a river. Beyond the cry of the frogs there were the sounds of a boat moored somewhere, of its vague, clumsy reaching at the shore, those sounds that are recognized as being made by something sightless. When did boats have eyes—once? Nothing watched that their little part of the lake stayed roped off and protected; was it there now, the rope stretched frail-like between posts that swayed in mud? That rope was to mark how far the girls could swim. Beyond lay the deep part, some bottomless parts, said Moody. Here and there was the quicksand that stirred your foot-print and kissed your heel. All snakes, harmless and harmful, were freely playing now; they put a trailing, moony division between weed and weed—bright, turning, bright and turning.

Nina still lay dreamily, or she had waked in the night. She heard Gertrude Bowles gasp in a dream, beginning to get her stomach ache, and Etoile begin, slowly, her snore. She thought: Now I can think, in between them. She could not even feel Miss Moody fretting.

The orphan! she thought exultantly. The other way to live. There were secret ways. She thought, Time's really short, I've been only think-ing like the others. It's only interesting, only worthy, to try for the fiercest secrets. To slip into them all—to change. To change for a mo-ment into Gertrude, into Mrs. Gruenwald, into Twosie—into a boy. To *have been* an orphan.

Nina sat up on the cot and stared passionately before her at the night —the pale dark roaring night with its secret step, the Indian night. She felt the forehead, the beaded stars, look in thoughtfully at her.

The pondering night stood rude at the tent door, the opening fold would let it stoop in—it, him—he had risen up inside. Long-armed, or long-winged, he stood in the center there where the pole went up. Nina lay back, drawn quietly from him. But the night knew about Easter. All about her. Geneva had pushed her to the very edge of the cot. Easter's hand hung down, opened outward. Come here, night, Easter might say, tender to a giant, to such a dark thing. And the night, obedient and graceful, would kneel to her. Easter's calloused hand hung open there to the night that had got wholly into the tent.

Nina let her own arm stretch forward opposite Easter's. Her hand too opened, of itself. She lay there a long time motionless, under the night's gaze, its black cheek, looking immovably at her hand, the only part of her now which was not asleep. Its gesture was like Easter's, but Easter's hand slept and her own hand knew—shrank and knew, yet offered still.

"Instead . . . me instead. . . ."

In the cup of her hand, in her filling skin, in the fingers' bursting weight and stillness, Nina felt it: compassion and a kind of competing that were all one, a single ecstasy, a single longing. For the night was not impartial. No, the night loved some more than others, served some more than others. Nina's hand lay open there for a long time, as if its fingers would be its eyes. Then it too slept. She dreamed her hand was helpless to the tearing teeth of wild beasts. At reveille she woke up lying on it. She could not move it. She hit it and bit it until like a cluster of bees it stung back and came to life.

— 5 —

They had seen, without any idea of what he would do—and yet it was just like him—little old Exum toiling up the rough barky ladder and dreaming it up, clinging there monkeylike among the leaves, all eyes and wrinkled forehead.

Exum was apart too, boy and nigger to boot; he constantly moved along an even further fringe of the landscape than Loch, wearing the man's stiff straw hat brilliant as a snowflake. They would see Exum in the hat bobbing along the rim of the swamp like a fisherman's cork, elevated just a bit by the miasma and illusion of the landscape he moved in. It was Exum persistent as a little bug, inching along the foot of the swamp wall, carrying around a fishing cane and minnow can, fishing around the bend from their side of the lake, catching all kinds of things. Things, things. He claimed all he caught, gloating—dangled it and loved it, clasped it with suspicious glee—wouldn't a soul dispute him that? The Boy Scout asked him if he could catch an electric eel and Exum promised it readily—a gift; the challenge was a siesta-long back-and-forth across the water.

Now all rolling eyes, he hung on the ladder, too little to count as looking—too everything-he-was to count as anything.

Beyond him on the diving-board, Easter was standing—high above the others at their swimming lesson. She was motionless, barefooted, and tall with her outgrown, printed dress on her and the sky under her. She had not answered when they called things up to her. They splashed noisily under her calloused, coral-colored foot that hung over.

"How are you going to get down, Easter!" shouted Gertrude Bowles.

Miss Moody smiled understandingly up at Easter. How far, in the water, could Miss Parnell Moody be transformed from a schoolteacher? They had wondered. She wore a canary yellow bathing cap lumpy over her hair, with a rubber butterfly on the front. She wore a brassiere and bloomers under her bathing suit because, said Jinny Love, that was exactly how good she was. She scarcely looked for trouble, immediate trouble—though this was the last day at Moon Lake.

Exum's little wilted black fingers struck at his lips as if playing a tune on them. He put out a foolishly long arm. He held a green willow switch. Later they every one said they saw him—but too late. He gave Easter's heel the tenderest, obscurest little brush, with something of nigger persuasion about it.

She dropped like one hit in the head by a stone from a sling. In their retrospect, her body, never turning, seemed to languish upright for a moment, then descend. It went to meet and was received by blue air. It dropped as if handed down all the way and was let into the brown water almost on Miss Moody's crown, and went out of sight at once. There was something so positive about its disappearance that only the instinct of caution made them give it a moment to come up again; it didn't come up. Then Exum let loose a girlish howl and clung to the ladder as though a fire had been lighted under it.

Nobody called for Loch Morrison. On shore, he studiously hung his bugle on the tree. He was enormously barefooted. He took a frog dive and when he went through the air they noticed that the powdered-on dirt gave him lavender soles. Now he swam destructively into the water, cut through the girls, and began to hunt Easter where all the fingers began to point.

They cried while he hunted, their chins dropping into the brown buggy stuff and their mouths sometimes swallowing it. He didn't give a glance their way. He stayed under as though the lake came down a lid on him, at each dive. Sometimes, open-mouthed, he appeared with something awful in his hands, showing not them, but the world, or himself— long ribbons of green and terrible stuff, shapeless black matter, nobody's shoe. Then he would up-end and go down, hunting her again. Each dive was a call on Exum to scream again.

"Shut up! Get out of the way! You stir up the lake!" Loch Morrison yelled once—blaming them. They looked at one another and after one loud cry all stopped crying. Standing in the brown that cut them off where they waited, ankle-deep, waist-deep, knee-deep, chin-deep, they made a little V, with Miss Moody in front and partly obscuring their vision with her jerky butterfly cap. They felt his insult. They stood so still as to be almost carried away, in the pictureless warm body of lake around them, until they felt the weight of the currentless water pulling anyhow. Their shadows only, like the curled back edges of a split drum, showed where they each protruded out of Moon Lake.

Up above, Exum howled, and further up, some fulsome, vague clouds with uneasy hearts blew peony-like. Exum howled up, down, and all around. He brought Elberta, mad, from the cook tent, and surely Mrs. Gruenwald was dead to the world—asleep or reading—or she would be coming too, by now, capering down her favorite trail. It was Jinny Love, they realized, who had capered down, and now stood strangely signaling from shore. The painstaking work of Miss Moody, white bandages covered her arms and legs; poison ivy had appeared that morning. Like Easter, Jinny Love had no intention of going in the lake.

"Ahhhhh!" everybody said, long and drawn out, just as he found her.

Of course he found her, there was her arm sliding through his hand. They saw him snatch the hair of Easter's head, the way a boy will snatch anything he wants, as if he won't have invisible opponents snatching first. Under the water he joined himself to her. He spouted, and with engine-like jerks brought her in.

There came Mrs. Gruenwald. With something like a skip, she came to a stop on the bank and waved her hands. Her middy blouse flew up, showing her loosened corset. It was red. They treasured that up. But her voice was pre-emptory.

"This minute! Out of the lake! Out of the lake, out-out! Parnell! Discipline! March them out."

"One's drowned!" shrieked poor Miss Moody.

Loch stood over Easter. He sat her up, folding, on the shore, wheeled her arm over, and by that dragged her clear of the water before he dropped her, a wrapped bundle in the glare. He shook himself in the sun like a dog, blew his nose, spat, and shook his ears, all in a kind of leisurely trance that kept Mrs. Gruenwald off—as though he had no notion that he was interrupting things at all. Exum could now be heard shrieking for Miss Marybelle Steptoe, the lady who had had the camp last year and was now married and living in the Delta.

Miss Moody and all her girls now came out of the lake. Tardy, drooping, their hair heavy-wet and their rubber shoes making wincing sounds, they edged the shore.

Loch returned to Easter, spread her out, and then they could all get at her, but they watched the water lake in her lap. The sun like a weight fell on them. Miss Moody wildly ran and caught up Easter's ankle and pushed on her, like a lady with a wheelbarrow. The Boy Scout looped Easter's arms like sashes on top of her and took up his end, the shoulders. They carried her, looking for shade. One arm fell, touching ground. Jinny Love, in the dazzling bandages, ran up and scooped Easter's arm in both of hers. They proceeded, zigzag, Jinny Love turning her head toward the rest of them, running low, bearing the arm.

They put her down in the only shade on earth, after all, the table under the tree. It was where they ate. The table was itself still mostly tree, as the ladder and diving board were half tree too; a camp table had to be round and barky on the underside, and odorous of having been chopped down. They knew that splintery surface, and the ants that crawled on it. Mrs. Gruenwald, with her strong cheeks, blew on the table, but she might have put a cloth down. She stood between table and girls; her tennis shoes, like lesser corsets, tied her feet solid there; and they did not go any closer, but only to where they could see.

"I got her, please ma'am."

In the water, the lifesaver's face had held his whole impatience; now it was washed pure, blank. He pulled Easter his way, away from Miss Moody—who, however, had got Easter's sash ends wrung out—and then, with a turn, hid her from Mrs. Gruenwald. Holding her folded up to him, he got her clear, and the next moment, with a spread of his hand, had her lying there before him on the table top.

They were silent. Easter lay in a mold of wetness from Moon Lake, on her side; sharp as a flatiron her hipbone pointed up. She was arm to arm and leg to leg in a long fold, wrong-colored and pressed together as unopen leaves are. Her breasts, too, faced together. Out of the water Easter's hair was darkened, and lay over her face in long fern shapes. Miss Moody laid it back.

"You can tell she's not breathing," said Jinny Love.

Easter's nostrils were pinched-looking like an old country woman's. Her side fell slack as a dead rabbit's in the woods, with the flowers of her orphan dress all running together in some antic of their own, some belated mix-up of the event. The Boy Scout had only let her go to leap onto the table with her. He stood over her, put his hands on her, and rolled her over; they heard the distant-like knock of her forehead on the solid table, and the knocking of her hip and knee.

Exum was heard being whipped in the willow clump; then they remembered Elberta was his mother. "You little black son-a-bitch!" they heard her yelling, and he howled through the woods.

Astride Easter the Boy Scout lifted her up between his legs and dropped her. He did it again, and she fell on one arm. He nodded—not to them.

There was a sigh, a Morgana sigh, not an orphans'. The orphans did not press forward, or claim to own or protect Easter any more. They did nothing except mill a little, and yet their group was delicately changed. In Nina's head, where the world was still partly leisurely, came a recollected scene: birds on a roof under a cherry tree; they were drunk.

The Boy Scout, nodding, took Easter's hair and turned her head. He left her face looking at them. Her eyes were neither open nor altogther shut but as if her ears heard a great noise, back from the time she fell; the whites showed under the lids pale and slick as watermelon seeds. Her lips were parted to the same degree; her teeth could be seen smeared with black mud.

The Boy Scout reached in and gouged out her mouth with his hand, an unbelievable act. She did not alter. He lifted up, screwed his toes, and with a groan of his own fell upon her and drove up and down upon her, into her, gouging the heels of his hands into her ribs again and again. She did not alter except that she let a thin stream of water out of her mouth, a dark stain down the fixed cheek. The children drew together. Lifesaving was much worse than they had dreamed. Worse still was the carelessness of Easter's body.

Jinny Love volunteered once more. She would wave a towel over things to drive the mosquitoes, at least, away. She chose a white towel. Her unspotted arms lifted and crisscrossed. She faced them now; her expression quietened and became ceremonious.

Easter's body lay up on the table to receive anything that was done to it. If *he* was brutal, her self, her body, the withheld life, was brutal too. While the Boy Scout as if he rode a runaway horse clung momently to her and arched himself off her back, dug his knees and fists into her and was flung back careening by his own tactics, she lay there.

Let him try and try!

The next thing Nina knew was a scent of home, an adult's thumb in her shoulder, and a cry, "Now what?" Miss Lizzie Stark rushed in front of her, where her hips and black purse swung to a full stop, blotting out everything. She was Jinny Love's mother and had arrived on her daily visit to see how the camp was running.

They never heard the electric car coming, but usually they saw it, watched for it in the landscape, as out of place as a piano rocking over the holes and taking the bumps, making a high wall of dust.

Nobody dared tell Miss Lizzie; only Loch Morrison's grunts could be heard.

"Some orphan get too much of it?" Then she said more loudly, "But what's *he* doing to her? Stop that."

The Morgana girls all ran to her and clung to her skirt.

"Get off me," she said. "Now look here, everybody. I've got a weak heart. You all know that—Is that *Jinny Love?*"

"Leave me alone, Mama," said Jinny Love, waving the towel.

Miss Lizzie, whose hands were on Nina's shoulders, shook Nina. "Jinny Love Stark, come here to me, Loch Morrison, get off that table and shame on you."

Miss Moody was the one brought to tears. She walked up to Miss Lizzie holding a towel in front of her breast and weeping. "He's our life saver, Miss Lizzie. Remember? Our Boy Scout. Oh, mercy, I'm thankful you've come, he's been doing that a long time. Stand in the shade, Miss Lizzie."

"Boy Scout? Why, he ought to be—he ought to be—I can't stand it, Parnell Moody."

"Can't any of us help it, Miss Lizzie. Can't any of us. It's what he came for." She wept.

"That's Easter," Geneva said. "That is."

"He ought to be put out of business," Miss Lizzie Stark said. She stood in the center of them all, squeezing Nina uncomfortably for Jinny Love, who flouted her up in front, and Nina could look up at her. The white rice powder which she used on the very front of her face twinkled on her faint mustache. She smelled of red pepper and lemon juice—she had been making them some mayonnaise. She was valiantly trying to make up for all the Boy Scout was doing by what she was thinking of him: that he was odious. Miss Lizzie's carelessly flung word to him on sight—the first day—had been, "You little rascal, I bet you run down and pollute the spring, don't you?" "Nome," the Boy Scout had said, show-ing the first evidence of his gloom,

"Tears won't help, Parnell," Miss Lizzie said. "Though some don't know what tears are." She glanced at Mrs. Gruenwald, who glanced back from another level; she had brought herself out a chair. "And our last afternoon. I'd thought we'd have a treat."

They looked around as here came Marvin, Miss Lizzie's yard boy, holding two watermelons like a mother with twins. He came toward the table and just stood there.

"Marvin. You can put those melons down, don't you see the table's got somebody on it?" Miss Lizzie said. "Put 'em down and wait."

Her presence made this whole happening seem more in the nature of things. They were glad Miss Lizzie had come! It was somehow for this that they had given those yells for Miss Lizzie as Camp Mother. Under her gaze the Boy Scout's actions seemed to lose a good deal of significance. He was reduced almost to a nuisance—a mosquito, with a mosquito's proboscis. "Get him off her," Miss Lizzie repeated, in her rich and yet careless, almost humorous voice, knowing it was no good. "Ah, get him off her." She stood hugging the other little girls, several of them, warmly. Her gaze only hardened on Jinny Love; they hugged her all the more.

She loved them. It seemed the harder it was to get out here and the harder a time she found them having, the better she appreciated them. They remembered now—while the Boy Scout still drove up and down on Easter's muddy back—how they were always getting ready for Miss Lizzie; the tents even now were straight and the ground picked up and raked for her, and the tea for supper was already made and sitting in a tub in the lake; and sure enough, the niggers' dog had barked at the car just as always, and now here she was. She could have stopped every-thing; and she hadn't stopped it. Even her opening protests seemed now like part of things—what she was supposed to say. Several of the little girls looked up at Miss Lizzie instead of at what was on the table. Her powdered lips flickered, her eyelids hooded her gaze, but she was there.

On the table, the Boy Scout spat, and took a fresh appraisal of Easter. He reached for a hold on her hair and pulled her head back. No longer were her lips faintly parted—her mouth was open. It gaped. So did his. He dropped her, the head with its suddenness bowed again on its cheek, and he started again.

"Easter's dead! Easter's d—" cried Gertrude Bowles in a rowdy voice, and she was slapped rowdily across the mouth to cut off the word, by Miss Lizzie's hand.

Jinny Love, with a persistence they had not dreamed of, deployed the towel. Could it be owing to Jinny Love's always being on the right side that Easter mustn't dare die and bring all this to a stop? Nina thought, It's I that's thinking. Easter's not thinking at all. And while not thinking, she is not dead, but unconscious, which is even harder to be. Easter had come among them and had held herself untouchable and intact. Of course, for one little touch could smirch her, make her fall so far, so deep. Except that by that time they were all saying the nigger deliberately poked her off in the water, meant her to drown.

"Don't touch her," they said tenderly to one another.

"Give up! Give up! Give up!" screamed Miss Moody—she who had rubbed them all the same, as if she rubbed chickens for the frying pan. Miss Lizzie without hesitation slapped her too.

"Don't touch her."

For they were crowding closer to the table all the time.

"If Easter's dead, I get her coat for winter, all right," said Geneva.

"Hush, orphan."

"Is she then?"

"You shut up." The Boy Scout looked around and panted at Geneva. "You can ast *me* when I ast you to ast me."

The niggers' dog was barking again, had been barking.

"Now who?"

"A big boy. It's old Ran MacLain and he's coming."

"He would."

He came right up, wearing a cap.

"Get away from me, Ran MacLain," Miss Lizzie called toward him. "You and dogs and guns, keep away. We've already got all we can put up with out here."

She put her foot down on his asking any questions, getting up on the table, or leaving, now that he'd come. Under his cap bill, Ran MacLain set his gaze—he was twenty-three, his seasoned gaze—on Loch and Easter on the table. He could not be prevented from considering them all. He moved under the tree. He held his gun under his arm. He let two dogs run loose, and almost imperceptibly, he chewed gum. Only Miss Moody did not move away from him.

And pressing closer to the table, Nina almost walked into Easter's arm flung out over the edge. The arm was turned at the elbow so that the hand opened upward. It held there the same as it had held when the night came in and stood in the tent, when it had come to Easter and not to Nina. It was the one hand, and it seemed the one moment.

"Don't touch her."

Nina fainted. She woke up to the cut-onion odor of Elberta's underarm. She was up on the table with Easter, foot to head. There was so much she loved at home, but there was only time to remember the front

yard. The silver, sweet-smelling paths strewed themselves behind the
lawn mower, the four-o'clocks blazed. Then Elberta raised her up, she
got down from the table, and was back with the others.

"Keep away. Keep away, I told you you better keep away. Leave me
alone," Loch Morrison was saying with short breaths. "I dove for her,
didn't I?"

They hated him, Nina most of all. Almost, they hated Easter.

They looked at Easter's mouth and at the eyes where they were con-
templating without sense the back side of the light. Though she had
bullied and repulsed them earlier, they began to speculate in another
kind of allurement: was there danger that Easter, turned in on herself,
might call out to them after all, from the other, worse, side of it? Her
secret voice, if soundless then possibly visible, might work out of her
terrible mouth like a vine, preening and sprung with flowers. Or a snake
would come out.

The Boy Scout crushed in her body and blood came out of her mouth.
For them all, it was like being spoken to.

"Nina, you! Come stand right here in my skirt," Miss Lizzie called.
Nina went and stood under the big bosom that started down, at the
neck of her dress, like a big cloven white hide.

Jinny Love was catching her mother's eye. Of course she had stolen
brief rests, but now her white arms lifted the white towel and whipped
it bravely. She looked at them until she caught their eye—as if in the
end the party was for *her*.

Marvin had gone back to the car and brought two more melons, which
he stood holding.

"Marvin. We aren't ready for our watermelon. I told you."

"Oh, Ran. How could you? Oh, Ran."

That was Miss Moody in still a third manifestation.

By now the Boy Scout seemed forever part of Easter and she part of
him, he in motion on the up-and-down and she stretched across. He was
dripping, while her skirt dried on the table; so in a manner they had
changed places too. Was time moving? Endlessly, Ran MacLain's dogs
frisked and played, with the niggers' dog between.

Time was moving because in the beginning Easter's face—the curve
of her brow, the soft upper lip and the milky eyes—partook of the
swoon of her fall—the almost forgotten fall that bathed her so purely in
blue for that long moment. The face was set now, and ugly with that
rainy color of seedling petunias, the kind nobody wants. Her mouth
surely by now had been open long enough, as long as any gape, bite,
cry, hunger, satisfaction lasts, any one person's grief, or even protest.

Not all the children watched, and their heads all were beginning to
hang, to nod. Everybody had forgotten about crying. Nina had spotted

three little shells in the sand she wanted to pick up when she could. And suddenly this seemed to her one of those moments out of the future, just as she had found one small brief one out of the past; this was far, far ahead of her—picking up the shells, one, another, another, without time moving any more, and Easter abandoned on a little edifice, beyond dying and beyond being remembered about.

"I'm so tired!" Gertrude Bowles said. "And hot. Ain't you tired of Easter, laying up there on that table?"

"My arms are about to break, you all," and Jinny Love stood and hugged them to her.

"I'm so tired of Easter," Gertrude said.

"Wish she'd go ahead and die and get it over with," said Little Sister Spights, who had been thumb-sucking all afternoon without a reprimand.

"I give up," said Jinny Love.

Miss Lizzie beckoned, and she came. "I and Nina and Easter all went out in the woods, and I was the only one that came back with poison ivy," she said, kissing her mother.

Miss Lizzie sank her fingers critically into the arms of the girls at her skirt. They all rose on tiptoe. Was Easter dead then?

Looking out for an instant from precarious holds, they took in sharply for memory's sake that berated figure, the mask formed and set on the face, one hand displayed, one jealously clawed under the waist, as if a secret handful had been groveled for, the spread and spotted legs. It was a betrayed figure, the betrayal was over, it was a memory. And then as the blows, automatic now, swung down again, the figure itself gasped.

"Get back. Get back." Loch Morrison spoke between cruel, gritted teeth to them, and crouched over.

And when they got back, her toes webbed outward. Her belly arched and drew up from the board under her. She fell, but she kicked the Boy Scout.

Ridiculously, he tumbled backwards off the table. He fell almost into Miss Lizzie's skirt; she halved herself on the instant, and sat on the ground with her lap spread out before her like some magnificent hat that has just got crushed. Ran MacLain hurried politely over to pick her up, but she fought him off.

"Why don't you go home—now!" she said.

Before their eyes, Easter got to her knees, sat up, and drew her legs up to her. She rested her head on her knees and looked out at them, while she slowly pulled her ruined dress downward.

The sun was setting. They felt it directly behind them, the warmth flat as a hand. Easter leaned slightly over the table's edge, as if to gaze down at what might move, and blew her nose; she accomplished that with the aid of her finger, like people from away in the country. Then she sat looking out again; in another moment her legs dropped and hung down. The girls looked back at her, through the yellow and violet streams of dust—just now reaching them from Ran MacLain's flivver— the air coarse as sacking let down from the tree branches. Easter lifted one arm and shaded her eyes, but the arm fell in her lap like a clod.

There was a sighing sound from them. For the first time they noticed there was an old basket on the table. It held their knives, forks, tin cups and plates.

"Carry me." Easter's words had no inflection. Again, "Carry me."

She held out her arms to them, stupidly.

Then Ran MacLain whistled to his dogs.

The girls ran forward all together. Mrs. Gruenwald's fists rose in the air as if she lifted—no, rather had lowered—a curtain and she began with a bleating sound, "Pa-a-ack—

> —up your troubles in your old kit bag
> And smile, smile, smile!"

The Negroes were making a glorious commotion, all of them came up now, and then Exum escaped them all and ran waving away to the woods, dainty as a loosened rabbit.

"Who was he, that big boy?" Etoile was asking Jinny Love.

"Ran MacLain, slow-poke."

"What did he want?"

"He's just waiting on the camp. *They're* coming out tomorrow, hunting. I heard all he said to Miss Moody."

"Did Miss Moody *know* him?"

"Anybody knows him, and his twin brother too."

Nina, running up in the front line with the others, sighed—the sigh she gave when she turned in her examination papers at school. Then with each step she felt a defiance of her own. She screamed, "Easter!"

In that passionate instant, when they reached Easter and took her up, many feelings returned to Nina, some joining and some conflicting. At least what had happened to Easter was out in the world, like the table itself. There it remained—mystery, if only for being hard and cruel and, by something Nina felt inside her body, murderous.

Now they had Easter and carried her up to the tent, Mrs. Gruenwald still capering backwards and leading on,

> "—in your old kit bag!
> Smile, girls-instead-of-boys, that's the style!"

Miss Lizzie towered along darkly, groaning. She grabbed hold of Little Sister Spights, and said, "Can *you* brush me off!" She would be taking charge soon, but for now she asked for a place to sit down and a glass of cold water. She did not speak to Marvin yet; he was shoving the watermelons up onto the table.

Their minds could hardly capture it again, the way Easter was standing free in space, then handled and turned over by the blue air itself. Some of them looked back and saw the lake, rimmed around with its wall-within-walls of woods, into which the dark had already come. There were the water wings of Little Sister Spights, floating yet, white as a bird. "I know another Moon Lake," one girl had said yesterday. "Oh, my child, Moon Lakes are all over the world," Mrs. Gruenwald had interrupted. "I know of one in Austria. . . ." And into each fell a girl, they dared, now, to think.

The lake grew darker, then gleamed, like the water of a rimmed well. Easter was put to bed, they sat quietly on the ground outside the tent, and Miss Lizzie sipped water from Nina's cup. The sky's rising clouds lighted all over, like one spread-out blooming mimosa tree that could be seen from where the trunk itself should rise.

— 6 —

Nina and Jinny Love, wandering down the lower path with arms entwined, saw the Boy Scout's tent. It was after the watermelon feast, and Miss Lizzie's departure. Miss Moody, in voile and tennis shoes, had a date with old "Rudy" Loomis, and Mrs. Gruenwald was trying to hold the girls with a sing before bedtime. Easter slept; Twosie watched her.

Nina and Jinny Love could hear the floating songs, farewell-like, the cheers and yells between. An owl hooted in a tree, closer by. The wind stirred.

On the other side of the tent wall the slats of the Boy Scout's legs shuttered open and shut like a fan when he moved back and forth. He had a lantern in there, or perhaps only a candle. He finished off his own shadow by opening the flap of his tent. Jinny Love and Nina halted on the path, quiet as old campers.

The Boy Scout, little old Loch Morrison, was undressing in his tent for the whole world to see. He took his time wrenching off each garment; then he threw it to the floor as hard as he would throw a ball; yet that seemed, in him, meditative.

His candle—for that was all it was—jumping a little now, he stood there studying and touching his case of sunburn in a Kress mirror like theirs. He was naked and there was his little tickling thing hung on him like the last drop on the pitcher's lip. He ceased or exhausted study and came to the tent opening again and stood leaning on one raised arm, with his weight on one foot—just looking out into the night, which was clamorous.

It seemed to them he had little to do!

Hadn't he surely, just before they caught him, been pounding his chest with his fists? Bragging on himself? It seemed to them they could still hear in the beating air of night the wild tattoo of pride he must have struck off. His silly, brief, overriding little show they could well imagine there in his tent of separation in the middle of the woods, in the night. Minnowy thing that matched his candle flame, naked as he was with that, he thought he shone forth too. Didn't he?

Nevertheless, standing there with the tent slanting over him and his arm knobby as it reached up and his head bent a little, he looked rather at loose ends.

"We can call like an owl," Nina suggested. But Jinny Love thought in terms of the future. "I'll tell on him, in Morgana tomorrow. He's the most conceited Boy Scout in the whole troop; and's bowlegged.

"You and I will always be old maids," she added.

Then they went up and joined the singing.

William Faulkner (1897–1962)

WAS

Most of Faulkner's fiction projects, like the gossip spun on Southern porches, a leisurely saga, Gothic in its violences and its genealogical intricacy, of characters who need not be "presented" because from story to story everyone has come to know them. The humor of his splendid absurdities, often latent, is overt in "Was," which shapes a family myth out of the comedy of the tall tale. The year is 1859; the novel of which this is the first chapter spans nearly a century.

— 1 —

WHEN Cass Edmonds and Uncle Buck ran back to the house from discovering that Tomey's Turl had run again, they heard Uncle Buddy cursing and bellowing in the kitchen, then the fox and the dogs came out of the kitchen and crossed the hall into the dogs' room and they heard them run through the dogs' room into his and Uncle Buck's room, then they saw them cross the hall again into Uncle Buddy's room and heard them run through Uncle Buddy's room into the kitchen again and this time it sounded like the whole kitchen chimney had come down and Uncle Buddy bellowing like a steamboat blowing, and this time the fox and the dogs and five or six sticks of firewood all came out of the kitchen together with Uncle Buddy in the middle of them hitting at everything in sight with another stick. It was a good race.

When Cass and Uncle Buck ran into their room to get Uncle Buck's necktie, the fox had treed behind the clock on the mantel. Uncle Buck got the necktie from the drawer and kicked the dogs off and lifted the fox down by the scruff of the neck and shoved it back into the crate under the bed and they went to the kitchen, where Uncle Buddy was picking the breakfast up out of the ashes and wiping it off with his apron. "What in damn's hell do you mean," he said, "turning that damn fox out with the dogs all loose in the house?"

"Damn the fox," Uncle Buck said. "Tomey's Turl has broke out again. Give me and Cass some breakfast quick. We might just barely catch him before he gets there."

Because they knew exactly where Tomey's Turl had gone, he went there every time he could slip off, which was about twice a year. He was heading for Mr. Hubert Beauchamp's place just over the edge of the next county, that Mr. Hubert's sister, Miss Sophonsiba (Mr. Hubert was a bachelor too, like Uncle Buck and Uncle Buddy) was still trying to make people call Warwick after the place in England that she said Mr. Hubert was probably the true earl of only he never even had enough pride, not to mention energy, to take the trouble to establish his just rights. Tomey's Turl would go there to hang around Mr. Hubert's girl Tennie, until somebody came and got him. They couldn't keep him at home by buying Tennie from Mr. Hubert because Uncle Buck said he and Uncle Buddy had so many niggers already that they could hardly walk around on their own land for them, and they couldn't sell Tomey's Turl to Mr. Hubert because Mr. Hubert said he not only wouldn't buy Tomey's Turl, he wouldn't have that damn white half-McCaslin on his place even as a free gift, not even if Uncle Buck and Uncle Buddy were to pay board and keep for him. And if somebody didn't go and get Tomey's Turl right away, Mr. Hubert would fetch him back himself, bringing Miss Sophonsiba, and they would stay for a week or longer, Miss Sophonsiba living in Uncle Buddy's room and Uncle Buddy moved clean out of the house, sleeping in one of the cabins in the quarters where the niggers used to live in his great-grandfather's time until his great-grandfather died and Uncle Buck and Uncle Buddy moved all the niggers into the big house which his great-grandfather had not had time to finish, and not even doing the cooking while they were there and not even coming to the house any more except to sit on the front gallery after supper, sitting in the darkness between Mr. Hubert and Uncle Buck until after a while even Mr. Hubert would give up telling how many more head of niggers and acres of land he would add to what he would give Miss Sophonsiba when she married, and go to bed. And one midnight last summer Uncle Buddy just happened by accident to be awake and hear Mr. Hubert drive out of the lot and by the time he waked them and they got Miss Sophonsiba up and dressed and the team put to the wagon and caught Mr. Hubert, it was almost daylight. So it was always he and Uncle Buck who went to fetch Tomey's Turl because Uncle Buddy never went anywhere, not even to town and not even to fetch Tomey's Turl from Mr. Hubert's, even though they all knew that Uncle Buddy could have risked it ten times as much as Uncle Buck could have dared.

They ate breakfast fast. Uncle Buck put on his necktie while they were running toward the lot to catch the horses. The only time he wore the necktie was on Tomey's Turl's account and he hadn't even had it

out of the drawer since that night last summer when Uncle Buddy had
waked them in the dark and said, "Get up out of that bed and damn
quick." Uncle Buddy didn't own a necktie at all; Uncle Buck said
Uncle Buddy wouldn't take that chance even in a section like theirs,
where ladies were so damn seldom thank God that a man could ride
for days in a straight line without having to dodge a single one. His
grandmother (she was Uncle Buck's and Uncle Buddy's sister; she had
raised him following his mother's death. That was where he had got
his christian name: McCaslin, Carothers McCaslin Edmonds) said that
Uncle Buck and Uncle Buddy both used the necktie just as another
way of daring people to say they looked like twins, because even at sixty
they would still fight anyone who claimed he could not tell them apart;
whereupon his father had answered that any man who ever played
poker once with Uncle Buddy would never mistake him again for Uncle
Buck or anybody else.

Jonas had the two horses saddled and waiting. Uncle Buck didn't
mount a horse like he was any sixty years old either, lean and active as
a cat, with his round, close-cropped white head and his hard little gray
eyes and his white-stubbed jaw, his foot in the iron and the horse already moving, already running at the open gate when Uncle Buck came
into the seat. He scrabbled up too, onto the shorter pony, before Jonas
could boost him up, clapping the pony with his heels into its own stiff,
short-coupled canter, out the gate after Uncle Buck, when Uncle Buddy
(he hadn't even noticed him) stepped out from the gate and caught
the bit. "Watch him," Uncle Buddy said. "Watch Theophilus. The
minute anything begins to look wrong, you ride to hell back here and
get me. You hear?"

"Yes, sir," he said. "Lemme go now. I won't even ketch Uncle Buck,
let alone Tomey's Turl—"

Uncle Buck was riding Black John, because if they could just catch
sight of Tomey's Turl at least one mile from Mr. Hubert's gate, Black
John would ride him down in two minutes. So when they came out on
the long flat about three miles from Mr. Hubert's, sure enough, there
was Tomey's Turl on the Jake mule about a mile ahead. Uncle Buck
flung his arm out and back, reining in, crouched on the big horse, his
little round head and his gnarled neck thrust forward like a cooter's.
"Stole away!" he whispered. "You stay back where he won't see you and
flush. I'll circle him through the woods and we will bay him at the
creek ford."

He waited until Uncle Buck had vanished into the woods. Then he
went on. But Tomey's Turl saw him. He closed in too fast; maybe he
was afraid he wouldn't be there in time to see him when he treed. It
was the best race he had ever seen. He had never seen old Jake go that
fast, and nobody had ever known Tomey's Turl to go faster than his

natural walk, even riding a mule. Uncle Buck whooped once from the woods, running on sight, then Black John came out of the trees, driving, soupled out flat and level as a hawk, with Uncle Buck right up behind his ears now and yelling so that they looked exactly like a big black hawk with a sparrow riding it, across the field and over the ditch and across the next field, and he was running too; the mare went out before he even knew she was ready, and he was yelling too. Because, being a nigger, Tomey's Turl should have jumped down and run for it afoot as soon as he saw them. But he didn't; maybe Tomey's Turl had been running off from Uncle Buck for so long that he had even got used to running away like a white man would do it. And it was like he and old Jake had added Tomey's Turl's natural walking speed to the best that old Jake had ever done in his life, and it was just exactly enough to beat Uncle Buck to the ford. Because when he and the pony arrived, Black John was blown and lathered and Uncle Buck was down, leading him around in a circle to slow him down, and they could already hear Mr. Hubert's dinner horn a mile away.

Only, for a while Tomey's Turl didn't seem to be at Mr. Hubert's either. The boy was still sitting on the gatepost, blowing the horn—there was no gate there; just two posts and a nigger boy about his size sitting on one of them, blowing a fox-horn; this was what Miss Sophonsiba was still reminding people was named Warwick even when they had already known for a long time that's what she aimed to have it called, until when they wouldn't call it Warwick she wouldn't even seem to know what they were talking about and it would sound as if she and Mr. Hubert owned two separate plantations covering the same area of ground, one on top of the other. Mr. Hubert was sitting in the spring-house with his boots off and his feet in the water, drinking a toddy. But nobody there had seen Tomey's Turl; for a time it looked like Mr. Hubert couldn't even place who Uncle Buck was talking about. "Oh, that nigger," he said at last. "We'll find him after dinner."

Only it didn't seem as if they were going to eat either. Mr. Hubert and Uncle Buck had a toddy, then Mr. Hubert finally sent to tell the boy on the gatepost he could quit blowing, and he and Uncle Buck had another toddy and Uncle Buck was saying, "I just want my nigger. Then we got to get on back toward home."

"After dinner," Mr. Hubert said. "If we don't start him somewhere around the kitchen, we'll put the dogs on him. They'll find him if it's in the power of mortal Walker dogs to do it."

But at last a hand began waving a handkerchief or something white through the broken place in an upstairs shutter. They went to the house, crossing the back gallery, Mr. Hubert warning them again, as he always did, to watch out for the rotted floor-board he hadn't got around to having fixed yet. Then they stood in the hall, until presently there was a

jangling and swishing noise and they began to smell the perfume, and
Miss Sophonsiba came down the stairs. Her hair was roached under a
lace cap; she had on her Sunday dress and beads and a red ribbon
around her throat and a little nigger girl carrying her fan and he stood
quietly a step behind Uncle Buck, watching her lips until they opened
and he could see the roan tooth. He had never known anyone before
with a roan tooth and he remembered how one time his grandmother
and his father were talking about Uncle Buddy and Uncle Buck and
his grandmother said that Miss Sophonsiba had matured into a fine-
looking woman once. Maybe she had. He didn't know. He wasn't but
nine.

"Why, Mister Theophilus," she said. "And McCaslin," she said.
She had never looked at him and she wasn't talking to him and he knew
it, although he was prepared and balanced to drag his foot when Uncle
Buck did. "Welcome to Warwick."

He and Uncle Buck dragged their foot. "I just come to get my nigger,"
Uncle Buck said. "Then we got to get on back home."

Then Miss Sophonsiba said something about a bumblebee, but he
couldn't remember that. It was too fast and there was too much of it,
the earrings and beads clashing and jingling like little trace chains on a
toy mule trotting and the perfume stronger too, like the earrings and
beads sprayed it out each time they moved and he watched the roan-
colored tooth flick and glint between her lips; something about Uncle
Buck was a bee sipping from flower to flower and not staying long anywhere and all that stored sweetness to be wasted on Uncle Buddy's
desert air, calling Uncle Buddy Mister Amodeus like she called Uncle
Buck Mister Theophilus, or maybe the honey was being stored up
against the advent of a queen and who was the lucky queen and when?
"Ma'am?" Uncle Buck said. Then Mr. Hubert said:

"Hah. A buck bee. I reckon that nigger's going to think he's a buck
hornet, once he lays hands on him. But I reckon what Buck's thinking
about sipping right now is some meat gravy and biscuit and a cup of
coffee. And so am I."

They went into the dining room and ate and Miss Sophonsiba said
how seriously now neighbors just a half day's ride apart ought not to
go so long as Uncle Buck did, and Uncle Buck said Yessum, and Miss
Sophonsiba said Uncle Buck was just a confirmed roving bachelor from
the cradle born and this time Uncle Buck even quit chewing and looked
and said, Yes, ma'am, he sure was, and born too late at it to ever change
now but at least he could thank God no lady would ever have to suffer
the misery of living with him and Uncle Buddy, and Miss Sophonsiba
said Ah, that maybe Uncle Buck just ain't met the woman yet who
would not only accept what Uncle Buck was pleased to call misery, but

who would make Uncle Buck consider even his freedom a small price to pay, and Uncle Buck said, "Nome. Not yet."

Then he and Mr. Hubert and Uncle Buck went out to the front gallery and sat down. Mr. Hubert hadn't even got done taking his shoes off again and inviting Uncle Buck to take his off, when Miss Sophonsiba came out the door carrying a tray with another toddy on it. "Damnit, Sibbey," Mr. Hubert said. "He's just et. He don't want to drink that now." But Miss Sophonsiba didn't seem to hear him at all. She stood there, the roan tooth not flicking now but fixed because she wasn't talking now, handing the toddy to Uncle Buck until after a while she said how her papa always said nothing sweetened a Missippi toddy like the hand of a Missippi lady and would Uncle Buck like to see how she use to sweeten her papa's toddy for him? She lifted the toddy and took a sip of it and handed it again to Uncle Buck and this time Uncle Buck took it. He dragged his foot again and drank the toddy and said if Mr. Hubert was going to lay down, he would lay down a while too, since from the way things looked Tomey's Turl was fixing to give them a long hard race unless Mr. Hubert's dogs were a considerable better than they used to be.

Mr. Hubert and Uncle Buck went into the house. After a while he got up too and went around to the back yard to wait for them. The first thing he saw was Tomey's Turl's head slipping along above the lane fence. But when he cut across the yard to turn him, Tomey's Turl wasn't even running. He was squatting behind a bush, watching the house, peering around the bush at the back door and the upstairs windows, not whispering exactly but not talking loud either: "Whut they doing now?"

"They're taking a nap now," he said. "But never mind that; they're going to put the dogs on you when they get up."

"Hah," Tomey's Turl said. "And nem you mind that neither. I got protection now. All I needs to do is to keep Old Buck from ketching me unto I gets the word."

"What word?" he said. "Word from who? Is Mr. Hubert going to buy you from Uncle Buck?"

"Huh," Tomey's Turl said again. "I got more protection than whut Mr. Hubert got even." He rose to his feet. "I gonter tell you something to remember: anytime you wants to git something done, from hoeing out a crop to getting married, just get the womenfolks to working at it. Then all you needs to do is set down and wait. You member that."

Then Tomey's Turl was gone. And after a while he went back to the house. But there wasn't anything but the snoring coming out of the room where Uncle Buck and Mr. Hubert were, and some more light-sounding snoring coming from upstairs. He went to the spring-house and sat with his feet in the water as Mr. Hubert had been doing, because soon now it would be cool enough for a race. And sure enough, after a while Mr. Hubert and Uncle Buck came out onto the back gallery, with Miss Sophonsiba right behind them with the toddy tray only this time Uncle Buck drank his before Miss Sophonsiba had time to sweeten it, and Miss Sophonsiba told them to get back early, that all Uncle Buck knew of Warwick was just dogs and niggers and now that she had him, she wanted to show him her garden that Mr. Hubert and nobody else had any sayso in. "Yessum," Uncle Buck said. "I just want to catch my nigger. Then we got to get on back home."

Four or five niggers brought up the three horses. They could already hear the dogs waiting still coupled in the lane, and they mounted and went on down the lane, toward the quarters, with Uncle Buck already out in front of even the dogs. So he never did know just when and where they jumped Tomey's Turl, whether he flushed out of one of the cabins or not. Uncle Buck was away out in front on Black John and they hadn't even cast the dogs yet when Uncle Buck roared, "Gone away! I godfrey, he broke cover then!" and Black John's feet clapped four times like pistol shots while he was gathering to go out, then he and Uncle Buck vanished over the hill like they had run at the blank edge of the world itself. Mr. Hubert was roaring too: "Gone away! Cast them!" and they all piled over the crest of the hill just in time to see Tomey's Turl away out across the flat, almost to the woods, and the dogs streaking down the hill and out onto the flat. They just tongued once and when they came boiling up around Tomey's Turl it looked like they were trying to jump up and lick him in the face until even Tomey's Turl slowed down and he and the dogs all went into the woods together, walking, like they were going home from a rabbit hunt. And when they caught up with Uncle Buck in the woods, there was no Tomey's Turl and no dogs either, nothing but old Jake about a half an hour later, hitched in a clump of bushes with Tomey's Turl's coat tied on him for a saddle and near a half bushel of Mr. Hubert's oats scattered around on the ground that old Jake never even had enough appetite left to nuzzle up and spit back out again. It wasn't any race at all.

"We'll get him tonight though," Mr. Hubert said. "We'll bait for him. We'll throw a picquet of niggers and dogs around Tennie's house about midnight, and we'll get him."

"Tonight, hell," Uncle Buck said. "Me and Cass and that nigger all three are going to be half way home by dark. Ain't one of your niggers got a fyce or something that will trail them hounds?"

"And fool around here in the woods for half the night too?" Mr. Hubert said. "When I'll bet you five hundred dollars that all you got to do to catch that nigger is to walk up to Tennie's cabin after dark and call him?"

"Five hundred dollars?" Uncle Buck said. "Done! Because me and him neither one are going to be anywhere near Tennie's house by dark. Five hundred dollars!" He and Mr. Hubert glared at one another.

"Done!" Mr. Hubert said.

So they waited while Mr. Hubert sent one of the niggers back to the house on old Jake and in about a half an hour the nigger came back with a little bobtailed black fyce and a new bottle of whiskey. Then he rode up to Uncle Buck and held something out to him wrapped in a piece of paper. "What?" Uncle Buck said.

"It's for you," the nigger said. Then Uncle Buck took it and unwrapped it. It was the piece of red ribbon that had been on Miss Sophonsiba's neck and Uncle Buck sat there on Black John, holding the ribbon like it was a little water moccasin only he wasn't going to let anybody see he was afraid of it, batting his eyes fast at the nigger. Then he stopped batting his eyes.

"What for?" he said.

"She just sont hit to you," the nigger said. "She say to tell you 'success.'"

"She said what?" Uncle Buck said.

"I don't know, sir," the nigger said. "She just say 'success.'"

"Oh," Uncle Buck said. And the fyce found the hounds. They heard them first, from a considerable distance. It was just before sundown and they were not trailing, they were making the noise dogs make when they want to get out of something. They found what that was too. It was a ten-foot-square cotton-house in a field about two miles from Mr. Hubert's house and all eleven of the dogs were inside it and the door wedged with a chunk of wood. They watched the dogs come boiling out when the nigger opened the door, Mr. Hubert sitting his horse and looking at the back of Uncle Buck's neck.

"Well, well," Mr. Hubert said. "That's something, anyway. You can use them again now. They don't seem to have no more trouble with your nigger than he seems to have with them."

"Not enough," Uncle Buck said. "That means both of them. I'll stick to the fyce."

"All right," Mr. Hubert said. Then he said, "Hell, 'Filus, come on. Let's go eat supper. I tell you, all you got to do to catch that nigger is—"

"Five hundred dollars," Uncle Buck said.

"What?" Mr. Hubert said. He and Uncle Buck looked at each other. They were not glaring now. They were not joking each other either. They sat there in the beginning of twilight, looking at each other, just blinking a little. "What five hundred dollars?" Mr. Hubert said. "That you won't catch that nigger in Tennie's cabin at midnight tonight?"

"That me or that nigger neither ain't going to be near nobody's house but mine at midnight tonight." Now they did glare at each other.

"Five hundred dollars," Mr. Hubert said. "Done."

"Done," Uncle Buck said.

"Done," Mr. Hubert said.

"Done," Uncle Buck said.

So Mr. Hubert took the dogs and some of the niggers and went back to the house. Then he and Uncle Buck and the nigger with the fyce went on, the nigger leading old Jake with one hand and holding the fyce's leash (it was a piece of gnawed plowline) with the other. Now Uncle Buck let the fyce smell Tomey's Turl's coat; it was like for the first time now the fyce found out what they were after and they would have let him off the leash and kept up with him on the horses, only about that time the nigger boy began blowing the fox-horn for supper at the house and they didn't dare risk it.

Then it was full dark. And then—he didn't know how much later nor where they were, how far from the house, except that it was a good piece and it had been dark for good while and they were still going on, with Uncle Buck leaning down from time to time to let the fyce have another smell of Tomey's Turl's coat while Uncle Buck took another drink from the whiskey bottle—they found that Tomey's Turl had doubled and was making a long swing back toward the house. "I godfrey, we've got him," Uncle Buck said. "He's going to earth. We'll cut back to the house and head him before he can den." So they left the nigger to cast the fyce and follow him on old Jake, and he and Uncle Buck rode for Mr. Hubert's, stopping on the hills to blow the horses and listen to the fyce down in the creek bottom where Tomey's Turl was still making his swing.

But they never caught him. They reached the dark quarters; they could see lights still burning in Mr. Hubert's house and somebody was blowing the fox-horn again and it wasn't any boy and he had never heard a fox-horn sound mad before either, and he and Uncle Buck scattered out on the slope below Tennie's cabin. Then they heard the fyce, not trailing now but yapping, about a mile away, then the nigger whooped and they knew the fyce had faulted. It was at the creek. They hunted the banks both ways for more than an hour, but they couldn't straighten Tomey's Turl out. At last even Uncle Buck gave up and they started back toward the house, the fyce riding too now, in front of the nigger on the mule. They were just coming up the lane to the quarters; they could see on along the ridge to where Mr. Hubert's house was all dark now, when all of a sudden the fyce gave a yelp and jumped down from old Jake and hit the ground running and yelling every jump, and Uncle Buck was down too and had snatched him off the pony almost before he could clear his feet from the irons, and they ran too, on past the dark cabins toward the one where the fyce had treed. "We got him!"

Uncle Buck said. "Run around to the back. Don't holler; just grab up a stick and knock on the back door, loud."

Afterward, Uncle Buck admitted that it was his own mistake, that he had forgotten when even a little child should have known: not ever to stand right in front of or right behind a nigger when you scare him; but always to stand to one side of him. Uncle Buck forgot that. He was standing facing the front door and right in front of it, with the fyce right in front of him yelling fire and murder every time it could draw a new breath; he said the first he knew was when the fyce gave a shriek and whirled and Tomey's Turl was right behind it. Uncle Buck said he never even saw the door open; that the fyce just screamed once and ran between his legs and then Tomey's Turl ran right clean over him. He never even bobbled; he knocked Uncle Buck down and then caught him before he fell without even stopping, snatched him up under one arm, still running, and carried him along for about ten feet, saying, "Look out of here, old Buck. Look out of here, old Buck," before he threw him away and went on. By that time they couldn't even hear the fyce any more at all.

Uncle Buck wasn't hurt; it was only the wind knocked out of him where Tomey's Turl had thrown him down on his back. But he had been carrying the whiskey bottle in his back pocket, saving the last drink until Tomey's Turl was captured, and he refused to move until he knew for certain if it was just whiskey and not blood. So Uncle Buck laid over on his side easy, and he knelt behind him and raked the broken glass out of his pocket. Then they went on to the house. They walked. The nigger came up with the horses, but nobody said anything to Uncle Buck about riding again. They couldn't hear the fyce at all now. "He was going fast, all right," Uncle Buck said. "But I don't believe that even he will catch that fyce, I godfrey, what a night."

"We'll catch him tomorrow," he said.

"Tomorrow, hell," Uncle Buck said. "We'll be at home tomorrow. And the first time Hubert Beauchamp or that nigger either one set foot on my land, I'm going to have them arrested for trespass and vagrancy."

The house was dark. They could hear Mr. Hubert snoring good now, as if he had settled down to road-gaiting at it. But they couldn't hear anything from upstairs, even when they were inside the dark hall, at the foot of the stairs. "Likely hers will be at the back," Uncle Buck said. "Where she can holler down to the kitchen without having to get up. Besides, an unmarried lady will sholy have her door locked with strangers in the house." So Uncle Buck eased himself down onto the bottom step, and he knelt and drew Uncle Buck's boots off. Then he removed his own and set them against the wall, and he and Uncle Buck mounted the stairs, feeling their way up and into the upper hall. It was dark too, and still there was no sound anywhere except Mr. Hubert snoring below, so they felt their way along the hall toward the front of the house, until they felt a door. They could hear nothing beyond the door, and when Uncle Buck tried the knob, it opened. "All right," Uncle Buck whispered. "Be quiet." They could see a little now, enough to see the shape of the bed and the mosquito-bar. Uncle Buck threw down his suspenders and unbuttoned his trousers and went to the bed and eased himself carefully down onto the edge of it, and he knelt again and drew Uncle Buck's trousers off and he was just removing his own when Uncle Buck lifted the mosquito-bar and raised his feet and rolled into the bed. That was when Miss Sophonsiba sat up on the other side of Uncle Buck and gave the first scream.

— 2 —

When he reached home just before dinner time the next day, he was just about worn out. He was too tired to eat, even if Uncle Buddy had waited to eat dinner first; he couldn't have stayed on the pony another mile without going to sleep. In fact, he must have gone to sleep while he was telling Uncle Buddy, because the next thing he knew it was late afternoon and he was lying on some hay in the jolting wagon-bed, with Uncle Buddy sitting on the seat above him exactly the same way he sat a horse or sat in his rocking chair before the kitchen hearth while he was cooking, holding the whip exactly as he held the spoon or fork he stirred and tasted with. Uncle Buddy had some cold bread and meat and a jug of buttermilk wrapped in damp towsacks waiting when he waked up. He ate, sitting in the wagon in almost the last of the afternoon. They must have come fast, because they were not more than two miles from Mr. Hubert's. Uncle Buddy waited for him to eat. Then he said, "Tell me again," and he told it again: how he and Uncle Buck finally found a room without anybody in it, and Uncle Buck sitting on the side of the bed saying, "O godfrey, Cass. O godfrey, Cass," and then they heard Mr. Hubert's feet on the stairs and watched the light come down the hall and Mr. Hubert came in, in his nightshirt, and walked over and set the candle on the table and stood looking at Uncle Buck.

"Well, 'Filus," he said. "She's got you at last."

"It was an accident," Uncle Buck said. "I swear to godfrey—"

"Hah," Mr. Hubert said. "Don't tell me. Tell her that."

"I did," Uncle Buck said. "I did tell her. I swear to God—"

"Sholy," Mr. Hubert said. "And just listen." They listened a minute. He had been hearing her all the time. She was nowhere near as loud as at first; she was just steady. "Don't you want to go back in there and tell her again it was an accident, that you never meant nothing and to just excuse you and forget about it? All right."

"All right what?" Uncle Buck said.

"Go back in there and tell her again," Mr. Hubert said. Uncle Buck looked at Mr. Hubert for a minute. He batted his eyes fast.

"Then what will I come back and tell you?" he said.

"To me?" Mr. Hubert said. "I would call that a horse of another color. Wouldn't you?"

Uncle Buck looked at Mr. Hubert. He batted his eyes fast again. Then he stopped again. "Wait," he said. "Be reasonable. Say I did walk into a lady's bedroom, even Miss Sophonsiba's; say, just for the sake of the argument, there wasn't no other lady in the world but her and so I walked into hers and tried to get in bed with her, would I have took a nine-year-old boy with me?"

"Reasonable is just what I'm being," Mr. Hubert said. "You come into bear-country of your own free will and accord. All right; you were a grown man and you knew it was bear-country and you knew the way back out like you knew the way in and you had your chance to take it. But no. You had to crawl into the den and lay down by the bear. And whether you did or didn't know the bear was in it don't make any difference. So if you got back out of that den without even a claw-mark on you, I would not only be unreasonable, I'd be a damned fool. After all, I'd like a little peace and quiet and freedom myself, now I got a chance for it. Yes, sir. She's got you, 'Filus, and you know it. You run a hard race and you run a good one, but you skun the henhouse one time too many."

"Yes," Uncle Buck. He drew his breath in and let it out again, slow and not loud. But you could hear it. "Well," he said. "So I reckon I'll have to take the chance then."

"You already took it," Mr. Hubert said. "You did that when you came back here." Then he stopped too. Then he batted his eyes, but only about six times. Then he stopped and looked at Uncle Buck for more than a minute. "What chance?" he said.

"That five hundred dollars," Uncle Buck said.

"What five hundred dollars?" Mr. Hubert said. He and Uncle Buck looked at one another. Now it was Mr. Hubert that batted his eyes again and then stopped again. "I thought you said you found him in Tennie's cabin."

"I did," Uncle Buck said. "What you bet me was I would catch him there. If there had been ten of me standing in front of that door, we wouldn't have caught him." Mr. Hubert blinked at Uncle Buck, slow and steady.

"So you aim to hold me to that fool bet," he said.

"You took your chance too," Uncle Buck said. Mr. Hubert blinked at Uncle Buck. Then he stopped. Then he went and took the candle from the table and went out. They sat on the edge of the bed and watched the light go down the hall and heard Mr. Hubert's feet on the stairs.

After a while they began to see the light again and they heard Mr. Hubert's feet coming back up the stairs. Then Mr. Hubert entered and went to the table and set the candle down and laid a deck of cards by it.

"One hand," he said. "Draw. You shuffle, I cut, this boy deals. Five hundred dollars against Sibbey. And we'll settle this nigger business once and for all too. If you win, you buy Tennie; if I win, I buy that boy of yours. The price will be the same for each one: three hundred dollars."

"Win?" Uncle Buck said. "The one that wins buys the niggers?"

"Wins Sibbey, damn it!" Mr. Hubert said. "Wins Sibbey! What the hell else are we setting up till midnight arguing about? The lowest hand wins Sibbey and buys the niggers."

"All right," Uncle Buck said. "I'll buy the damn girl then and we'll call the rest of this foolishness off."

"Hah," Mr. Hubert said again. "This is the most serious foolishness you ever took part in in your life. No. You said you wanted your chance, and now you've got it. Here it is, right here on this table, waiting for you."

So Uncle Buck shuffled the cards and Mr. Hubert cut them. Then he took up the deck and dealt in turn until Uncle Buck and Mr. Hubert had five. And Uncle Buck looked at his hand a long time and then said two cards and he gave them to him, and Mr. Hubert looked at his hand quick and said one card and he gave it to him and Mr. Hubert flipped his discard onto the two which Uncle Buck had discarded and slid the new card into his hand and opened it out and looked at it quick again and closed it and looked at Uncle Buck and said, "Well? Did you help them threes?"

"No," Uncle Buck said.

"Well I did," Mr. Hubert said. He shot his hand across the table so that the cards fell face-up in front of Uncle Buck and they were three kings and two fives, and said, "By God, Buck McCaslin, you have met your match at last."

"And that was all?" Uncle Buddy said. It was late then, near sunset; they would be at Mr. Hubert's in another fifteen minutes.

"Yes, sir," he said, telling that too: how Uncle Buck waked him at daylight and he climbed out a window and got the pony and left, and how Uncle Buck said that if they pushed him too close in the meantime, he would climb down the gutter too and hide in the woods until Uncle Buddy arrived.

"Hah," Uncle Buddy said. "Was Tomey's Turl there?"

"Yes, sir," he said. "He was waiting in the stable when I got the pony. He said, 'Ain't they settled it yet?'"

"And what did you say?" Uncle Buddy said.

"I said, 'Uncle Buck looks like he's settled. But Uncle Buddy ain't got here yet.'"

"Hah," Uncle Buddy said.

And that was about all. They reached the house. Maybe Uncle Buck was watching them, but if he was, he never showed himself, never came out of the woods. Miss Sophonsiba was nowhere in sight either, so at least Uncle Buck hadn't quite given up; at least he hadn't asked her yet. And he and Uncle Buddy and Mr. Hubert ate supper and they came in from the kitchen and cleared the table, leaving only the lamp on it and the deck of cards.

Then it was just like it was the night before, except that Uncle Buddy had no necktie and Mr. Hubert wore clothes now instead of a night-shirt and it was a shaded lamp on the table instead of a candle, and Mr. Hubert sitting at his end of the table with the deck in his hands, riffling the edges with his thumb and looking at Uncle Buddy. Then he tapped the edges even and set the deck out in the middle of the table, under the lamp, and folded his arms on the edge of the table and leaned forward a little on the table, looking at Uncle Buddy, who was sitting at his end of the table with his hands in his lap, all one gray color, like an old gray rock or a stump with gray moss on it, that still, with his round white head like Uncle Buck's but he didn't blink like Uncle Buck and he was a little thicker than Uncle Buck, as if from sitting down so much watching food cook, as if the things he cooked had made him a little thicker than he would have been and the things he cooked with, the flour and such, had made him all one same quiet color.

"Little toddy before we start?" Mr. Hubert said.

"I don't drink," Uncle Buddy said.

"That's right," Mr. Hubert said. "I knew there was something else besides just being woman-weak that makes 'Filus seem human. But no matter." He batted his eyes twice at Uncle Buddy. "Buck McCaslin against the land and niggers you have heard me promise as Sophonsiba's dowry on the day she marries. If I beat you, 'Filus marries Sibbey without any dowry. If you beat me, you get 'Filus. But I still get the three hundred dollars 'Filus owes me for Tennie. Is that correct?"

"That's correct," Uncle Buddy said.

"Stud," Mr. Hubert said. "One hand. You to shuffle, me to cut, this boy to deal."

"No," Uncle Buddy said. "Not Cass. He's too young. I don't want him mixed up in any gambling."

"Hah," Mr. Hubert said. "It's said that a man playing cards with Amodeus McCaslin ain't gambling. But no matter." But he was still looking at Uncle Buddy; he never even turned his head when he spoke: "Go to the back door and holler. Bring the first creature that answers, animal mule or human, that can deal ten cards."

So he went to the back door. But he didn't have to call because Tomey's Turl was squatting against the wall just outside the door, and they returned to the dining room where Mr. Hubert still sat with his arms folded on his side of the table and Uncle Buddy sat with his hands in his lap on his side and the deck of cards face-down under the lamp between them. Neither of them even looked up when he and Tomey's Turl entered. "Shuffle," Mr. Hubert said. Uncle Buddy shuffled and set the cards back under the lamp and put his hands back into his lap and Mr. Hubert cut the deck and folded his arms back onto the table edge. "Deal," he said. Still neither he nor Uncle Buddy looked up. They just sat there while Tomey's Turl's saddle-colored hands came into the light and took up the deck and dealt, one card face-down to Mr. Hubert and one face-down to Uncle Buddy, and one face-up to Mr. Hubert and it was a king, and one face-up to Uncle Buddy and it was a six.

"Buck McCaslin against Sibbey's dowry," Mr. Hubert said. "Deal." And the hand dealt Mr. Hubert a card and it was a three, and Uncle Buddy a card and it was a two. Mr. Hubert looked at Uncle Buddy. Uncle Buddy rapped once with his knuckles on the table.

"Deal," Mr. Hubert said. And the hand dealt Mr. Hubert a card and it was another three, and Uncle Buddy a card and it was a four. Mr. Hubert looked at Uncle Buddy's cards. Then he looked at Uncle Buddy and Uncle Buddy rapped on the table again with his knuckles.

"Deal," Mr. Hubert said, and the hand dealt him an ace and Uncle Buddy a five and now Mr. Hubert just sat still. He didn't look at anything or move for a whole minute; he just sat there and watched Uncle Buddy put one hand onto the table for the first time since he shuffled and pinch up one corner of his face-down card and look at it and then put his hand back into his lap. "Check," Mr. Hubert said.

"I'll bet you them two niggers," Uncle Buddy said. He didn't move either. He sat there just like he sat in the wagon or on a horse or in the rocking chair he cooked from.

"Against what?" Mr. Hubert said.

"Against the three hundred dollars Theophilus owes you for Tennie, and the three hundred you and Theophilus agreed on for Tomey's Turl," Uncle Buddy said.

"Hah," Mr. Hubert said, only it wasn't loud at all this time, nor even short. Then he said "Hah. Hah. Hah" and not loud either. Then he said, "Well." Then he said, "Well, well." Then he said: "We'll check up for a minute. If I win, you take Sibbey without dowry and the two niggers, and I don't owe 'Filus anything. If you win—"

"—Theophilus is free. And you owe him the three hundred dollars for Tomey's Turl," Uncle Buddy said.

"That's just if I call you," Mr. Hubert said. "If I don't call you, 'Filus won't owe me nothing and I won't owe 'Filus nothing, unless I take that nigger which I have been trying to explain to you and him both for years that I won't have on my place. We will be right back where all this foolishness started from, except for that. So what it comes down to is, I either got to give a nigger away, or risk buying one that you done already admitted you can't keep at home." Then he stopped talking. For about a minute it was like he and Uncle Buddy had both gone to sleep. Then Mr. Hubert picked up his face-down card and turned it over. It was another three, and Mr. Hubert sat there without looking at anything at all, his fingers beating a tattoo, slow and steady and not very loud, on the table. "H'm," he said. "And you need a trey and there ain't but four of them and I already got three. And you just shuffled. And I cut afterward. And if I call you, I will have to buy that nigger. Who dealt these cards, Amodeus?" Only he didn't wait to be answered. He reached out and tilted the lamp-shade, the light moving up Tomey's Turl's arms that were supposed to be black but were not quite white, up his Sunday shirt that was supposed to be white but wasn't quite either, that he put on every time he ran away just as Uncle Buck put on the necktie each time he went to bring him back, and on to his face; and Mr. Hubert sat there, holding the lampshade and looking at Tomey's Turl. Then he tilted the shade back down and took up his cards and turned them face-down and pushed them toward the middle of the table. "I pass, Amodeus," he said.

— 3 —

He was still too worn out for sleep to sit on a horse, so this time he and Uncle Buddy and Tennie all three rode in the wagon, while Tomey's Turl led the pony from old Jake. And when they got home just after daylight, this time Uncle Buddy never even had time to get breakfast started and the fox never even got out of the crate, because the dogs were right there in the room. Old Moses went right into the crate with the fox, so that both of them went right on through the back end of it. That is, the fox went through, because when Uncle Buddy opened the door to come in, old Moses was still wearing most of the crate around his neck until Uncle Buddy kicked it off of him. So they just made one run, across the front gallery and around the house and they could hear the fox's claws when he went scrabbling up the lean-pole, onto the roof—a fine race while it lasted, but the tree was too quick.

"What in damn's hell do you mean," Uncle Buddy said, "casting that damn thing with all the dogs right in the same room?"

"Damn the fox," Uncle Buck said. "Go on and start breakfast. It seems to me I've been away from home a whole damn month."

Henry James (1843–1916)

THE TONE OF TIME

---

*"Moon Lake" and "Was" establish the kind of consciousness with
which their events are to be viewed; Henry James, in many of his
stories, goes further and dramatizes the point of view completely.
The narrator of "The Tone of Time" is not merely a convention but
a functioning character, everyone's errand-boy, fussily anxious to
help, and by temperament excluded from such ruinous passion as lies
in the background of the story.*

*By dramatizing the reader's curiosity, the narrator gives the reader
someone inside the story to feel identified with. By the end of the
story, do you still feel that identifying yourself with this man was a
good idea?*

— 1 —

I was too pleased with what it struck me that, as an old, old friend, I
had done for her, not to go to her that very afternoon with the news.
I knew she worked late, as in general I also did; but I sacrificed for her
sake a good hour of the February daylight. She was in her studio, as I
had believed she would be, where her card ("Mary J. Tredick"—not
Mary Jane, but Mary Juliana) was manfully on the door; a little tired,
a little old and a good deal spotted, but with her ugly spectacles taken
off, as soon as I appeared, to greet me. She kept on, while she scraped
her palette and wiped her brushes, the big stained apron that covered
her from head to foot and that I have often enough before seen her retain
in conditions giving the measure of her renunciation of her desire to
dazzle. Every fresh reminder of this brought home to me that she had
given up everything but her work, and that there had been in her history
some reason. But I was as far from the reason as ever. She had given up
too much; this was just why one wanted to lend her a hand. I told her,
at any rate, that I had a lovely job for her.

"To copy something I do like?"

From *The Better Sort*. Reprinted by permission of Paul R. Reynolds & Son.

Her complaint, I knew, was that people only gave orders, if they gave them at all, for things she did not like. But this wasn't a case of copying—not at all, at least, in the common sense. "It's for a portrait—quite in the air."

"Ah, you do portraits yourself!"

"Yes, and you know how. My trick won't serve for this. What's wanted is a pretty picture."

"Then of whom?"

"Of nobody. That is of anybody. Anybody you like."

She naturally wondered. "Do you mean I'm myself to choose my sitter?"

"Well, the oddity is that there is to be no sitter."

"Whom then is the picture to represent?"

"Why, a handsome, distinguished, agreeable man, of not more than forty, clean-shaven, thoroughly well-dressed, and a perfect gentleman."

She continued to stare. "And I'm to find him myself?"

I laughed at the term she used. "Yes, as you 'find' the canvas, the colours and the frame." After which I immediately explained. "I've just had the 'rummest' visit, the effect of which was to make me think of you. A lady, unknown to me and unintroduced, turned up at my place at three o'clock. She had come straight, she let me know, without preliminaries, on account of one's high reputation—the usual thing—and of her having admired one's work. Of course I instantly saw—I mean I saw it as soon as she named her affair—that she hadn't understood my work at all. What am I good for in the world but just the impression of the given, the presented case? I can do but the face I see."

"And do you think I can do the face I don't?"

"No, but you see so many more. You see them in fancy and memory, and they've come out, for you, from all the museums you've haunted and all the great things you've studied. I know you'll be able to see the one my visitor wants and to give it—what's the crux of the business—the tone of time."

She turned the question over. "What does she want it for?"

"Just for that—for the tone of time. And, except that it's to hang over her chimney, she didn't tell me. I've only my idea that it's to represent, to symbolise, as it were, her husband, who's not alive and who perhaps never was. This is exactly what will give you a free hand."

"With nothing to go by—no photographs or other portraits?"

"Nothing."

"She only proposes to describe him?"

"Not even; she wants the picture itself to do that. Her only condition is that he be a très-bel homme."

She had begun at last, a little thoughtfully, to remove her apron. "Is she French?"

"I don't know. I give it up. She calls herself Mrs. Bridgenorth."

Mary wondered. "*Connais pas!* I never heard of her."

"You wouldn't."

"You mean it's not her real name?"

I hesitated. "I mean that she's a very downright fact, full of the implication that she'll pay a downright price. It's clear to me that you can ask what you like; and it's therefore a chance that I can't consent to your missing." My friend gave no sign either way, and I told my story. "She's a woman of fifty, perhaps of more, who has been pretty, and who still presents herself, with her grey hair a good deal powdered, as I judge, to carry it off, extraordinarily well. She was a little frightened and a little free; the latter because of the former. But she did uncommonly well, I thought, considering the oddity of her wish. This oddity she quite admits; she began indeed by insisting on it so in advance that I found myself expecting I didn't know what. She broke at moments into French, which was perfect, but no better than her English, which isn't vulgar; not more at least than that of everybody else. The things people *do* say, and the way they say them, to artists! She wanted immensely, I could see, not to fail of her errand, not to be treated as absurd; and she was extremely grateful to me for meeting her so far as I did. She was beautifully dressed and she came in a brougham."

My listener took it in; then, very quietly, "Is she respectable?" she inquired.

"Ah, there you are!" I laughed; "and how you always pick the point right out, even when one has endeavoured to diffuse a specious glamour! She's extraordinary," I pursued after an instant; "and just what she wants of the picture, I think, is to make her a little less so."

"Who is she, then? What is she?" my companion simply went on.

It threw me straightway back on one of my hobbies. "Ah, my dear, what is so interesting as life? What is, above all, so stupendous as London? There's everything in it, everything in the world, and nothing too amazing not some day to pop out at you. What is a woman, faded, preserved, pretty, powdered, vague, odd, dropping on one without credentials, but with a carriage and very good lace? What is such a person but a person who *may* have had adventures, and have made them, in one way or another, pay? They're, however, none of one's business; it's scarcely on the cards that one should ask her. I should like, with Mrs. Bridgenorth, to see a fellow ask! She goes in for propriety, the real thing. If I suspect her of being the creation of her own talents, she has clearly, on the other hand, seen a lot of life. Will you meet her?" I next demanded.

My hostess waited. "No."

"Then you won't try?"

"Need I meet her to try?" And the question made me guess that, so far as she had understood, she began to feel herself a little taken. "It seems strange," she none the less mused, "to attempt to please her on such a basis. To attempt," she presently added, "to please her at all. It's your idea that she's not married?" she, with this, a trifle inconsequentially asked.

"Well," I replied, "I've only had an hour to think of it, but I somehow already see the scene. Not immediately, not the day after, or even perhaps the year after the thing she desires is set up there, but in due process of time and on convenient opportunity, the transfiguration will occur. 'Who is that awfully handsome man?' 'That? Oh, that's an old sketch of my dear dead husband.' Because I told her—insidiously sounding her—that she would want it to look old, and that the tone of time is exactly what you're full of."

"I believe I am," Mary sighed at last.

"Then put on your hat." I had proposed to her on my arrival to come out to tea with me, and it was when left alone in the studio while she went to her room that I began to feel sure of the success of my errand. The vision that had an hour before determined me grew deeper and brighter for her while I moved about and looked at her things. There were more of them there on her hands than one liked to see; but at least they sharpened my confidence, which was pleasant for me in view of that of my visitor, who had accepted without reserve my plea for Miss Tredick. Four or five of her copies of famous portraits—ornaments of great public and private collections—were on the walls, and to see them again together was to feel at ease about my guarantee. The mellow manner of them was what I had had in my mind in saying, to excuse myself to Mrs. Bridgenorth, "Oh, my things, you know, look as if they had been painted tomorrow!" It made no difference that Mary's Van-dykes and Gainsboroughs were reproductions and replicas, for I had known her more than once to amuse herself with doing the thing quite, as she called it, off her own bat. She had copied so bravely so many brave things that she had at the end of her brush an extraordinary bag of tricks. She had always replied to me that such things were mere clever humbug, but mere clever humbug was what our client happened to want. The thing was to let her have it—one could trust her for the rest. And at the same time that I mused in this way I observed to myself that there was already something more than, as the phrase is, met the eye in such response as I felt my friend had made. I had touched, without intention, more than one spring; I had set in motion more than one impulse. I found myself indeed quite certain of this after she had come back in her hat and her jacket. She was different—her idea had flowered; and she smiled at me from under her tense veil, while she drew over her

firm, narrow hands a pair of fresh gloves, with a light distinctly new.
"Please tell your friend that I'm greatly obliged to both of you and that
I take the order."

"Good. And to give him all his good looks?"

"It's just to do *that* that I accept. I shall make him supremely beautiful—and supremely base."

"Base?" I just demurred.

"The finest gentleman you'll ever have seen, and the worst friend."

I wondered, as I was startled; but after an instant I laughed for joy.
"Ah well, so long as he's not mine! I see we *shall* have him," I said as we
went, for truly I had touched a spring. In fact I had touched *the* spring.

It rang, more or less, I was presently to find, all over the place. I went,
as I had promised, to report to Mrs. Bridgenorth on my mission, and
though she declared herself much gratified at the success of it I could
see she a little resented the apparent absence of any desire on Miss
Tredick's part for a preliminary conference. "I only thought she might
have liked just to see me, and have imagined I might like to see *her*."

But I was full of comfort. "You'll see her when it's finished. You'll see
her in time to thank her."

"And to pay her, I suppose," my hostess laughed, with an asperity
that was, after all, not excessive. "Will she take very long?"

I thought. "She's so full of it that my impression would be that she'll
do it off at a heat."

"She *is* full of it then?" she asked; and on hearing to what tune,
though I told her but half, she broke out with admiration. "You artists
are the most extraordinary people!" It was almost with a bad conscience
that I confessed we indeed were, and while she said that what she
meant was that we seemed to understand everything, and I rejoined that
this was also what *I* meant, she took me into another room to see the
place for the picture—a proceeding of which the effect was singularly to
confirm the truth in question. The place for the picture—in her own
room, as she called it, a boudoir at the back, overlooking the general
garden of the approved modern row and, as she said, only just wanting
that touch—proved exactly the place (the space of a large panel in the
white woodwork over the mantel) that I had spoken of to my friend. She
put it quite candidly, "Don't you see what it will do?" and looked at me,
wonderfully, as for a sign that I could sympathetically take from her
what she didn't literally say. She said it, poor woman, so very nearly
that I had no difficulty whatever. The portrait, tastefully enshrined
there, of the finest gentleman one should ever have seen, would do even
more for herself than it would do for the room.

I may as well mention at once that my observation of Mrs. Bridgenorth was not in the least of a nature to unseat me from the hobby I

have already named. In the light of the impression she made on me life seemed quite as prodigious and London quite as amazing as I had ever contended, and nothing could have been more in the key of that experience than the manner in which everything was vivid between us and nothing expressed. We remained on the surface with the tenacity of shipwrecked persons clinging to a plank. Our plank was our concentrated gaze at Mrs. Bridgenorth's mere present. We allowed her past to exist for us only in the form of the prettiness that she had gallantly rescued from it and to which a few scraps of its identity still adhered. She was amiable, gentle, consistently proper. She gave me more than anything else the sense, simply, of waiting. She was like a house so freshly and successfully "done up" that you were surprised it wasn't occupied. She was waiting for something to happen—for somebody to come. She was waiting, above all, for Mary Tredick's work. She clearly counted that it would help her.

I had foreseen the fact—the picture was produced at a heat; rapidly, directly, at all events, for the sort of thing it proved to be. I left my friend alone at first, left the ferment to work, troubling her with no questions and asking her for no news; two or three weeks passed, and I never went near her. Then at last, one afternoon as the light was failing, I looked in. She immediately knew what I wanted. "Oh yes, I'm doing him."

"Well," I said, "I've respected your intensity, but I *have* felt curious."

I may not perhaps say that she was never so sad as when she laughed, but it's certain that she always laughed when she was sad. When, however, poor dear, for that matter, was she, secretly, not? Her little gasps of mirth were the mark of her worst moments. But why should she have one of these just now? "Oh, I know your curiosity!" she replied to me; and the small chill of her amusement scarcely met it. "He's coming out, but I can't show him to you yet. I must muddle it through in my own way. It has insisted on being, after all, a 'likeness,'" she added. "But nobody will ever know."

"Nobody?"

"Nobody *she* sees."

"Ah, she doesn't, poor thing," I returned, "seem to see anybody!"

"So much the better. I'll risk it." On which I felt I should have to wait, though I had suddenly grown impatient. But I still hung about, and while I did so she explained. "If what I've done is really a portrait, the condition itself prescribed it. If I was to do the most beautiful man in the world I could do but one."

We looked at each other; then I laughed. "It can scarcely be *me!* But you're getting," I asked, "the great thing?"

"The infamy? Oh yes, please God."

It took away my breath a little, and I even for the moment scarce felt at liberty to press. But one could always be cheerful. "What I meant is the tone of time."

"Getting it, my dear man? Didn't I get it long ago? Don't I *show* it—the tone of time?" she suddenly, strangely sighed at me, with something in her face I had never yet seen. "I can't give it to him more than—for all these years—he was to have given it to *me*."

I scarce knew what smothered passion, what remembered wrong, what mixture of joy and pain my words had accidentally quickened. Such an effect of them could only become, for me, an instant pity, which, however, I brought out but indirectly. "It's the tone," I smiled, "in which you're speaking now."

This served, unfortunately, as something of a check. "I didn't mean to speak now." Then with her eyes on the picture, "I've said everything there. Come back," she added, "in three days. He'll be all right."

He was indeed when at last I saw him. She had produced an extraordinary thing—a thing wonderful, ideal, for the part it was to play. My only reserve, from the first, was that it was too fine for its part, that something much less "sincere" would equally have served Mrs. Bridgenorth's purpose, and that relegation to that lady's "own room"—whatever charm it was to work there—might only mean for it cruel obscurity. The picture is before me now, so that I could describe it if description availed. It represents a man of about five-and-thirty, seen only as to the head and shoulders, but dressed, the observer gathers, in a fashion now almost antique and which was far from contemporaneous with the date of the work. His high, slightly narrow face, which would be perhaps too aquiline but for the beauty of the forehead and the sweetness of the mouth, has a charm that even, after all these years, still stirs my imagination. His type has altogether a distinction that you feel to have been firmly caught and yet not vulgarly emphasized. The eyes are just too near together, but they are, in a wondrous way, both careless and intense, while lip, cheek, and chin, smooth and clear, are admirably drawn. Youth is still, you see, in all his presence, the joy and pride of life, the perfection of a high spirit and the expectation of a great fortune, which he takes for granted with unconscious insolence. Nothing has ever happened to humiliate or disappoint him, and if my fancy doesn't run away with me the whole presentation of him is a guarantee that he will die without having suffered. He is so handsome in short, that you can scarcely say what he means, and so happy that you can scarcely guess what he feels.

It is of course, I hasten to add, an appreciably feminine rendering, light, delicate, vague, imperfectly synthetic—insistent and evasive, above all, in the wrong places; but the composition, none the less, is beautiful and the suggestion infinite. The grandest air of the thing struck me in fact, when first I saw it, as coming from the high artistic impertinence with which it offered itself as painted about 1850. It would have been a rare flower of refinement for that dark day. The "tone"—that of such a past as it pretended to—was there almost to excess, a brown bloom into which the image seemed mysteriously to retreat. The subject of it looks at me now across more years and more knowledge, but what I felt at the moment was that he managed to be at once a triumphant trick and a plausible evocation. He hushed me, I remember, with so many kinds of awe that I shouldn't have dreamt of asking who he was. All I said, after my first incoherences of wonder at my friend's practised skill, was: "And you've arrived at this truth without documents?"

"It depends on what you call documents."

"Without notes, sketches, studies?"

"I destroyed them years ago."

"Then you once had them?"

She just hung fire. "I once had everything."

It told me both more and less than I had asked; enough at all events to make my next question, as I uttered it, sound even to myself a little foolish. "So that it's all memory?"

From where she stood she looked once more at her work; after which she jerked away and, taking several steps, came back to me with something new—whatever it was I had already seen—in her air and answer. "It's all *hate!*" she threw at me, and then went out of the room. It was not till she had gone that I quite understood why. Extremely affected by the impression visibly made on me, she had burst into tears but had wished me not to see them. She left me alone for some time with her wonderful subject, and I again, in her absence, made things out. He was dead—he had been dead for years; the sole humiliation, as I have called it, that he was to know had come to him in that form. The canvas held and cherished him, in any case, as it only holds the dead. She had suffered from him, it came to me, the worst that a woman can suffer, and the wound he had dealt her, though hidden, had never effectually healed. It had bled again while she worked. Yet when she at last reappeared there was but one thing to say. "The beauty, heaven knows, I see. But I don't see what you call the infamy."

She gave him a last look—again she turned away. "Oh, he was like that."

"Well, whatever he was like," I remember replying, "I wonder you can bear to part with him. Isn't it better to let her see the picture first here?"

As to this she doubted. "I don't think I want her to come."

I wondered. "You continue to object so to meet her?"

"What good will it do? It's quite impossible I should alter him for her."

"Oh, she won't want *that!*" I laughed. "She'll adore him as he is."

"Are you quite sure of your idea?"

"That he's to figure as Mr. Bridgenorth? Well, if I hadn't been from the first, my dear lady, I should be now. Fancy, with the chance, her *not* jumping at him! Yes, he'll figure as Mr. Bridgenorth."

"Mr. Bridgenorth!" she echoed, making the sound, with her small, cold laugh, grotesquely poor for him. He might really have been a prince, and I wondered if he hadn't been. She had, at all events, a new notion. "Do you mind my having it taken to your place and letting her come to see it there?" Which—as I immediately embraced her proposal, deferring to her reasons, whatever they were—was what was speedily arranged.

— 2 —

The next day therefore I had the picture in charge, and on the following Mrs. Bridgenorth, whom I had notified, arrived. I had placed it, framed and on an easel, well in evidence, and I have never forgotten the look and the cry that, as she became aware of it, leaped into her face and from her lips. It was an extraordinary moment, all the more that it found me quite unprepared—so extraordinary that I scarce knew at first what had happened. By the time I really perceived, moreover, more things had happened than one, so that when I pulled myself together it was to face the situation as a whole. She had recognized on the instant the subject; that came first and was irrepressibly vivid in her. Her recognition had, for the length of a flash, lighted for her the possibility that the stroke had been directed. That came second, and she flushed with it as with a blow in the face. What came third—and it was what was really most wondrous—was the quick instinct of getting both her strange recognition and her blind suspicion well in hand. She couldn't control, however, poor woman, the strong colour in her face and the quick tears in her eyes. She could only glare at the canvas, gasping, grimacing, and try to gain time. Whether in surprise or in resentment she intensely reflected, feeling more than anything else how little she might prudently show; and I was conscious even at the moment that nothing of its kind could have been finer than her effort to swallow her shock in ten seconds.

How many seconds she took I didn't measure; enough, assuredly, for me also to profit. I gained more time than she, and the greatest oddity doubtless was my own private maneuver—the quickest calculation that, acting from a mere confused instinct, I had ever made. If she had known the great gentleman represented there and yet had determined on the spot to carry herself as ignorant, all my loyalty to Mary Tredick came to the surface in a prompt countermove. What gave me opportunity was the red in her cheek. "Why, you've known him!"

I saw her ask herself for an instant if she mightn't successfully make her startled state pass as the mere glow of pleasure—her natural greeting to her acquisition. She was pathetically, yet at the same time almost comically, divided. Her line was so to cover her tracks that every avowal of a past connection was a danger; but it also concerned her safety to learn, in the light of our astounding coincidence, how far she already stood exposed. She meanwhile begged the question. She smiled through her tears. "He's too magnificent!"

But I gave her, as I say, all too little time. "Who is he? Who *was* he?"

It must have been my look still more than my words that determined her. She wavered but an instant longer, panted, laughed, cried again, and then, dropping into the nearest seat, gave herself up so completely that I was almost ashamed. "Do you think I'd tell you his *name?*" The burden of the backward years—all the effaced and ignored—lived again, almost like an accent unlearned but freshly breaking out at a touch, in the very sound of the words. These perceptions she, however, the next thing showed me, were a game at which two could play. She had to look at me but an instant. "Why, you really *don't* know it!"

I judged best to be frank. "I don't know it."

"Then how does *she?*"

"How do you?" I laughed. "I'm a different matter."

She sat a minute turning things round, staring at the picture. "The likeness, the likeness!" It was almost too much.

"It's so true?"

"Beyond everything."

I considered. "But a resemblance to a known individual—that wasn't what you wanted."

She sprang up at this in eager protest. "Ah, no one else would see it."

I showed again, I fear, my amusement. "No one but you and she?"

"It's her doing *him!*" She was held by her wonder. "Doesn't she, on your honour, know?"

"That his is the very head you would have liked if you had dared? Not a bit. How *should* she? She knows nothing—on my honour."

Mrs. Bridgenorth continued to marvel. "She just painted him for the kind of face—?"

"That corresponds with my description of what you wished? Precisely."

"But *how*—after so long? From memory? As a friend?"

"As a reminiscence—yes. Visual memory, you see, in our uncanny race, is wonderful. As the ideal thing, simply, for your purpose. You *are* then suited?" I, after an instant, added.

She had again been gazing, and at this turned her eyes on me; but I saw she couldn't speak, couldn't do more at least than sound, unutterably, "Suited!" so that I was positively not surprised when suddenly—just as Mary had done, the power to produce this effect seeming a property of the model—she burst into tears. I feel no harsher in relating it, however I may appear, than I did at the moment, but it is a fact that while she just wept I literally had a fresh inspiration on behalf of Miss Tredick's interests. I knew exactly, moreover, before my companion had recovered herself, what she would next ask me; and I consciously brought this appeal on in order to have it over. I explained that I had not the least idea of the identity of our artist's sitter, to which she had given me no clue. I had nothing but my impression that she had known him—known him well; and, from whatever material she had worked, the fact of his having also been known to Mrs. Bridgenorth was a coincidence pure and simple. It partook of the nature of prodigy, but such prodigies did occur. My visitor listened with avidity and credulity. She was so far reassured. Then I saw her question come. "Well, if she doesn't dream he was ever anything to me—or what he will be now—I'm going to ask you, as a very particular favour, never to tell her. She will want to know of course exactly how I've been struck. You'll naturally say that I'm delighted, but may I exact from you that you say nothing else?"

There was supplication in her face, but I had to think. "There are conditions I must put to you first, and one of them is also a question, only more frank than yours. Was this mysterious personage—frustrated by death—to have married you?"

She met it bravely. "Certainly, if he had lived."

I was only amused at an artlessness in her "certainly." "Very good. But why do you wish the coincidence—"

"Kept from her?" She knew exactly why. "Because if she suspects it she won't let me have the picture. Therefore," she added with decision, "you must let me pay for it on the spot."

"What do you mean by on the spot?"

"I'll send you a cheque as soon as I get home."

"Oh," I laughed, "let us understand. Why do you consider she won't let you have the picture?"

She made me wait a little for this, but when it came it was perfectly lucid. "Because she'll then see how much more I must want it."

"How much less—wouldn't it be rather, since the bargain was, as the more convenient thing, not for a likeness?"

"Oh," said Mrs. Bridgenorth with impatience, "the likeness will take care of itself. She'll put this and that together." Then she brought out her real apprehension. "She'll be jealous."

"Oh!" I laughed. But I was startled.

"She'll hate me!"

I wondered. "But I don't think she liked him."

"Don't think?" She stared at me, with her echo, over all that might be in it, then seemed to find little enough. "I *say!*"

It was almost comically the old Mrs. Bridgenorth. "But I gather from her that he was bad."

"Then what was *she?*"

I barely hesitated. "What were *you?*"

"That's my own business." And she turned again to the picture. "He was good enough for her to do *that* of him."

I took it in once more. "Artistically speaking, for the way it's done, it's one of the most curious things I've ever seen."

"It's a grand treat!" said poor Mrs. Bridgenorth more simply.

It was, it *is* really; which is exactly what made the case so interesting. "Yet I feel somehow that, as I say, it wasn't done with love."

It was wonderful how she understood. "It was done with rage."

"Then what have you to fear?"

She knew again perfectly. "What happened when he made *me* jealous. So much," she declared, "that if you'll give me your word for silence—"

"Well?"

"Why, I'll double the money."

"Oh," I replied, taking a turn about in the excitement of our concurrence, "that's exactly what—to do a still better stroke for her—it had just come to *me* to propose!"

"It's understood then, on your oath, as a gentleman?" She was so eager that practically this settled it, though I moved to and fro a little while she watched me in suspense. It vibrated all round us that she had gone out to the thing in a stifled flare, that a whole close relation had in the few minutes revived. We know it of the truly amiable person that he will strain a point for another that he wouldn't strain for himself. The stroke to put in for Mary was positively prescribed. The work represented really much more than had been covenanted, and if the purchaser chose so to value it this was her own affair. I decided. "If it's understood also on *your* word."

We were so at one that we shook hands on it. "And when may I send?"

"Well, I shall see her this evening. Say early tomorrow."

"Early tomorrow." And I went with her to her brougham, into which, I remember, as she took leave, she expressed regret that she mightn't then and there have introduced the canvas for removal. I consoled her with remarking that she couldn't have got it in—which was not quite true.

I saw Mary Tredick before dinner, and though I was not quite ideally sure of my present ground with her I instantly brought out my news. "She's so delighted that I felt I must in conscience do something still better for you. She's not to have it on the original terms. I've put up the price."

Mary wondered. "But to what?"

"Well, to four hundred. If you say so, I'll try even for five."

"Oh, she'll never give that."

"I beg your pardon."

"After the agreement?" She looked grave. "I don't like such leaps and bounds."

"But, my dear child, they're yours. You contracted for a decorative trifle, and you've produced a breathing masterpiece."

She thought. "Is that what she calls it?" Then, as having to think too, I hesitated, "What does she know?" she pursued.

"She knows she wants it."

"So much as that?"

At this I had to brace myself a little. "So much that she'll send me the cheque this afternoon, and that you'll have mine by the first post in the morning."

"Before she has even received the picture?"

"Oh, she'll send for it tomorrow." And as I was dining out and had still to dress, my time was up. Mary came with me to the door, where I repeated my assurance. "You shall receive my cheque by the first post." To which I added: "If it's little enough for a lady so much in need to pay for *any* husband, it isn't worth mentioning as the price of such a one as you've given her!"

I was in a hurry, but she held me. "Then you've felt your idea confirmed?"

"My idea?"

"That that's what I *have* given her?"

I suddenly fancied I had perhaps gone too far; but I had kept my cab and was already in it. "Well, put it," I called with excess of humour over the front, "that you've, at any rate, given *him* a wife!"

When on my return from dinner that night I let myself in, my first care, in my dusty studio, was to make light for another look at Mary's subject. I felt the impulse to bid him good night, but, to my astonishment, he was no longer there. His place was a void—he had already disappeared. I saw, however, after my first surprise, what had happened—saw it moreover, frankly, with some relief. As my servants were in bed I could ask no questions, but it was clear that Mrs. Bridgenorth, whose note, containing its cheque, lay on my table, had been after all unable to wait. The note, I found, mentioned nothing but the enclosure; but it had come by hand, and it was her silence that told the tale. Her messenger had been instructed to "act"; he had come with a vehicle, he had transferred to it canvas and frame. The prize was now therefore landed and the incident closed. I didn't altogether, the next morning, know why, but I had slept the better for the sense of these things, and as soon as my attendant came in I asked for details. It was on this that his answer surprised me. "No, sir, there was no man; she came herself. She had only a four-wheeler, but I helped her, and we got it in. It was a squeeze, sir, but she *would* take it."

I wondered. "She had a four-wheeler? and not her servant?"

"No, no, sir. She came, as you may say, single-handed."

"And not even in her brougham, which would have been larger."

My man, with his habit, weighed it. "But *have* she a brougham, sir?"

"Why, the one she was here in yesterday."

Then light broke. "Oh, *that* lady! It wasn't her, sir. It was Miss Tredick."

Light broke, but darkness a little followed it—a darkness that, after breakfast, guided my steps back to my friend. There, in its own first place, I met her creation; but I saw it would be a different thing meeting *her*. She immediately put down on a table, as if she had expected me, the cheque I had sent her overnight. "Yes, I've brought it away. And I can't take the money."

I found myself in despair. "You want to keep him?"

"I don't understand what has happened."

"You just back out?"

"I don't understand," she repeated, "what has happened." But what I had already perceived was, on the contrary, that she very nearly, that she in fact quite remarkably, did understand. It was as if in my zeal I had given away my case, and I felt that my test was coming. She had been thinking all night with intensity, and Mrs. Bridgenorth's generosity, coupled with Mrs. Bridgenorth's promptitude, had kept her awake. Thence, for a woman nervous and critical, imaginations, visions, questions. "Why, in writing me last night, did you take for granted it was *she* who had swooped down? Why," asked Mary Tredick, "should she swoop?"

Well, if I could drive a bargain for Mary, I felt I could *a fortiori* lie for her. "Because it's her way. She does swoop. She's impatient and uncontrolled. And it's affectation for you to pretend," I said with diplomacy, "that you see no reason for her falling in love—"

"Falling in love?" She took me straight up.

"With that gentleman. Certainly. What woman wouldn't? What woman didn't? I really don't see, you know, your right to back out."

"I won't back out," she presently returned, "if you'll answer me a question. Does she know the man represented?" Then as I hung fire: "It has come to me that she must. It would account for so much. For the strange way I feel," she went on, "and for the extraordinary sum you've been able to extract from her."

It was a pity, and I flushed with it, besides wincing at the word she used. But Mrs. Bridgenorth and I, between us, had clearly made the figure too high. "You think that, if she *had* guessed, I would naturally work it to 'extract' more?"

She turned away from me on this and, looking blank in her trouble, moved vaguely about. Then she stopped. "I see him set up there. I hear her say it. What you said she would make him pass for."

I believe I foolishly tried—though only for an instant—to look as if I didn't remember what I had said. "Her husband?"

"He wasn't."

The next minute I had risked it. "Was he yours?"

I don't know what I had expected, but I found myself surprised at her mere pacific headshake. "No."

"Then why mayn't he have been—?"

"Another woman's? Because he died, to my absolute knowledge, unmarried." She spoke as quietly. "He had known many women, and there was one in particular with whom he became—and too long remained—ruinously intimate. She tried to make him marry her, and he was very near it. Death, however, saved him. But she was the reason—"

"Yes?" I feared again from her a wave of pain, and I went on while she kept it back. "Did you know her?"

"She was one I wouldn't." Then she brought it out. "She was the reason he failed me." Her successful detachment somehow said all, reduced me to a flat, kind "Oh!" that marked my sense of her telling me, against my expectation, more than I knew what to do with. But it was just while I wondered how to turn her confidence that she repeated, in a changed voice, her challenge of a moment before. "Does she know the man represented?"

"I haven't the least idea." And having so acquitted myself I added, with what strikes me now as futility: "She certainly—yesterday—didn't name him."

"Only recognized him?"

"If she did she brilliantly concealed it."

"So that you got nothing from her?"

It was a question that offered me a certain advantage. "I thought you accused me of getting too much."

She gave me a long look, and I now saw everything in her face. "It's very nice—what you're doing for me, and you do it handsomely. It's beautiful—beautiful, and I thank you with all my heart. But I know."

"And what do you know?"

She went about now preparing her usual work. "What he must have been to her."

"You mean she was the person?"

"Well," she said, putting on her old spectacles, "she was one of them."

"And you accept so easily the astounding coincidence—?"

"Of my finding myself, after years, in so extraordinary a relation with her? What do you call easily? I've passed a night of torment."

"But what put it into your head—?"

"That I had so blindly and strangely given him back to her? *You* put it—yesterday."

"And how?"

"I can't tell you. You didn't in the least mean to—on the contrary. But you dropped the seed. The plant, after you had gone," she said with a businesslike pull at her easel, "the plant began to grow. I *saw* them there—in your studio—face to face."

"You were jealous?" I laughed.

She gave me through her glasses another look, and they seemed, from this moment, in their queerness, to have placed her quite on the other side of the gulf of time. She was firm there; she was settled; I couldn't get at her now. "I see she told you I *would* be." I doubtless kept down too little my start at it, and she immediately pursued. "You say I accept the coincidence, which is of course prodigious. But such things happen. Why shouldn't I accept it if you do?"

"*Do* I?" I smiled.

She began her work in silence, but she presently exclaimed: "I'm glad I didn't meet her!"

"I don't yet see why you wouldn't."

"Neither do I. It was an instinct."

"Your instincts"—I tried to be ironic—"are miraculous."

"They *have* to be, to meet such accidents. I must ask you kindly to tell her, when you return her gift, that now I have done the picture I find I must after all keep it for myself."

"Giving no reason?"

She painted away. "She'll know the reason."

Well, by this time I knew it too; I knew so many things that I feared my resistance was weak. If our wonderful client hadn't been his wife in fact, she was not to be helped to become his wife in fiction. I knew almost more than I can say, more at any rate than I could then betray. He had been bound in common mercy to stand by my friend, and he had basely forsaken her. This indeed brought up the obscure, into which I shyly gazed. "Why, even granting your theory, should you grudge her the portrait? It was painted in bitterness."

"Yes. Without that—!"

"It wouldn't have come? Precisely. Is it in bitterness, then, you'll keep it?"

She looked up from her canvas. "In what would *you* keep it?"

It made me jump. "Do you mean I *may*?" Then I had my idea. "I'd give you her price for it!"

Her smile through her glasses was beautiful. "And afterwards make it over to her? You shall have it when I die." With which she came away from her easel, and I saw that I was staying her work and should properly go. So I put out my hand to her. "It took—whatever you will!—to paint it," she said, "but I shall keep it in joy." I could answer nothing now—had to cease to pretend; the thing was in her hands. For a moment we stood there, and I had again the sense, melancholy and final, of her being, as it were, remotely glazed and fixed into what she had done. "He's taken from me, and for all those years he's kept. Then she herself, by a prodigy—!" She lost herself again in the wonder of it.

"Unwittingly gives him back?"

She fairly, for an instant over the marvel, closed her eyes. "Gives him back."

Then it was I saw how he would be kept! But it was the end of my vision. I could only write, ruefully enough, to Mrs. Bridgenorth, whom I never met again, but of whose death—preceding by a couple of years Mary Tredick's—I happened to hear. This is an old man's tale. I have inherited the picture, in the deep beauty of which, however, darkness still lurks. No one, strange to say, has ever recognized the model, but everyone asks his name. I don't even know it.

D. H. Lawrence (1885–1930)

THE SHADOW IN THE ROSE GARDEN

As usual, Lawrence spurns narrators and works with unsettling close-ness to his characters. This study in reciprocal cruelty springing from an intimacy neither protagonist can govern is itself intimate, as though the reader were present, invisible, at confrontations not meant for anyone's eye. Thus, as a condition of getting the story told at all, we are made to participate ourselves in the story's theme of violated privacy.

Find two places in the story at which you suddenly discover that your own desire to know what has been going on is acutely shared by one of the characters.

A rather small young man sat by the window of a pretty seaside cottage trying to persuade himself that he was reading the newspaper. It was about half-past eight in the morning. Outside, the glory roses hung in the morning sunshine like little bowls of fire tipped up. The young man looked at the table, then at the clock, then at his own big silver watch. An expression of stiff endurance came on to his face. Then he rose and reflected on the oil paintings that hung on the walls of the room, giving careful but hostile attention to "The Stag at Bay." He tried the lid of the piano, and found it locked. He caught sight of his own face in a little mirror, pulled his brown moustache, and an alert interest sprang into his eyes. He was not ill-favored. He twisted his moustache. His figure was rather small, but alert and vigorous. As he turned from the mirror a look of self-commiseration mingled with his appreciation of his own physiognomy.

In a state of self-suppression, he went through into the garden. His jacket, however, did not look dejected. It was new, and had a smart and self-confident air, sitting upon a confident body. He contemplated the Tree of Heaven that flourished by the lawn, then sauntered on to the next plant. There was more promise in a crooked apple tree covered with brown-red fruit. Glancing round, he broke off an apple and, with his back to the house, took a clean, sharp bite. To his surprise the fruit was sweet. He took another. Then again he turned to survey the bedroom windows overlooking the garden. He started, seeing a woman's figure; but it was only his wife. She was gazing across to the sea, apparently ignorant of him.

For a moment or two he looked at her, watching her. She was a good-looking woman, who seemed older than he, rather pale, but healthy, her face yearning. Her rich auburn hair was heaped in folds on her forehead. She looked apart from him and his world, gazing away to the sea. It irked her husband that she should continue abstracted and in ignorance of him; he pulled poppy fruits and threw them at the window. She started, glanced at him with a wild smile, and looked away again. Then almost immediately she left the window. He went indoors to meet her. She had a fine carriage, very proud, and wore a dress of soft white muslin.

"I've been waiting long enough," he said.

"For me or for breakfast?" she said lightly. "You know we said nine o'clock. I should have thought you could have slept after the journey."

"You know I'm always up at five, and I couldn't stop in bed after six. You might as well be in pit as in bed, on a morning like this."

"I shouldn't have thought the pit would occur to you, here."

She moved about examining the room, looking at the ornaments under glass covers. He, planted on the hearth-rug, watched her rather uneasily, and grudgingly indulgent. She shrugged her shoulders at the apartment.

"Come," she said, taking his arm, "let us go into the garden till Mrs. Coates brings the tray."

"I hope she'll be quick," he said, pulling his moustache. She gave a short laugh, and leaned on his arm as they went. He had lighted a pipe.

Mrs. Coates entered the room as they went down the steps. The delightful, erect old lady hastened to the window for a good view of her visitors. Her china-blue eyes were bright as she watched the young couple go down the path, he walking in an easy, confident fashion, with his wife on his arm. The landlady began talking to herself in a soft, Yorkshire accent.

"Just of a height they are. She wouldn't ha' married a man less than herself in stature, I think, though he's not her equal otherwise." Here her granddaughter came in, setting a tray on the table. The girl went to the old woman's side.

"He's been eating the apples, Gran'," she said.

"Has he, my pet? Well, if he's happy, why not?"

Outside, the young, well-favored man listened with impatience to the chink of the teacups. At last, with a sigh of relief, the couple came in to breakfast. After he had eaten for some time, he rested a moment and said:

"Do you think it's any better place than Bridlington?"

"I do," she said, "infinitely! Besides, I am at home here—it's not like a strange seaside place to me."

"How long were you here?"

"Two years."

He ate reflectively.

"I should ha' thought you'd rather go to a fresh place," he said at length.

She sat very silent, and then, delicately, put out a feeler.

"Why?" she said. "Do you think I shan't enjoy myself?"

He laughed comfortably, putting the marmalade thick on his bread.

"I hope so," he said.

She again took no notice of him.

"But don't say anything about it in the village, Frank," she said casually. "Don't say who I am, or that I used to live here. There's nobody I want to meet, particularly, and we should never feel free if they knew me again."

"Why did you come, then?"

"'Why?' Can't you understand why?"

"Not if you don't want to know anybody."

"I came to see the place, not the people."

He did not say any more.

"Women," she said, "are different from men. I don't know why I wanted to come—but I did."

She helped him to another cup of coffee, solicitously.

"Only," she resumed, "don't talk about me in the village." She laughed shakily. "I don't want my past brought up against me, you know." And she moved the crumbs on the cloth with her finger tip.

He looked at her as he drank his coffee; he sucked his moustache, and putting down his cup, said phlegmatically:

"I'll bet you've had a lot of past."

She looked with a little guiltiness, that flattered him, down at the tablecloth.

"Well," she said, caressive, "you won't give me away, who I am, will you?"

"No," he said, comforting, laughing. "I won't give you away."

He was pleased.

She remained silent. After a moment or two she lifted her head, saying:

"I've got to arrange with Mrs. Coates, and do various things. So you'd better go out by yourself this morning—and we'll be in to dinner at one."

"But you can't be arranging with Mrs. Coates all morning," he said.

"Oh, well—then I've got some letters to write, and I must get that mark out of my skirt. I've got plenty of little things to do this morning. You'd better go out by yourself."

He perceived that she wanted to be rid of him, so that when she went upstairs, he took his hat and lounged out on to the cliffs, suppressedly angry.

Presently she too came out. She wore a hat with roses, and a long lace scarf hung over her white dress. Rather nervously, she put up her sunshade, and her face was half hidden in its colored shadow. She went along the narrow track of flagstones that were worn hollow by the feet of the fishermen. She seemed to be avoiding her surroundings, as if she remained safe in the little obscurity of her parasol.

She passed the church, and went down the lane till she came to a high wall by the wayside. Under this she went slowly, stopping at length by an open doorway, which shone like a picture of light in the dark wall. There in the magic beyond the doorway, patterns of shadow lay on the sunny court, on the blue and white sea-pebbles of its paving, while a green lawn glowed beyond, where a bay tree glittered at the edges. She tiptoed nervously into the courtyard, glancing at the house that stood in shadow. The uncurtained windows looked black and soulless, the kitchen door stood open. Irresolutely she took a step forwards, and again forward, leaning, yearning, towards the garden beyond.

She had almost gained the corner of the house when a heavy step came crunching through the trees. A gardener appeared before her. He held a wicker tray on which were rolling great, dark red gooseberries, overripe. He moved slowly.

"The garden isn't open today," he said quietly to the attractive woman, who was poised for retreat.

For a moment she was silent with surprise. How should it be public at all?

"When is it open?" she asked, quick-witted.

"The rector lets visitors in on Fridays and Tuesdays."

She stood still, reflecting. How strange to think of the rector opening his garden to the public!

"But everybody will be at church," she said coaxingly to the man. "There'll be nobody here, will there?"

He moved, and the big gooseberries rolled.

"The rector lives at the new rectory," he said.

The two stood still. He did not like to ask her to go. At last she turned to him with a winning smile.

"Might I have *one* peep at the roses?" she coaxed, with pretty wilfulness.

"I don't suppose it would matter," he said, moving aside; "you won't stop long—"

She went forward, forgetting the gardener in a moment. Her face became strained, her movements eager. Glancing round, she saw all the windows giving on to the lawn were curtainless and dark. The house had a sterile appearance, as if it were still used, but not inhabited. A shadow seemed to go over her. She went across the lawn towards the garden, through an arch of crimson ramblers, a gate of color. There beyond lay the soft blue sea within the bay, misty with morning, and the farthest headland of black rock jutting dimly out between blue and blue of the sky and water. Her face began to shine, transfigured with pain and joy. At her feet the garden fell steeply, all a confusion of flowers, and away below was the darkness of treetops covering the beck.

She turned to the garden that shone with sunny flowers around her. She knew the little corner where was the seat beneath the yew tree. Then there was the terrace where a great host of flowers shone, and from this, two paths went down, one at each side of the garden. She closed her sunshade and walked slowly among the many flowers. All round were rose bushes, big banks of roses, then roses hanging and tumbling from pillars, or roses balanced on the standard bushes. By the open earth were many other flowers. If she lifted her head, the sea was upraised beyond, and the Cape.

Slowly she went down one path, lingering, like one who has gone back into the past. Suddenly she was touching some heavy crimson roses that were soft as velvet, touching them thoughtfully, without knowing, as a mother sometimes fondles the hand of her child. She leaned slightly forward to catch the scent. Then she wandered on in abstraction. Sometimes a flame-colored, scentless rose would hold her arrested. She stood gazing at it as if she could not understand it. Again the same softness of intimacy came over her, as she stood before a tumbling heap of pink petals. Then she wondered over the white rose, that was greenish, like ice, in the center. So, slowly, like a white, pathetic butterfly, she drifted down the path, coming at last to a tiny terrace all full of roses. They seemed to fill the place, a sunny, gay throng. She was shy of them, they were so many and so bright. They seemed to be conversing and laughing. She felt herself in a strange crowd. It exhilarated her, carried her out of her herself. She flushed with excitement. The air was pure scent.

Hastily, she went to a little seat among the white roses, and sat down. Her scarlet sunshade made a hard blot of color. She sat quite still, feeling her own existence lapse. She was no more than a rose, a rose that could not quite come into blossom, but remained tense. A little fly dropped on her knee, on her white dress. She watched it, as if it had fallen on a rose. She was not herself.

Then she started cruelly as a shadow crossed her and a figure moved into her sight. It was a man who had come in slippers, unheard. He wore a linen coat. The morning was shattered, the spell vanished away. She was only afraid of being questioned. He came forward. She rose. Then, seeing him, the strength went from her and she sank on the seat again.

He was a young man, military in appearance, growing slightly stout. His black hair was brushed smooth and bright, his moustache was waxed. But there was something rambling in his gait. She looked up, blanched to the lips, and saw his eyes. They were black, and stared without seeing. They were not a man's eyes. He was coming towards her.

He stared at her fixedly, made an unconscious salute, and sat down beside her on the seat. He moved on the bench, shifted his feet, saying, in a gentlemanly, military voice:

"I don't disturb you—do I?"

She was mute and helpless. He was scrupulously dressed in dark clothes and a linen coat. She could not move. Seeing his hands, with the ring she knew so well upon the little finger, she felt as if she were going dazed. The whole world was deranged. She sat unavailing. For his hands, her symbols of passionate love, filled her with horror as they rested now on his strong thighs.

"May I smoke?" he asked intimately, almost secretly, his hand going to his pocket.

She could not answer, but it did not matter, he was in another world. She wondered, craving, if he recognized her—if he could recognize her. She sat pale with anguish. But she had to go through with it.

"I haven't got any tobacco," he said thoughtfully.

But she paid no heed to his words, only she attended to him. Could he recognize her, or was it all gone? She sat still in a frozen kind of suspense.

"I smoke John Cotton," he said, "and I must economize with it, it is expensive. You know, I'm not very well off while these lawsuits are going on."

"No," she said, and her heart was cold, her soul kept rigid.

He moved, made a loose salute, rose, and went away. She sat motionless. She could see his shape, the shape she had loved with all her passion: his compact, soldier's head, his fine figure now slackened. And it was not he. It only filled her with horror too difficult to know.

Suddenly he came again, his hand in his jacket pocket.

"Do you mind if I smoke?" he said. "Perhaps I shall be able to see things more clearly."

He sat down beside her again, filling a pipe. She watched his hands with the fine strong fingers. They had always inclined to tremble slightly. It surprised her, long ago, in such a healthy man. Now they moved inaccurately, and the tobacco hung raggedly out of the pipe.

"I have legal business to attend to. Legal affairs are always so uncertain. I tell my solicitor exactly, precisely what I want, but I can never get it done."

She sat and heard him talking. But it was not he. Yet those were the hands she had kissed, there were the glistening, strange black eyes that she had loved. Yet it was not he. She sat motionless with horror and silence. He dropped his tobacco pouch, and groped for it on the ground. Yet she must wait to see if he would recognize her. Why could she not go? In a moment he rose.

"I must go at once," he said. "The owl is coming." Then he added confidentially: "His name isn't really the owl, but I call him that. I must go and see if he has come."

She rose too. He stood before her, uncertain. He was a handsome, soldierly fellow, and a lunatic. Her eyes searched him, and searched him, to see if he would recognize her, if she could discover him.

"You don't know me?" she asked, from the terror of her soul, standing alone.

He looked back at her quizzically. She had to bear his eyes. They gleamed on her, but with no intelligence. He was drawing nearer to her.

"Yes, I do know you," he said, fixed, intent, but mad, drawing his face nearer hers. Her horror was too great. The powerful lunatic was coming too near to her.

A man approached, hastening.

"The garden isn't open this morning," he said.

The deranged man stopped and looked at him. The keeper went to the seat and picked up the tobacco pouch left lying there.

"Don't leave your tobacco, sir," he said, taking it to the gentleman in the linen coat.

"I was just asking this lady to stay to lunch," the latter said politely. "She is a friend of mine."

The woman turned and walked swiftly, blindly, between the sunny roses, out from the garden, past the house with the blank, dark windows, through the sea-pebbled courtyard to the street. Hastening and blind, she went forward without hesitating, not knowing whither. Directly she came to the house she went upstairs, took off her hat, and sat down on the bed. It was as if some membrane had been torn in two in her, so that she was not an entity that could think and feel. She sat staring across at the window, where an ivy spray waved slowly up and down in the sea wind. There was some of the uncanny luminousness of the sunlit sea in the air. She sat perfectly still, without any being. She only felt she might be sick, and it might be blood that was loose in her torn entrails. She sat perfectly still and passive.

After a time she heard the hard tread of her husband on the floor below, and, without herself changing, she registered his movement. She heard his rather disconsolate footsteps go out again, then his voice speaking, answering, growing cheery, and his solid tread drawing near.

He entered, ruddy, rather pleased, an air of complacency about his alert, sturdy figure. She moved stiffly. He faltered in his approach.

"What's the matter?" he asked, a tinge of impatience in his voice. "Aren't you feeling well?"

This was torture to her.

"Quite," she replied.

His brown eyes became puzzled and angry.

"What is the matter?" he said.

"Nothing."

He took a few strides, and stood obstinately, looking out of the window.

"Have you run up against anybody?" he asked.

"Nobody who knows me," she said.

His hands began to twitch. It exasperated him, that she was no more sensible of him than if he did not exist. Turning on her at length, driven, he asked:

"Something has upset you, hasn't it?"

"No, why?" she said, neutral. He did not exist for her, except as an irritant.

His anger rose, filling the veins of his throat.

"It seems like it," he said, making an effort not to show his anger, because there seemed no reason for it. He went away downstairs. She sat still on the bed, and with the residue of feeling left to her, she disliked him because he tormented her. The time went by. She could smell the dinner being served, the smoke of her husband's pipe from the garden. But she could not move. She had no being. There was a tinkle of the bell. She heard him come indoors. And then he mounted the stairs again. At every step her heart grew tight in her. He opened the door.

"Dinner is on the table," he said.

It was difficult for her to endure his presence, for he would interfere with her. She could not recover her life. She rose stiffly and went down. She could neither eat nor talk during the meal. She sat absent, torn, without any being of her own. He tried to go on as if nothing were the matter. But at last he became silent with fury. As soon as it was possible, she went upstairs again, and locked the bedroom door. She must be alone. He went with his pipe into the garden. All his suppressed anger against her who held herself superior to him filled and blackened his heart. Though he had not known it, yet he had never really won her, she had never loved him. She had taken him on sufferance. This had foiled him. He was only a laboring electrician in the mine, she was superior to him. He had always given way to her. But all the while, the injury and ignominy had been working in his soul because she did not hold him seriously. And now all his rage came up against her.

He turned and went indoors. The third time, she heard him mounting the stairs. Her heart stood still. He turned the catch and pushed the door—it was locked. He tried it again, harder. Her heart was standing still.

"Have you fastened the door?" he asked quietly, because of the landlady.

"Yes. Wait a minute."

She rose and turned the lock, afraid he would burst in. She felt hatred towards him, because he did not leave her free. He entered, his pipe between his teeth, and she returned to her old position on the bed. He closed the door and stood with his back to it.

"What's the matter?" he asked determinedly.

She was sick of him. She could not look at him.

"Can't you leave me alone?" she replied, averting her face from him.

He looked at her quickly, wincing with ignominy. Then he seemed to consider for a moment.

"There's something up with you, isn't there?" he asked definitely.

"Yes," she said, "but that's no reason why you should torment me."

"I don't torment you. What's the matter?"

"Why should you know?" she cried, in hate and desperation.

Something snapped. He started and caught his pipe as it fell from his mouth. Then he pushed forward the bitten-off mouthpiece with his tongue, took it from off his lips, and looked at it. Then he put out his pipe, and brushed the ash from his waistcoat. After which he raised his head.

"I want to know," he said. His face was greyish pale, and set uglily.

Neither looked at the other. She knew he was fired now. His heart was pounding heavily. She hated him, but she could not withstand him. Suddenly she lifted her head and turned on him.

"What right have you to know?" she asked.

He looked at her. She felt a pang of surprise for his tortured eyes and his fixed face. But her heart hardened swiftly. She had never loved him. She did not love him now.

But suddenly she lifted her head again swiftly, like a thing that tries to get free. She wanted to be free of it. It was not him so much, but it, something she had put on herself, that bound her so horribly. And having put the bond on herself, it was hardest to take it off. But now she hated everything and felt destructive. He stood with his back to the door, fixed, as if he would oppose her eternally, till she was extinguished. She looked at him. Her eyes were cold and hostile. His workman's hands spread on the panels of the door behind him.

"You know I used to live here?" she began, in a hard voice, as if wilfully to wound him. He braced himself against her, and nodded.

"Well, I was companion to Miss Birch of Torril Hall—she and the rector were friends, and Archie was the rector's son." There was a pause. He listened without knowing what was happening. He stared at his wife. She was squatted in her white dress on the bed, carefully folding and refolding the hem of her skirt. Her voice was full of hostility.

"He was an officer—a sublieutenant—then he quarreled with his colonel and came out of the army. At any rate"—she plucked at her skirt hem, her husband stood motionless, watching her movements which filled his veins with madness—"he was awfully fond of me, and I was of him—awfully."

"How old was he?" asked the husband.

"When—when I first knew him? Or when he went away—?"

"When you first knew him."

"When I first knew him, he was twenty-six—he's thirty-one—nearly thirty-two—because I'm twenty-nine, and he is nearly three years older—"

She lifted her head and looked at the opposite wall.

"And what then?" said her husband.

She hardened herself, and said callously:

"We were as good as engaged for nearly a year, though nobody knew —at least—they talked—but—it wasn't open. Then he went away—"

"He chucked you?" said the husband brutally, wanting to hurt her into contact with himself. Her heart rose wildly with rage. Then "Yes," she said, to anger him. He shifted from one foot to the other, giving a "Pah!" of rage. There was silence for a time.

"Then," she resumed, her pain giving a mocking note to her words, "he suddenly went out to fight in Africa, and almost the very day I first met you, I heard from Miss Birch he'd got sunstroke—and two months after, that he was dead—"

"That was before you took on with me?" said the husband.

There was no answer. Neither spoke for a time. He had not understood. His eyes were contracted uglily.

"So you've been looking at your old courting places!" he said. "That was what you wanted to go out by yourself for this morning."

Still she did not answer him anything. He went away from the door to the window. He stood with his hands behind him, his back to her. She looked at him. His hands seemed gross to her, the back of his head paltry.

At length, almost against his will, he turned round, asking:

"How long were you carrying on with him?"

"What do you mean?" she replied coldly.

"I mean how long were you carrying on with him?"

She lifted her head, averting her face from him. She refused to answer. Then she said:

"I don't know what you mean, by carrying on. I loved him from the first days I met him—two months after I went to stay with Miss Birch."

"And do you reckon he loved you?" he jeered.

"I know he did."

"How do you know, if he'd have no more to do with you?"

There was a long silence of hate and suffering.

"And how far did it go between you?" he asked at length, in a frightened, stiff voice.

"I hate your not-straightforward questions," she cried, beside herself with his baiting. "We loved each other, and we *were* lovers—we were. I don't care what *you* think: what have you got to do with it? We were lovers before I knew you—"

"Lovers—lovers," he said, white with fury. "You mean you had your fling with an army man, and then came to me to marry when you'd had done—"

She sat swallowing her bitterness. There was a long pause.

"Do you mean to say you used to go—the whole hogger?" he asked, still incredulous.

"Why, what else do you think I mean?" she cried brutally.

He shrank, and became white, impersonal. There was a long, paralyzed silence. He seemed to have gone small.

"You never thought to tell me all this before I married you," he said, with bitter irony, at last.

"You never asked me," she replied.

"I never thought there was any need."

"Well, then, you *should* think."

He stood with expressionless, almost childlike set face, revolving many thoughts, whilst his heart was mad with anguish.

Suddenly she added:

"And I saw him today," she said. "He is not dead, he's mad."

"Mad!" he said involuntarily.

"A lunatic," she said. It almost cost her her reason to utter the word. There was a pause.

"Did he know you?" asked the husband, in a small voice.

"No," she said.

He stood and looked at her. At last he had learned the width of the breach between them. She still squatted on the bed. He could not go near her. It would be violation to each of them to be brought into contact with the other. The thing must work itself out. They were both shocked so much, they were impersonal, and no longer hated each other. After some minutes he left her and went out.

William Carlos Williams (1883–1963)

LENA

Lena half-playing at half-having an affair with Don, Pete and Don good-humoredly indulging Lena without quite knowing what she wants, are all three jesting in the dark. The carefully transcribed, apparently artless dialogue both conceals and expresses what no one in the story knows how to articulate. Despite the vastly different scale of the stories—this one is no more than a sketch—Lena may be compared with another inarticulate heroine, Flaubert's Félicité.

You got good fish here, said Pete.

Yeah, said the man back of the bar. Best in the States. He was leaning forward, facing his two customers, his hands busy behind the counter, so that when he spoke he had to look up at them with his big, watery eyes.

It's the butter, said Lena. Don's inquiring stare shifted from the one who had first spoken to the gray-haired woman erect at his left. He made no reply.

I see you have to keep your windows screened though, said Lena. Then, to the hulk of a man sitting next to her, Funny to see lemons growing on a tree; can't get used to it. Smells nice, too. Just like the medahs in the early spring.

You like it? said the man in the dirty white coat back of the bar.

No, she don't like it, said Pete.

Any better up in Jersey this time of year?

The two on the high chairs looked down at him. How did you know we come from Jersey?

Look, Pop. People from all over the United States come into this place and nobody ever says medahs the way she said it just now. I come from Rutherford myself. You know where that is? I thought so. How long you been here?

Two days and she wants to go already back. You own this business?

No, I just work here. First time you been down?

First and last, said Lena. There was no one else in the place at that time of morning and the two on the high chairs seemed disinclined to move. Heinselman's my name, said the big guy. Pigs. Secaucus. This is my wife, Lena. What's your name?

Don. Just Don. So she don't like it, huh? Stick around. It'll grow on you.

I like it all right, but I don't want it. She turned sidewise and looked across the courtyard with its palm trees and oleanders, toward the arcades of the big dining room opposite. Twenty bucks, that's what we had to pay when we eat in there last night.

Hell, Lena, said her husband. We're down here on a vacation—the first we had together. That was expensive food, that's right. . . .

But you gotta admit it's good, said the man behind the counter, and if we didn't make 'em pay they wouldn't like it. But I'll tell you, you get the same food right here in this bar. What d'yuh say? The coconut cream pie's good today.

No, just a cup of coffee.

You act as if you were homesick. What are you, bride and groom?

The big man laughed. Bride and groom! That's good. What you say, Lena, are we bride and groom?

Seeing there was no answer forthcoming from the woman, Don spoke up again. Looking hard at her, his lower lip hanging down in the way he had, There's something familiar about you, he said. Were you ever over in Richfield?

Sure, I guess so.

Did you ever stop at Don's Clam Bar?

Why not?

That was my place. Then, turning to the big fellow, Look, he said. I'm getting out of here at two o'clock. Stick around. Lemme show you some of the high spots. O.K., Lena?

Fresh guy. But something in the way he said it made her smile. Sure, why not? Anything from up home.

Take it away! cried Don. I knew you the first time I saw you. We'll get along fine.

They were sitting on one of the park benches facing the water where far across the bay you could see the flashing lights of the outer city. Lena was in the middle, flanked by the two men.

I had a chance to make a pile of dough one time. And I did too. Sand-pit up near Haverstraw. A woman gummed it up on me.

And drink, maybe, said Lena.

But the thing that really finished me was that oldest boy of mine. He didn't even get into the war, just a training flight. He flew out from somewhere near New Orleans—that's a place you ought to see—and never came back. Ran out of gas, as simple as that. They got his body for me.

That must have been some time ago, said Lena shifting her position.

Yeah, kind of stiffens you up sitting here on these benches. What do you say we go over to my place for a little game of pinochle?

Come on, Lena, said her husband. And some beer, huh?

Sure, the place is lousy with food. And I'll show you the model I got for a machine to clean shrimp.

You make it?

No, I invented it. Come on, just a half a block down the street here. O.K., Lena? It's only nine o'clock, kid. Come on.

By eleven o'clock Lena wanted to go back to the hotel. We leave tomorrow morning.

Can't get you to change your mind?

Na, Lena. A couple of weeks. Here it's warm and pretty. What can we do home?

Work.

I ask you, Don, what a woman! said the big man shaking his head.

You're lucky you got her. What do you say, Lena? I don't meet many people I can pal up with down here. I'll give you a good time.

Where's your wife and the other two kids you was telling us about? Lena countered. I don't trust you. You just like to talk and hit the booze. I know your kind.

Don laughed. Look Lena, stick around and we'll take old Peter here for a hayride. I mean it. You ain't seen nothing yet.

What you want to do this for me for? I'm no young chicken. You trying to make a fool out of me? I don't get you.

Tomorrow morning. I can't go with you, I'll be working, but there's a swell trip you can take around the lagoon and. . . .

On what? We haven't got that kind of money.

It's on me. I got a 1948 Cadillac. It's a honey. And a kid to drive it for you. Anything you like.

What'n the hell's the matter with you? said Lena. You don't know us.

Look, you're from up where I came from. Look. You think I'm putting up a game on you?

Lena, said her big husband. Don is a good guy. He wants to be nice to us. He wants you to stay here, I want you to stay here—for a couple of weeks. We got the cash.

Yes, but not to throw away on a dump like this. Well O.K. I'll stay till Sunday if that'll satisfy you.

Atta girl! Ever see a cockfight, Pete? And we can take in the ponies Sat'day afternoon.

Betting too, no less, said Lena.

Ten bucks! What can you lose? I'll treat you right.

He's getting drunk, she said sidewise to her husband.

No, said Don at the little metal table under an awning where they'd been sitting since the last race on the card. He'd cleaned up thirty bucks. She'd lost. Pete had come out about even, more or less. I'm not drunk, only a little sticky. I never get drunk.

Well then, stop drinking, said Lena.

's all right by me. Stop drinking, she says, so I stop drinking. And he took the half-full bottle of Old Grand-dad by the neck and threw it out onto the grass under the palm trees where it rolled crazily about, spilling whisky, until it landed against the concrete wall of the neighboring pavilion and stopped there, without breaking. She's right. Stop drinking, Don. For you I stop drinking. Because it's you. You got a heart, But that bitch I married. . . . Sorry. Sorry I said that. She's got no heart. She's got the two girls. What the hell more does she want? What have I got? And that ain't the half of it.

Lena looked as though she were about to push the table into his lap and go. She glowered at him and bit her lip. Her husband, a little sunken about the eyes, was watching her, waiting for what she would do next. She was staring at Don who was leaning forward, mouth open, his arms hanging between his knees, fascinated.

Let's have another round of beer, said Lena. Then we'll go home.

Where is she? said Don next morning at the bar. Sleeping it off?

I wasn't sure you'd be open this morning.

What's she up to?

Packing up our suitcases to go home. Thanks for the use of the car. I had a good time.

She can't do that to me, said Don. Tell her to come down here. I wanna talk to her.

She's a funny girl. You know how I made my money, huh? Pigs.

Yeah, said Don. She told me.

It smells bad. So I buy her a little house out in the country.

Yeah, yeah, said Don. She told me.

A fine little farm, just like she said she wanted. The finest farm country in the state. Pine trees, grass. It smells good. We got a few chickens, everything she wants. Everything convenient. I just put in the latest combination dishwasher, laundry and sink, just the way she wanted it. And what do you think she says?

Hell knows, said Don, what a woman wants.

She wants to sell the whole damn place. She wants to go back down where I got my business, in the medahs. That's why I married her, to get her out of that place.

Don looked down at the glass he was polishing.

So I said to her, Come on down to Miami for a couple of weeks, maybe you'll change your mind.

Take it easy, said Don, without raising his eyes. She's coming up behind you. Then looking up and pretending suddenly to have seen her, Hi there, Lena, old muskrat. What'll it be?

She smiled. How I'd like to see a mus'rat again. Just a cup of coffee. Plain. I feel like a new woman, I do. We're flying back this afternoon.

Flying, no less!

Yep, it's the quickest way. She was in high spirits. Do you know what I was thinking about last night? You know, Pete?

I never know what you thinking.

I was thinking, lying there with the planes going over my head the way they do down here. I was thinking of a story one of the boys told me once, one of my two young brothers I brought up after my father and mother died. They used to go hunting in the medahs, when they was big enough. You know once they brought me home three, what they call Canada geese they shot. But they was pretty fishy.

The way you give it to us you'd think it was an estate you had up in Westchester. I knew the medahs too when I was a kid, don't think I didn't.

Yeah, but you never loved it the way I do, said Lena.

She lived in a little shack down there with the boys when she was young, said Pete. It was all she had.

Come on, give it to us—about the dream.

She supped her coffee, fiery hot and looked at Don reproachfully over the far edge of the cup.

Look out you don't burn your tongue, said her husband.

Well, I was thinking, said Lena of what one of my boys told me. I remember that day, I thought he'd never come home. I thought maybe he shot himself—it was so late. The thing is he wanted to see how the blackbirds come in at night so he hid himself early in the cattails and caneys for hours. For hours he had to wait for them.

To shoot 'em, huh?

But mostly to see. He hid himself good. Because to fool things like that you really got to know how. He was lying on his back almost asleep when he began to hear like firecrackers goin' off all around him. At first he didn't know what it was. He was scared. And what do you think it was?

I don't know. Jesse James and his brothers?

The birds. They're pretty heavy, you know, those blackbirds. And when they come down, hundreds of them, maybe thousands and when they light on those long, dried reeds they break off like pistol shots, he said. That's what he heard—all around him and the birds coming down to roost on those reeds. I never forgot it.

There was a long pause.

You know, Don? Last night thinking about you I taught myself something. I'm a wife now. I forgot that. I guess I got to give up all those things.

Gustave Flaubert (1821–1880)

A SIMPLE HEART

No translator has ever matched Flaubert's resourcefulness in making
even densely factual passages flow from active verb to active verb;
the French original uses only two forms of "to be" in the first four
paragraphs of this story, as against nine in the translation. Yet the
translator's impoverished resources do not wholly betray Flaubert's
conception of a lifelong dreariness from which sanctity flowers. Structure and detail alike are borrowed from saints' lives, but without comment; we are left to interpret the closing miracle as we please, without
doubting its appropriateness.

   The opening paragraphs are really about the people rather than
about the house; we are being given a catalogue of their sacred objects. Find other places and other ways in which people are charac-
terized without being talked about directly.

— 1 —

MADAME Aubain's servant Félicité was the envy of the ladies of Pont-
l'Évêque for half a century.

She received four pounds a year. For that she was cook and general
servant, and did the sewing, washing, and ironing; she could bridle a
horse, fatten poultry, and churn butter—and she remained faithful to
her mistress, unamiable as the latter was.

Madame Aubain had married a gay bachelor without money who died
at the beginning of 1809, leaving her with two small children and a
quantity of debts. She then sold all her property except the farms of
Toucques and Geffosses, which brought in two hundred pounds a year
at most, and left her house in Saint-Melaine for a less expensive one that
had belonged to her family and was situated behind the market.

This house had a slate roof and stood between an alley and a lane
that went down to the river. There was an unevenness in the levels of
the rooms which made you stumble. A narrow hall divided the kitchen

From *Three Tales*. Translated by Arthur McDowell. Copyright 1924 by Alfred A.
Knopf, Inc. Reprinted by permission of Alfred A. Knopf, Inc.

from the "parlour" where Mme. Aubain spent her day, sitting in a wicker easy chair by the window. Against the panels, which were painted white, was a row of eight mahogany chairs. On an old piano under the barometer a heap of wooden and cardboard boxes rose like a pyramid. A stuffed armchair stood on either side of the Louis-Quinze chimney-piece, which was in yellow marble with a clock in the middle of it modeled like a temple of Vesta. The whole room was a little musty, as the floor was lower than the garden.

The first floor began with "Madame's" room: very large, with a paleflowered wallpaper and a portrait of "Monsieur" as a dandy of the period. It led to a smaller room, where there were two children's cots without mattresses. Next came the drawing room, which was always shut up and full of furniture covered with sheets. Then there was a corridor leading to a study. The shelves of a large bookcase were respectably lined with books and papers, and its three wings surrounded a broad writing table in darkwood. The two panels at the end of the room were covered with pen drawings, water-color landscape, and engravings by Audran, all relics of better days and vanished splendour. Félicité's room on the top floor got its light from a dormer window, which looked over the meadows.

She rose at daybreak to be in time for Mass, and worked till evening without stopping. Then, when dinner was over, the plates and dishes in order, and the door shut fast, she thrust the log under the ashes and went to sleep in front of the hearth with her rosary in her hand. Félicité was the stubbornest of all bargainers; and as for cleanness, the polish on her saucepans was the despair of other servants. Thrifty in all things, she ate slowly, gathering off the table in her fingers the crumbs of her loaf— a twelve-pound loaf expressly baked for her, which lasted for three weeks.

At all times of year she wore a print handkerchief fastened with a pin behind, a bonnet that covered her hair, grey stockings, a red skirt, and a bibbed apron—such as hospital nurses wear—over her jacket.

Her face was thin and her voice sharp. At twenty-five she looked like forty. From fifty onwards she seemed of no particular age; and with her silence, straight figure, and precise movements she was like a woman made of wood, and going by clockwork.

— 2 —

She had had her love story like another.

Her father, a mason, had been killed by falling off some scaffolding. Then her mother died, her sisters scattered, and a farmer took her in and employed her, while she was still quite little, to herd the cows at pasture.

She shivered in rags and would lie flat on the ground to drink water from the ponds; she was beaten for nothing, and finally turned out for the theft of a shilling which she did not steal. She went to another farm, where she became dairy maid; and, as she was liked by her employers, her companions were jealous of her.

One evening in August (she was then eighteen) they took her to the assembly at Colleville. She was dazed and stupefied in an instant by the noise of the fiddlers, the lights in the trees, the gay medley of dresses, the lace, the gold crosses, and the throng of people jigging all together. While she kept shyly apart a young man with a well-to-do air, who was leaning on the shaft of a cart and smoking his pipe, came up to ask her to dance. He treated her to cider, coffee, and cake, and bought her a silk handkerchief; and then, imagining she had guessed his meaning, offered to see her home. At the edge of a field of oats he pushed her roughly down. She was frightened and began to cry out; and he went off.

One evening later she was on the Beaumont road. A big hay wagon was moving slowly along; she wanted to get in front of it, and as she brushed past the wheels she recognized Theodore. He greeted her quite calmly, saying she must excuse it all because it was "the fault of the drink." She could not think of any answer and wanted to run away.

He began at once to talk about the harvest and the worthies of the commune, for his father had left Colleville for the farm at Les Écots, so that now he and she were neighbors. "Ah!" she said. He added that they thought of settling him in life. Well, he was in no hurry; he was waiting for a wife to his fancy. She dropped her head; and then he asked her if she thought of marrying. She answered with a smile that it was mean to make fun of her.

"But I am not, I swear!"—and he passed his left hand round her waist. She walked in the support of his embrace; their steps grew slower. The wind was soft, the stars glittered, the huge wagonload of hay swayed in front of them, and dust rose from the dragging steps of the four horses. Then, without a word of command, they turned to the right. He clasped her once more in his arms, and she disappeared into the shadow.

The week after Theodore secured some assignations with her.

They met at the end of farmyards, behind a wall, or under a solitary tree. She was not innocent as young ladies are—she had learned knowledge from the animals—but her reason and the instinct of her honor would not let her fall. Her resistance exasperated Theodore's passion; so much so that to satisfy it—or perhaps quite artlessly—he made her an offer of marriage. She was in doubt whether to trust him, but he swore great oaths of fidelity.

Soon he confessed to something troublesome; the year before his parents had bought him a substitute for the army, but any day he might be taken again, and the idea of serving was a terror to him. Félicité took this cowardice of his as a sign of affection, and it redoubled hers. She stole away at night to see him, and when she reached their meeting place Theodore racked her with his anxieties and urgings.

At last he declared that he would go himself to the prefecture for information, and would tell her the result on the following Sunday, between eleven and midnight.

When the moment came she sped towards her lover. Instead of him she found one of his friends.

He told her that she would not see Theodore any more. To ensure himself against conscription he had married an old woman, Madame Lehoussais, of Toucques, who was very rich.

There was an uncontrollable burst of grief. She threw herself on the ground, screamed, called to the God of mercy, and moaned by herself in the fields till daylight came. Then she came back to the farm and announced that she was going to leave; and at the end of the month she received her wages, tied all her small belongings with a handkerchief, and went to Pont-l'Évêque.

In front of the inn there she made inquiries of a woman in a widow's cap, who, as it happened, was just looking for a cook. The girl did not know much, but her willingness seemed so great and her demands so small that Mme. Aubain ended by saying:

"Very well, then, I will take you."

A quarter of an hour afterwards Félicité was installed in her house.

She lived there at first in a tremble, as it were, at "the style of the house" and the memory of "Monsieur" floating over it all. Paul and Virginie, the first aged seven and the other hardly four, seemed to her beings of a precious substance; she carried them on her back like a horse; it was a sorrow to her that Mme. Aubain would not let her kiss them every minute. And yet she was happy there. Her grief had melted in the pleasantness of things all round.

Every Thursday regular visitors came in for a game of boston, and Félicité got the cards and foot-warmers ready beforehand. They arrived punctually at eight and left before the stroke of eleven.

On Monday mornings the dealer who lodged in the covered passage spread out all his old iron on the ground. Then a hum of voices began to fill the town, mingled with the neighing of horses, bleating of lambs, grunting of pigs, and the sharp rattle of carts along the street. About noon, when the market was at its height, you might see a tall, hook-nosed old countryman with his cap pushed back making his appearance at the door. It was Robelin, the farmer of Geffosses. A little later came Liébard, the farmer from Toucques—short, red, and corpulent—in a grey jacket and gaiters shod with spurs.

Both had poultry or cheese to offer their landlord. Félicité was invariably a match for their cunning, and they went away filled with respect for her.

At vague intervals Mme. Aubain had a visit from the Marquis de Gremanville, one of her uncles, who had ruined himself by debauchery and now lived at Falaise on his last remaining morsel of land. He invariably came at the luncheon hour, with a dreadful poodle whose paws left all the furniture in a mess. In spite of efforts to show his breeding, which he carried to the point of raising his hat every time he mentioned "my late father," habit was too strong for him; he poured himself out glass after glass and fired off improper remarks. Félicité edged him politely out of the house—"You have had enough, Monsieur de Gremanville! Another time!"—and she shut the door on him.

She opened it with pleasure to M. Bourais, who had been a lawyer. His baldness, his white stock, frilled shirt, and roomy brown coat, his way of rounding the arm as he took snuff—his whole person, in fact, created that disturbance of mind which overtakes us at the sight of extraordinary men.

As he looked after the property of "Madame" he remained shut up with her for hours in "Monsieur's" study, though all the time he was afraid of compromising himself. He respected the magistracy immensely, and had some pretensions to Latin.

To combine instruction and amusement he gave the children a geography book made up of a series of prints. They represented scenes in different parts of the world: cannibals with feathers on their heads, a monkey carrying off a young lady, Bedouins in the desert, the harpooning of a whale, and so on. Paul explained these engravings to Félicité; and that, in fact, was the whole of her literary education. The children's education was undertaken by Guyot, a poor creature employed at the town hall, who was famous for his beautiful hand and sharpened his penknife on his boots.

When the weather was bright the household set off early for a day at Geffosses Farm.

Its courtyard is on a slope, with the farmhouse in the middle, and the sea looks like a grey streak in the distance.

Félicité brought slices of cold meat out of her basket, and they breakfasted in a room adjoining the dairy. It was the only surviving fragment of a country house which was now no more. The wallpaper hung in tatters, and quivered in the draughts. Mme. Aubain sat with bowed head, overcome by her memories; the children became afraid to speak. "Why don't you play, then?" she would say, and off they went.

Paul climbed into the barn, caught birds, played at ducks and drakes over the pond, or hammered with his stick on the big casks which boomed like drums. Virginie fed the rabbits or dashed off to pick corn-flowers, her quick legs showing their embroidered little drawers.

One autumn evening they went home by the fields. The moon was in its first quarter, lighting part of the sky; and mist floated like a scarf over the windings of the Toucques. Cattle, lying out in the middle of the grass, looked quietly at the four people as they passed. In the third meadow some of them got up and made a half-circle in front of the walkers. "There's nothing to be afraid of," said Félicité, as she stroked the nearest on the back with a kind of crooning song; he wheeled round and the others did the same. But when they crossed the next pasture there was a formidable bellow. It was a bull, hidden by the mist. Mme. Aubain was about to run. "No! no! don't go so fast!" They mended their pace, however, and heard a loud breathing behind them which came nearer. His hoofs thudded on the meadow grass like hammers; why, he was galloping now! Félicité turned round, and tore up clods of earth with both hands and threw them in his eyes. He lowered his muzzle, waved his horns, and quivered with fury, bellowing terribly. Mme. Aubain, now at the end of the pasture with her two little ones, was look-ing wildly for a place to get over the high bank. Félicité was retreating, still with her face to the bull, keeping up a shower of clods which blinded him, and crying all the time, "Be quick! be quick!"

Mme. Aubain went down into the ditch, pushed Virginie first and then Paul, fell several times as she tried to climb the bank, and managed it at last by dint of courage.

The bull had driven Félicité to bay against a rail fence; his slaver was streaming into her face; another second, and he would have gored her. She had just time to slip between two of the rails, and the big animal stopped short in amazement.

This adventure was talked of at Pont-l'Évêque for many a year. Féli-cité did not pride herself on it in the least, not having the barest sus-picion that she had done anything heroic.

Virginie was the sole object of her thoughts, for the child developed a nervous complaint as a result of her fright, and M. Poupart, the doctor, advised sea bathing at Trouville. It was not a frequented place then. Mme. Aubain collected information, consulted Bourais, and made prep-arations as though for a long journey.

Her luggage started a day in advance, in Liébard's cart. The next day he brought round two horses, one of which had a lady's saddle with a velvet back to it, while a cloak was rolled up to make a kind of seat on the crupper of the other. Mme. Aubain rode on that, behind the farmer. Félicité took charge of Virginie, and Paul mounted M. Lechaptois' donkey, lent on condition that great care was taken of it.

The road was so bad that its five miles took two hours. The horses sank in the mud up to their pasterns, and their haunches jerked abruptly in the effort to get out; or else they stumbled in the ruts, and at other moments had to jump. In some places Liébard's mare came suddenly to a halt. He waited patiently until she went on again, talking about the people who had properties along the road, and adding moral reflections to their history. So it was that as they were in the middle of Toucques, and passed under some windows bowered with nasturtiums, he shrugged his shoulders and said: "There's a Mme. Lehoussais lives there; instead of taking a young man she. . . ." Félicité did not hear the rest; the horses were trotting and the donkey galloping. They all turned down a bypath; a gate swung open and two boys appeared; and the party dismounted in front of a manure heap at the very threshold of the farmhouse door.

When Mme. Liébard saw her mistress she gave lavish signs of joy. She served her a luncheon with a sirloin of beef, tripe, black pudding, a fricassee of chicken, sparkling cider, a fruit tart, and brandied plums; seasoning it all with compliments to Madame, who seemed in better health; Mademoiselle, who was "splendid" now; and Monsieur Paul, who had "filled out" wonderfully. Nor did she forget their deceased grandparents, whom the Liébards had known, as they had been in the service of the family for several generations. The farm, like them, had the stamp of antiquity. The beams on the ceiling were worm-eaten, the walls blackened with smoke, and the windowpanes grey with dust. There was an oak dresser laden with every sort of useful article—jugs, plates, pewter bowls, wolf traps, and sheep-shears; and a huge syringe made the children laugh. There was not a tree in the three courtyards without mushrooms growing at the bottom of it or a tuft of mistletoe on its boughs. Several of them had been thrown down by the wind. They had taken root again at the middle; and all were bending under their wealth of apples. The thatched roofs, like brown velvet and of varying thickness, withstood the heaviest squalls. The cart shed, however, was falling into ruin. Mme. Aubain said she would see about it, and ordered the animals to be saddled again.

It was another half-hour before they reached Trouville. The little caravan dismounted to pass Écores—it was an overhanging cliff with boats below it—and three minutes later they were at the end of the quay and entered the courtyard of the Golden Lamb, kept by good Mme. David.

From the first days of their stay Virginie began to feel less weak, thanks to the change of air and the effect of the sea baths. These, for want of a bathing dress, she took in her chemise; and her nurse dressed her afterwards in a coastguard's cabin which was used by the bathers.

In the afternoons they took the donkey and went off beyond the Black Rocks, in the direction of Hennequeville. The path climbed at first through ground with dells in it like the green sward of a park, and then reached a plateau where grass fields and arable lay side by side. Hollies rose stiffly out of the briary tangle at the edge of the road; and here and there a great withered tree made zigzags in the blue air with its branches.

They nearly always rested in a meadow, with Deauville on their left, Havre on their right, and the open sea in front. It glittered in the sunshine, smooth as a mirror and so quiet that its murmur was scarcely to be heard; sparrows chirped in hiding and the immense sky arched over it all. Mme. Aubain sat doing her needlework; Virginie plaited rushes by her side; Félicité pulled up lavender, and Paul was bored and anxious to start home.

Other days they crossed the Toucques in a boat and looked for shells. When the tide went out sea urchins, starfish, and jellyfish were left exposed; and the children ran in pursuit of the foam flakes which scudded in the wind. The sleepy waves broke on the sand and unrolled all along the beach; it stretched away out of sight, bounded on the land side by the dunes which parted it from the Marsh, a wide meadow shaped like an arena. As they came home that way, Trouville, on the hill slope in the background, grew bigger at every step, and its miscellaneous throng of houses seemed to break into a gay disorder.

On days when it was too hot they did not leave their room. From the dazzling brilliance outside light fell in streaks between the laths of the blinds. There were no sounds in the village; and on the pavement below not a soul. This silence round them deepened the quietness of things. In the distance, where men were caulking, there was a tap of hammers as they plugged the hulls, and a sluggish breeze wafted up the smell of tar.

The chief amusement was the return of the fishing boats. They began to tack as soon as they had passed the buoys. The sails came down on two of the three masts; and they drew on with the foresail swelling like a balloon, glided through the splash of the waves, and when they had reached the middle of the harbor suddenly dropped anchor. Then the boats drew up against the quay. The sailors threw quivering fish over the side; a row of carts was waiting, and women in cotton bonnets darted out to take the baskets and give their men a kiss.

One of them came up to Félicité one day, and she entered the lodgings a little later in a state of delight. She had found a sister again—and then Nastasie Barette, "wife of Leroux," appeared, holding an infant at her breast and another child with her right hand, while on her left was a little cabin boy with his hands on his hips and a cap over his ear.

After a quarter of an hour Mme. Aubain sent them off; but they were always to be found hanging about the kitchen, or encountered in the course of a walk. The husband never appeared.

Félicité was seized with affection for them. She bought them a blanket, some shirts, and a stove; it was clear that they were making a good thing out of her. Mme. Aubain was annoyed by this weakness of hers, and she did not like the liberties taken by the nephew, who said "thee" and "thou" to Paul. So as Virginie was coughing and the fine weather gone, she returned to Pont-l'Évêque.

There M. Bourais enlightened her on the choice of a boys' school. The one at Caen was reputed to be the best, and Paul was sent to it. He said his good-byes bravely, content enough at going to live in a house where he would have companions. Mme. Aubain resigned herself to her son's absence as a thing that had to be. Virginie thought about it less and less. Félicité missed the noise he made. But she found an occupation to distract her; from Christmas onward she took the little girl to catechism every day.

— *3* —

After making a genuflexion at the door she walked up between the double row of chairs under the lofty nave, opened Mme. Aubain's pew, sat down, and began to look about her. The choir stalls were filled with the boys on the right and the girls on the left, and the curé stood by the lectern. On a painted window in the apse the Holy Ghost looked down upon the Virgin. Another window showed her on her knees before the child Jesus, and a group carved in wood behind the altar shrine represented St. Michael overthrowing the dragon.

The priest began with a sketch of sacred history. The Garden, the Flood, the Tower of Babel, cities in flames, dying nations, and overturned idols passed like a dream before her eyes; and the dizzying vision left her with reverence for the Most High and fear of His wrath. Then she wept at the story of the Passion. Why had they crucified Him, when He loved the children, fed the multitudes, healed the blind, and had willed, in His meekness, to be born among the poor, on the dung heap of a stable? The sowings, harvests, winepresses, all the familiar things the Gospel speaks of, were a part of her life. They had been made holy by God's passing; and she loved the lambs more tenderly for her love of the Lamb, and the doves because of the Holy Ghost.

She found it hard to imagine Him in person, for He was not merely a bird, but a flame as well, and a breath at other times. It may be His light, she thought, which flits at night about the edge of the marshes, His breathing which drives on the clouds, His voice which gives harmony to the bells; and she would sit rapt in adoration, enjoying the cool walls and the quiet of the church.

Of doctrines, she understood nothing—did not even try to understand.

The curé discoursed, the children repeated their lesson, and finally she went to sleep, waking up with a start when their wooden shoes clattered on the flagstones as they went away.

It was thus that Félicité, whose religious education had been neglected in her youth, learned the catechism by dint of hearing it; and from that time she copied all Virginie's observances, fasting as she did and confessing with her. On Corpus Christi Day they made a festal altar together.

The first communion loomed distractingly ahead. She fussed over the shoes, the rosary, the book and gloves; and how she trembled as she helped Virginie's mother to dress her!

All through the mass she was racked with anxiety. She could not see one side of the choir because of M. Bourais; but straight in front of her was the flock of maidens, with white crowns above their hanging veils, making the impression of a field of snow; and she knew her dear child at a distance by her dainty neck and thoughtful air. The bell tinkled. The heads bowed, and there was silence. As the organ pealed, singers and congregation took up the "Agnus Dei"; then the procession of the boys began, and after them the girls rose. Step by step, with their hands joined in prayer, they went towards the lighted altar, knelt on the first step, received the sacrament in turn, and came back in the same order to their places. When Virginie's turn came Félicité leaned forward to see her; and with the imaginativeness of deep and tender feeling it seemed to her that she actually was the child; Virginie's face became hers, she was dressed in her clothes, it was her heart beating in her breast. As the moment came to open her mouth she closed her eyes and nearly fainted.

She appeared early in the sacristy next morning for Monsieur the curé to give her the communion. She took it with devotion, but it did not give her the same exquisite delight.

Mme. Aubain wanted to make her daughter into an accomplished person; and as Guyot could not teach her music or English she decided to place her in the Ursuline Convent at Honfleur as a boarder. The child made no objection. Félicité sighed and thought that Madame lacked feeling. Then she reflected that her mistress might be right; matters of this kind were beyond her.

So one day an old spring-van drew up at the door, and out of it stepped a nun to fetch the young lady. Félicité hoisted the luggage on to the top, admonished the driver, and put six pots of preserves, a dozen pears, and a bunch of violets under the seat.

At the last moment Virginie broke into a fit of sobbing; she threw her arms round her mother, who kissed her on the forehead, saying over and over "Come, be brave! be brave!" The step was raised, and the carriage drove off.

Then Mme. Aubain's strength gave way; and in the evening all her friends—the Lormeau family, Mme. Lechaptois, the Rochefeuille ladies, M. de Houppeville, and Bourais—came in to console her.

To be without her daughter was very painful for her at first. But she heard from Virginie three times a week, wrote to her on the other days, walked in the garden, and so filled up the empty hours.

From sheer habit Félicité went into Virginie's room in the mornings and gazed at the walls. It was boredom to her not to have to comb the child's hair now, lace up her boots, tuck her into bed—and not to see her charming face perpetually and hold her hand when they went out together. In this idle condition she tried making lace. But her fingers were too heavy and broke the threads; she could not attend to anything, she had lost her sleep, and was, in her own words, "destroyed."

To "divert herself" she asked leave to have visits from her nephew Victor.

He arrived on Sundays after mass, rosy-cheeked, bare-chested, with the scent of the country he had walked through still about him. She laid her table promptly and they had lunch, sitting opposite each other. She ate as little as possible herself to save expense, but stuffed him with food so generously that at last he went to sleep. At the first stroke of vespers she woke him up, brushed his trousers, fastened his tie, and went to church, leaning on his arm with maternal pride.

Victor was always instructed by his parents to get something out of her—a packet of moist sugar, it might be, a cake of soap, spirits, or even money at times. He brought his things for her to mend and she took over the task, only too glad to have a reason for making him come back.

In August his father took him off on a coasting voyage. It was holiday time, and she was consoled by the arrival of the children. Paul, however, was getting selfish, and Virginie was too old to be called "thou" any longer; this put a constraint and barrier between them.

Victor went to Morlaix, Dunkirk, and Brighton in succession and made Félicité a present on his return from each voyage. It was a box made of shells the first time, a coffee cup the next, and on the third occasion a large gingerbread man. Victor was growing handsome. He was well made, had a hint of a moustache, good honest eyes, and a small leather hat pushed backwards like a pilot's. He entertained her by telling stories embroidered with nautical terms.

On a Monday, July 14, 1819 (she never forgot the date), he told her that he had signed on for the big voyage and next night but one he would take the Honfleur boat and join his schooner, which was to weigh anchor from Havre before long. Perhaps he would be gone two years.

The prospect of this long absence threw Félicité into deep distress; one more good-bye she must have, and on the Wednesday evening, when

Madame's dinner was finished, she put on her clogs and made short work of the twelve miles between Pont-l'Évêque and Honfleur.

When she arrived in front of the Calvary she took the turn to the right instead of the left, got lost in the timber yards, and retraced her steps; some people to whom she spoke advised her to be quick. She went all round the harbor basin, full of ships, and knocked against hawsers; then the ground fell away, lights flashed across each other, and she thought her wits had left her, for she saw horses up in the sky.

Others were neighing by the quayside, frightened at the sea. They were lifted by a tackle and deposited in a boat, where passengers jostled each other among cider casks, cheese baskets, and sacks of grain; fowls could be heard clucking, the captain swore; and a cabin boy stood leaning over the bows, indifferent to it all. Félicité, who had not recognized him, called "Victor!" and he raised his head; all at once, as she was darting forwards, the gangway was drawn back.

The Honfleur packet, women singing as they hauled it, passed out of harbor. Its framework creaked and the heavy waves whipped its bows. The canvas had swung round, no one could be seen on board now; and on the moon-silvered sea the boat made a black speck which paled gradually, dipped, and vanished.

As Félicité passed by the Calvary she had a wish to commend to God what she cherished most, and she stood there praying a long time with her face bathed in tears and her eyes towards the clouds. The town was asleep, coastguards were walking to and fro; and water poured without cessation through the holes in the sluice, with the noise of a torrent. The clocks struck two.

The convent parlor would not be open before day. If Félicité were late Madame would most certainly be annoyed; and in spite of her desire to kiss the other child she turned home. The maids at the inn were waking up as she came in to Pont-l'Évêque.

So the poor slip of a boy was going to toss for months and months at sea! She had not been frightened by his previous voyages. From England or Brittany you came back safe enough; but America, the colonies, the islands—these were lost in a dim region at the other end of the world.

Félicité's thoughts from that moment ran entirely on her nephew. On sunny days she was harassed by the idea of thirst; when there was a storm she was afraid of the lightning on his account. As she listened to the wind growling in the chimney or carrying off the slates she pictured him lashed by that same tempest, at the top of a shattered mast, with his body thrown backwards under a sheet of foam; or else (with a reminiscence of the illustrated geography) he was being eaten by savages, captured in a wood by monkeys, or dying on a desert shore. And never did she mention her anxieties.

Mme. Aubain had anxieties of her own, about her daughter. The good sisters found her an affectionate but delicate child. The slightest emotion unnerved her. She had to give up the piano.

Her mother stipulated for regular letters from the convent. She lost patience one morning when the postman did not come, and walked to and fro in the parlour from her armchair to the window. It was really amazing; not a word for four days!

To console Mme. Aubain by her own example Félicité remarked:

"As for me, Madame, it's six months since I heard. . . ."

"From whom, pray?"

"Why . . . from my nephew," the servant answered gently.

"Oh! your nephew!" And Mme. Aubain resumed her walk with a shrug of the shoulders, as much as to say: "I was not thinking of him! And what is more, it's absurd! A scamp of a cabin boy—what does he matter? . . . whereas my daughter . . . why, just think!"

Félicité, though she had been brought up on harshness, felt indignant with Madame—and then forgot. It seemed the simplest thing in the world to her to lose one's head over the little girl. For her the two children were equally important; a bond in her heart made them one, and their destinies must be the same.

She heard from the chemist that Victor's ship had arrived at Havana. He had read this piece of news in a gazette.

Cigars—they made her imagine Havana as a place where no one does anything but smoke, and there was Victor moving among the negroes in a cloud of tobacco. Could you, she wondered, "in case you needed," return by land? What was the distance from Pont-l'Évêque? She questioned M. Bourais to find out.

He reached for his atlas and began explaining the longitudes; Félicité's consternation provoked a fine pedantic smile. Finally he marked with his pencil a black, imperceptible point in the indentations of an oval spot, and said as he did so, "Here it is." She bent over the map; the maze of coloured lines wearied her eyes without conveying anything; and on an invitation from Bourais to tell him her difficulty, she begged him to show her the house where Victor was living. Bourais threw up his arms, sneezed, and laughed immensely: a simplicity like hers was a positive joy. And Félicité did not understand the reason; how could she when she expected, very likely, to see the actual image of her nephew—so stunted was her mind!

A fortnight afterwards Liébard came into the kitchen at market time as usual and handed her a letter from her brother-in-law. As neither of them could read she took it to her mistress.

Mme. Aubain, who was counting the stitches in her knitting, put the work down by her side, broke the seal of the letter, started, and said in a low voice, with a look of meaning:

"It is bad news . . . that they have to tell you. Your nephew. . . ."
He was dead. The letter said no more.

Félicité fell onto a chair, leaning her head against the wainscot; and she closed her eyelids, which suddenly flushed pink. Then with bent forehead, hands hanging, and fixed eyes, she said at intervals:

"Poor little lad! poor little lad!"

Liébard watched her and heaved sighs. Mme. Aubain trembled a little.

She suggested that Félicité should go to see her sister at Trouville. Félicité answered by a gesture that she had no need.

There was a silence. The worthy Liébard thought it was time for them to withdraw.

Then Félicité said:

"They don't care, not they!"

Her head dropped again; and she took up mechanically, from time to time, the long needles on her work table.

Women passed in the yard with a barrow of dripping linen.

As she saw them through the windowpanes she remembered her washing; she had put it to soak the day before, today she must wring it out; and she left the room.

Her plank and tub were at the edge of the Toucques. She threw a pile of linen on the bank, rolled up her sleeves, and taking her wooden beater dealt lusty blows whose sound carried to the neighboring gardens. The meadows were empty, the river stirred in the wind; and down below long grasses wavered, like the hair of corpses floating in the water. She kept her grief down and was very brave until the evening; but once in her room she surrendered to it utterly, lying stretched on the mattress with her face in the pillow and her hands clenched against her temples.

Much later she heard, from the captain himself, the circumstances of Victor's end. They had bled him too much at the hospital for yellow fever. Four doctors held him at once. He had died instantly, and the chief had said:

"Bah! there goes another!"

His parents had always been brutal to him. She preferred not to see them again; and they made no advances, either because they forgot her or from the callousness of the wretchedly poor.

Virginie began to grow weaker.

Tightness in her chest, coughing, continual fever, and veinings on her cheekbones betrayed some deep-seated complaint. M. Poupart had advised a stay in Provence. Mme. Aubain determined on it, and would have brought her daughter home at once but for the climate of Pont-l'Évêque.

She made an arrangement with a job-master, and he drove her to the convent every Tuesday. There is a terrace in the garden, with a view over the Seine. Virginie took walks there over the fallen vine leaves, on her mother's arm. A shaft of sunlight through the clouds made her blink sometimes, as she gazed at the sails in the distance and the whole horizon from the castle of Tancarville to the lighthouses at Havre. Afterwards they rested in the arbor. Her mother had secured a little cask of excellent Malaga; and Virginie, laughing at the idea of getting tipsy, drank a thimbleful of it, no more.

Her strength came back visibly. The autumn glided gently away. Félicité reassured Mme. Aubain. But one evening, when she had been out on a commission in the neighborhood, she found M. Poupart's gig at the door. He was in the hall, and Mme. Aubain was tying her bonnet.

"Give me my foot-warmer, purse, gloves! Quicker, come!"

Virginie had inflammation of the lungs; perhaps it was hopeless.

"Not yet!" said the doctor, and they both got into the carriage under whirling flakes of snow. Night was coming on and it was very cold.

Félicité rushed into the church to light a taper. Then she ran after the gig, came up with it in an hour, and jumped lightly in behind. As she hung on by the fringes a thought came into her mind: "The courtyard has not been shut up; supposing burglars got in!" And she jumped down.

At dawn next day she presented herself at the doctor's. He had come in and started for the country again. Then she waited in the inn, thinking that a letter would come by some hand or other. Finally, when it was twilight, she took the Lisieux coach.

The convent was at the end of a steep lane. When she was about half-way up it she heard strange sounds—a death-bell tolling. "It is for someone else," thought Félicité, and she pulled the knocker violently.

After some minutes there was a sound of trailing slippers, the door opened ajar, and a nun appeared.

The good sister, with an air of compunction, said that "she had just passed away." On the instant the bell of St. Leonard's tolled twice as fast.

Félicité went up to the second floor.

From the doorway she saw Virginie stretched on her back, with her hands joined, her mouth open, and head thrown back under a black crucifix that leaned towards her, between curtains that hung stiffly, less pale than was her face. Mme. Aubain, at the foot of the bed which she clasped with her arms, was choking with sobs of agony. The mother superior stood on the right. Three candlesticks on the chest of drawers made spots of red, and the mist came whitely through the windows. Nuns came and took Mme. Aubain away.

For two nights Félicité never left the dead child. She repeated the same prayers, sprinkled holy water over the sheets, came and sat down again, and watched her. At the end of the first vigil she noticed that the face had grown yellow, the lips turned blue, the nose was sharper, and the eyes sunk in. She kissed them several times, and would not have been immensely surprised if Virginie had opened them again; to minds like hers the supernatural is quite simple. She made the girl's toilette, wrapped her in her shroud, lifted her down into her bier, put a garland on her head, and spread out her hair. It was fair, and extraordinarily long for her age. Félicité cut off a big lock and slipped half of it into her bosom, determined that she should never part with it.

The body was brought back to Pont-l'Évêque, as Mme. Aubain intended; she followed the hearse in a closed carriage.

It took another three-quarters of an hour after the Mass to reach the cemetery. Paul walked in front, sobbing. M. Bourais was behind, and then came the chief residents, the women shrouded in black mantles, and Félicité. She thought of her nephew; and because she had not been able to pay these honors to him her grief was doubled, as though the one were being buried with the other.

Mme. Aubain's despair was boundless. It was against God that she first rebelled, thinking it unjust of Him to have taken her daughter from her—she had never done evil and her conscience was so clear! Ah, no!—she ought to have taken Virginie off to the south. Other doctors would have saved her. She accused herself now, wanted to join her child, and broke into cries of distress in the middle of her dreams. One dream haunted her above all. Her husband, dressed as a sailor, was returning from a long voyage, and shedding tears he told her that he had been ordered to take Virginie away. Then they consulted how to hide her somewhere.

She came in once from the garden quite upset. A moment ago—and she pointed out the place—the father and daughter had appeared to her, standing side by side, and they did nothing, but they looked at her.

For several months after this she stayed inertly in her room. Félicité lectured her gently; she must live for her son's sake, and for the other, in remembrance of "her."

"Her?" answered Mme. Aubain, as though she were just waking up. "Ah, yes! . . . yes! . . . You do not forget her!" This was an allusion to the cemetery, where she was strictly forbidden to go.

Félicité went there every day.

Precisely at four she skirted the houses, climbed the hill, opened the gate, and came to Virginie's grave. It was a little column of pink marble with a stone underneath and a garden plot enclosed by chains. The beds were hidden under a coverlet of flowers. She watered their leaves, freshened the gravel, and knelt down to break up the earth better. When Mme. Aubain was able to come there she felt a relief and a sort of consolation.

Then years slipped away, one like another, and their only episodes were the great festivals as they recurred—Easter, the Assumption, All Saints' Day. Household occurrences marked dates that were referred to afterwards. In 1825, for instance, two glaziers whitewashed the hall; in 1827 a piece of the roof fell into the courtyard and nearly killed a man. In the summer of 1828 it was Madame's turn to offer the consecrated bread; Bourais, about this time, mysteriously absented himself; and one by one the old acquaintances passed away: Guyot, Liébard, Mme. Lechaptois, Robelin, and Uncle Gremanville, who had been paralyzed for a long time.

One night the driver of the mail coach announced the Revolution of July in Pont-l'Évêque. A new subprefect was appointed a few days later— Baron de Larsonnière, who had been consul in America, and brought with him, besides his wife, a sister-in-law and three young ladies, already growing up. They were to be seen about on their lawn, in loose blouses, and they had a negro and a parrot. They paid a call on Mme. Aubain which she did not fail to return. The moment they were seen in the distance Félicité ran to let her mistress know. But only one thing could really move her feelings—the letters from her son.

He was swallowed up in a tavern life and could follow no career. She paid his debts, he made new ones; and the sighs that Mme. Aubain uttered as she sat knitting by the window reached Félicité at her spinning wheel in the kitchen.

They took walks together along the espaliered wall, always talking of Virginie and wondering if such and such a thing would have pleased her and what, on some occasion, she would have been likely to say.

All her small belongings filled a cupboard in the two-bedded room. Mme. Aubain inspected them as seldom as she could. One summer day she made up her mind to it—and some moths flew out of the wardrobe.

Virginie's dresses were in a row underneath a shelf, on which there were three dolls, some hoops, a set of toy pots and pans, and the basin that she used. They took out her petticoats as well, and the stockings and handkerchiefs, and laid them out on the two beds before folding them up again. The sunshine lit up these poor things, bringing out their stains and the creases made by the body's movements. The air was warm and blue, a blackbird warbled, life seemed bathed in a deep sweetness. They found a little plush hat with thick, chestnut-colored pile; but it was eaten all over by moths. Félicité begged it for her own. Their eyes met fixedly and filled with tears; at last the mistress opened her arms, the servant threw herself into them, and they embraced each other, satisfying their grief in a kiss that made them equal.

It was the first time in their lives, Mme. Aubain's nature not being expansive. Félicité was as grateful as though she had received a favor, and cherished her mistress from that moment with the devotion of an animal and a religious worship.

The kindness of her heart unfolded.

When she heard the drums of a marching regiment in the street she posted herself at the door with a pitcher of cider and asked the soldiers to drink. She nursed cholera patients and protected the Polish refugees; one of these even declared that he wished to marry her. They quarrelled, however; for when she came back from the Angelus one morning she found that he had got into her kitchen and made himself a vinegar salad which he was quietly eating.

After the Poles came Father Colmiche, an old man who was supposed to have committed atrocities in '93. He lived by the side of the river in the ruins of a pigsty. The little boys watched him through the cracks in the wall, and threw pebbles at him which fell on the pallet where he lay constantly shaken by a catarrh; his hair was very long, his eyes inflamed, and there was a tumor on his arm bigger than his head. She got him some linen and tried to clean up his miserable hole; her dream was to establish him in the bakehouse, without letting him annoy Madame. When the tumor burst she dressed it every day; sometimes she brought him cake, and would put him in the sunshine on a truss of straw. The poor old man, slobbering and trembling, thanked her in his worn-out voice, was terrified that he might lose her, and stretched out his hands when he saw her go away. He died; and she had a Mass said for the repose of his soul.

That very day a great happiness befell her; just at dinner time appeared Mme. de Larsonnière's negro, carrying the parrot in its cage, with perch, chain, and padlock. A note from the baroness informed Mme. Aubain that her husband had been raised to a prefecture and they were starting that evening; she begged her to accept the bird as a memento and mark of her regard.

For a long time he had absorbed Félicité's imagination, because he came from America; and that name reminded her of Victor, so much so that she made inquiries of the negro. She had once gone so far as to say, "How Madame would enjoy having him!"

The negro repeated the remark to his mistress; and as she could not take the bird away with her she chose this way of getting rid of him.

— *4* —

His name was Loulou. His body was green and the tips of his wings rose-pink; his forehead was blue and his throat golden.

But he had the tiresome habits of biting his perch, tearing out his feathers, sprinkling his dirt about, and spattering the water of his tub. He annoyed Mme. Aubain, and she gave him to Félicité for good.

She endeavored to train him; soon he could repeat "Nice boy! Your servant, sir! Good morning, Marie!" He was placed by the side of the door, and astonished several people by not answering to the name Jacquot, for all parrots are called Jacquot. People compared him to a turkey and a log of wood, and stabbed Félicité to the heart each time. Strange obstinacy on Loulou's part!—directly you looked at him he refused to speak.

None the less he was eager for society; for on Sundays, while the Rochefeuille ladies, M. de Houppeville, and new familiars—Onfroy the apothecary, Monsieur Varin, and Captain Mathieu—were playing their game of cards, he beat the windows with his wings and threw himself about so frantically that they could not hear each other speak.

Bourais' face, undoubtedly, struck him as extremely droll. Directly he saw it he began to laugh—and laugh with all his might. His peals rang through the courtyard and were repeated by the echo; the neighbors came to their windows and laughed too; while M. Bourais, gliding along under the wall to escape the parrot's eye, and hiding his profile with his hat, got to the river and then entered by the garden gate. There was a lack of tenderness in the looks which he darted at the bird.

Loulou had been slapped by the butcher boy for making so free as to plunge his head into his basket; and since then he was always trying to nip him through his shirt. Fabu threatened to wring his neck, although he was not cruel, for all his tattooed arms and large whiskers. Far from it; he really rather liked the parrot, and in a jovial humor even wanted to teach him to swear. Félicité, who was alarmed by such proceedings, put the bird in the kitchen. His little chain was taken off and he roamed about the house.

His way of going downstairs was to lean on each step with the curve of his beak, raise the right foot, and then the left; and Félicité was afraid that these gymnastics brought on fits of giddiness. He fell ill and could not talk or eat any longer. There was a growth under his tongue, such as fowls have sometimes. She cured him by tearing the pellicle off with her fingernails. Mr. Paul was thoughtless enough one day to blow some cigar smoke into his nostrils, and another time when Mme. Lormeau was teasing him with the end of her umbrella he snapped at the ferrule. Finally he got lost.

Félicité had put him on the grass to refresh him, and gone away for a minute, and when she came back—no sign of the parrot! She began by looking for him in the shrubs, by the waterside, and over the roofs, without listening to her mistress's cries of "Take care, do! You are out of your wits!" Then she investigated all the gardens in Pont-l'Évêque, and stopped the passers-by. "You don't ever happen to have seen my parrot, by any chance, do you?" And she gave a description of the parrot to those who did not know him. Suddenly, behind the mills at the foot of the hill she thought she could make out something green that fluttered. But on the top of the hill there was nothing. A hawker assured her that he had come across the parrot just before, at Saint-Melaine, in Mère Simon's shop. She rushed there; they had no idea of what she meant. At last she came home exhausted, with her slippers in shreds and despair in her soul; and as she was sitting in the middle of the garden seat at Madame's side, telling the whole story of her efforts, a light weight dropped onto her shoulder—it was Loulou! What on earth had he been doing? Taking a walk in the neighborhood, perhaps!

She had some trouble in recovering from this, or rather never did recover. As the result of a chill she had an attack of quinsy, and soon afterwards an earache. Three years later she was deaf; and she spoke very loud, even in church. Though Félicité's sins might have been published in every corner of the diocese without dishonor to her or scandal to anybody, his Reverence the priest thought it right now to hear her confession in the sacristy only.

Imaginary noises in the head completed her upset. Her mistress often said to her, "Heavens! how stupid you are!" "Yes, Madame," she replied, and looked about for something.

Her little circle of ideas grew still narrower; the peal of church bells and the lowing of cattle ceased to exist for her. All living beings moved as silently as ghosts. One sound only reached her ears now—the parrot's voice.

Loulou, as though to amuse her, reproduced the click-clack of the turn-spit, the shrill call of a man selling fish, and the noise of the saw in the joiner's house opposite; when the bell rang he imitated Mme. Aubain's "Félicité! the door! the door!"

They carried on conversations, he endlessly reciting the three phrases in his repertory, to which she replied with words that were just as disconnected but uttered what was in her heart. Loulou was almost a son and a lover to her in her isolated state. He climbed up her fingers, nibbled at her lips, and clung to her kerchief; and when she bent her forehead and shook her head gently to and fro, as nurses do, the great wings of her bonnet and the bird's wings quivered together.

When the clouds massed and the thunder rumbled Loulou broke into cries, perhaps remembering the downpours in his native forests. The streaming rain made him absolutely mad; he fluttered wildly about, dashed up to the ceiling, upset everything, and went out through the window to dabble in the garden; but he was back quickly to perch on one of the fire-dogs and hopped about to dry himself, exhibiting his tail and his beak in turn.

One morning in the terrible winter of 1837 she had put him in front of the fireplace because of the cold. She found him dead, in the middle of his cage; head downwards, with his claws in the wires. He had died from congestion, no doubt. But Félicité thought he had been poisoned with parsley, and though there was no proof of any kind her suspicions inclined to Fabu.

She wept so piteously that her mistress said to her, "Well, then, have him stuffed!"

She asked advice from a chemist, who had always been kind to the parrot. He wrote to Havre, and a person called Fellacher undertook the business. But as parcels sometimes got lost in the coach she decided to take the parrot as far as Honfleur herself.

Along the sides of the road were leafless apple trees, one after the other. Ice covered the ditches. Dogs barked about the farms; and Félicité, with her hands under her cloak, her little black sabots and her basket, walked briskly in the middle of the road.

She crossed the forest, passed High Oak, and reached St. Gatien.

A cloud of dust rose behind her, and in it a mail coach, carried away by the steep hill, rushed down at full gallop like a hurricane. Seeing this woman who would not get out of the way, the driver stood up in front and the postilion shouted too. He could not hold in his four horses, which increased their pace, and the two leaders were grazing her when he threw them to one side with a jerk of the reins. But he was wild with rage, and lifting his arm as he passed at full speed, gave her such a lash from waist to neck with his big whip that she fell on her back.

Her first act, when she recovered consciousness, was to open her basket. Loulou was happily none the worse. She felt a burn in her right cheek, and when she put her hands against it they were red; the blood was flowing.

She sat down on a heap of stones and bound up her face with her handkerchief. Then she ate a crust of bread which she had put in the basket as a precaution, and found a consolation for her wound in gazing at the bird.

When she reached the crest of Ecquemauville she saw the Honfleur lights sparkling in the night sky like a company of stars; beyond, the sea stretched dimly. Then a faintness overtook her and she stopped; her wretched childhood, the disillusion of her first love, her nephew's going away, and Virginie's death all came back to her at once like the waves of an oncoming tide, rose to her throat, and choked her.

Afterwards, at the boat, she made a point of speaking to the captain, begging him to take care of the parcel, though she did not tell him what was in it.

Fellacher kept the parrot a long time. He was always promising it for the following week. After six months he announced that a packing case had started, and then nothing more was heard of it. It really seemed as though Loulou was never coming back. "Ah, they have stolen him!" she thought.

He arrived at last, and looked superb. There he was, erect upon a branch which screwed into a mahogany socket, with a foot in the air and his head on one side, biting a nut which the bird-stuffer—with a taste for impressiveness—had gilded.

Félicité shut him up in her room. It was a place to which few people were admitted, and held so many religious objects and miscellaneous things that it looked like a chapel and bazaar in one.

A big cupboard impeded you as you opened the door. Opposite the window commanding the garden a little round one looked into the court; there was a table by the folding bed with a water jug, two combs, and a cube of blue soap in a chipped plate. On the walls hung rosaries, medals, several benign Virgins, and a holy water vessel made out of coconut; on the chest of drawers, which was covered with a cloth like an altar, was the shell box that Victor had given her, and after that a watering can, a toy balloon, exercise books, the illustrated geography, and a pair of young lady's boots; and, fastened by its ribbons to the nail of the looking glass, hung the little plush hat! Félicité carried observances of this kind so far as to keep one of Monsieur's frock coats. All the old rubbish which Mme. Aubain did not want any longer she laid hands on for her room. That was why there were artificial flowers along the edge of the chest of drawers and a portrait of the Comte d'Artois in the little window recess.

With the aid of a bracket Loulou was established over the chimney, which jutted into the room. Every morning when she woke up she saw him there in the dawning light, and recalled old days and the smallest details of insignificant acts in a deep quietness which knew no pain.

Holding, as she did, no communication with anyone, Félicité lived as insensibly as if she were walking in her sleep. The Corpus Christi processions roused her to life again. Then she went round begging mats and candlesticks from the neighbors to decorate the altar they put up in the street.

In church she was always gazing at the Holy Ghost in the window, and observed that there was something of the parrot in him. The likeness was still clearer, she thought, on a crude color-print representing the baptism of Our Lord. With his purple wings and emerald body he was the very image of Loulou.

She bought him, and hung him up instead of the Comte d'Artois, so that she could see them both together in one glance. They were linked in her thoughts; and the parrot was consecrated by his association with the Holy Ghost, which became more vivid to her eye and more intelligible. The Father could not have chosen to express Himself through a dove, for such creatures cannot speak; it must have been one of Loulou's ancestors, surely. And though Félicité looked at the picture while she said her prayers she swerved a little from time to time towards the parrot.

She wanted to join the Ladies of the Virgin but Mme. Aubain dissuaded her.

And then a great event loomed up before them—Paul's marriage.

He had been a solicitor's clerk to begin with, and then tried business, the Customs, the Inland Revenue, and made efforts, even, to get into the Rivers and Forests. By an inspiration from heaven he had suddenly, at thirty-six, discovered his real line—the Registrar's Office. And there he showed such marked capacity that an inspector had offered him his daughter's hand and promised him his influence.

So Paul, grown serious, brought the lady to see his mother.

She sniffed at the ways of Pont-l'Évêque, gave herself great airs, and wounded Félicité's feelings. Mme. Aubain was relieved at her departure.

The week after came news of M. Bourais' death in an inn in Lower Brittany. The rumor of suicide was confirmed, and doubts arose as to his honesty. Mme. Aubain studied his accounts, and soon found out the whole tale of his misdoings—embezzled arrears, secret sales of wood, forged receipts, etc. Besides that he had an illegitimate child, and "relations with a person at Dozulé."

These shameful facts distressed her greatly. In March 1853 she was seized with a pain in the chest; her tongue seemed to be covered with film, and leeches did not ease the difficult breathing. On the ninth evening of her illness she died, just at seventy-two.

She passed as being younger, owing to the bands of brown hair which framed her pale, pock-marked face. There were few friends to regret her, for she had a stiffness of manner which kept people at a distance.

But Félicité mourned for her as one seldom mourns for a master. It upset her ideas and seemed contrary to the order of things, impossible and monstrous, that Madame should die before her.

Ten days afterwards, which was the time it took to hurry there from Besançon, the heirs arrived. The daughter-in-law ransacked the drawers, chose some furniture, and sold the rest; and then they went back to their registering.

Madame's armchair, her small round table, her foot-warmer, and the eight chairs were gone! Yellow patches in the middle of the panels showed where the engravings had hung. They had carried off the two little beds and the mattresses, and all Virginie's belongings had disappeared from the cupboard. Félicité went from floor to floor dazed with sorrow.

The next day there was a notice on the door, and the apothecary shouted in her ear that the house was for sale.

She tottered, and was obliged to sit down. What distressed her most of all was to give up her rooom, so suitable as it was for poor Loulou. She enveloped him with a look of anguish when she was imploring the Holy

Ghost, and formed the idolatrous habit of kneeling in front of the parrot to say her prayers. Sometimes the sun shone in at the attic window and caught his glass eye, and a great luminous ray shot out of it and put her in an ecstasy.

She had a pension of fifteen pounds a year which her mistress had left her. The garden gave her a supply of vegetables. As for clothes, she had enough to last her to the end of her days, and she economized in candles by going to bed at dusk.

She hardly ever went out, as she did not like passing the dealer's shop, where some of the old furniture was exposed for sale. Since her fit of giddiness she dragged one leg; and as her strength was failing Mère Simon, whose grocery business had collapsed, came every morning to split the wood and pump water for her.

Her eyes grew feeble. The shutters ceased to be thrown open. Years and years passed, and the house was neither let nor sold.

Félicité never asked for repairs because she was afraid of being sent away. The boards on the roof rotted; her bolster was wet for a whole winter. After Easter she spat blood.

Then Mère Simon called in a doctor. Félicité wanted to know what was the matter with her. But she was too deaf to hear, and the only word which reached her was "pneumonia." It was a word she knew, and she answered softly, "Ah! like Madame," thinking it natural that she should follow her mistress.

The time for the festal shrines was coming near. The first one was always at the bottom of the hill, the second in front of the post office, and the third towards the middle of the street. There was some rivalry in the matter of this one, and the women of the parish ended by choosing Mme. Aubain's courtyard.

The hard breathing and fever increased. Félicité was vexed at doing nothing for the altar. If only she could at least have put something there! Then she thought of the parrot. The neighbors objected that it would not be decent. But the priest gave her permission, which so intensely delighted her that she begged him to accept Loulou, her sole possession, when she died.

From Tuesday to Saturday, the eve of the festival, she coughed more often. By the evening her face had shriveled, her lips stuck to her gums, and she had vomitings; and at twilight next morning, feeling herself very low, she sent for a priest.

Three kindly women were round her during the extreme unction. Then she announced that she must speak to Fabu. He arrived in his Sunday clothes, by no means at his ease in the funereal atmosphere.

"Forgive me," she said, with an effort to stretch out her arm; "I thought it was you who had killed him."

What did she mean by such stories? She suspected him of murder—a

man like him! He waxed indignant, and was on the point of making a
row.

"There," said the women, "she is no longer in her senses, you can see
it well enough!"

Félicité spoke to shadows of her own from time to time. The women
went away, and Mère Simon had breakfast. A little later she took Loulou and brought him close to Félicité with the words:

"Come, now, say good-bye to him!"

Loulou was not a corpse, but the worms devoured him; one of his
wings was broken, and the tow was coming out of his stomach. But she
was blind now; she kissed him on the forehead and kept him close
against her cheek. Mère Simon took him back from her to put him on
the altar.

— 5 —

Summer scents came up from the meadows; flies buzzed; the sun
made the river glitter and heated the slates. Mère Simon came back into
the room and fell softly asleep.

She woke at the noise of bells; the people were coming out from
vespers. Félicité's delirium subsided. She thought of the procession and
saw it as if she had been there.

All the school children, the church singers, and the firemen walked on
the pavement, while in the middle of the road the verger armed with his
hallebard and the beadle with a large cross advanced in front. Then came
the schoolmaster, with an eye on the boys, and the sister, anxious about
her little girls; three of the daintiest, with angelic curls, scattered rose
petals in the air; the deacon controlled the band with outstretched arms;
and two censer-bearers turned back at every step towards the Holy Sacrament, which was borne by Monsieur the curé, wearing his beautiful
chasuble, under a canopy of dark red velvet held up by four churchwardens. A crowd of people pressed behind, between the white cloths
covering the house walls, and they reached the bottom of the hill.

A cold sweat moistened Félicité's temples. Mère Simon sponged her
with a piece of linen, saying to herself that one day she would have to
go that way.

The hum of the crowd increased, was very loud for an instant, and
then went further away.

A fusillade shook the windowpanes. It was the postilions saluting the
monstrance. Félicité rolled her eyes and said as audibly as she could:
"Does he look well?" The parrot was weighing on her mind.

Her agony began. A death-rattle that grew more and more convulsed made her sides heave. Bubbles of froth came at the corners of her mouth and her whole body trembled.

Soon the booming of the ophicleides, the high voices of the children, and the deep voices of the men were distinguishable. At intervals all was silent, and the tread of feet, deadened by the flowers they walked on, sounded like a flock pattering on grass.

The clergy appeared in the courtyard. Mère Simon clambered on to a chair to reach the attic window, and so looked down straight upon the shrine. Green garlands hung over the altar, which was decked with a flounce of English lace. In the middle was a small frame with relics in it; there were two orange trees at the corners, and all along stood silver candlesticks and china vases, with sunflowers, lilies, peonies, foxgloves, and tufts of hortensia. This heap of blazing color slanted from the level of the altar to the carpet which went on over the pavement; and some rare objects caught the eye. There was a silver-gilt sugar basin with a crown of violets; pendants of Alençon stone glittered on the moss, and two Chinese screens displayed their landscapes. Loulou was hidden under roses, and showed nothing but his blue forehead, like a plaque of lapis lazuli.

The churchwardens, singers, and children took their places round the three sides of the court. The priest went slowly up the steps, and placed his great, radiant golden sun upon the lace. Everyone knelt down. There was a deep silence; and the censers glided to and fro on the full swing of their chains.

An azure vapor rose up into Félicité's room. Her nostrils met it; she inhaled it sensually, mystically; and then closed her eyes. Her lips smiled. The beats of her heart lessened one by one, vaguer each time and softer, as a fountain sinks, an echo disappears; and when she sighed her last breath she thought she saw an opening in the heavens, and a gigantic parrot hovering above her head.

Edward Loomis (1924–   )

FRIENDSHIP

Consider how this story would be changed were it retold according to Flaubert's convention of somber documentation. The attitudes of Loomis's narrator change it from a narrative of degradation into a study of the terrain between violence and amorousness, and it is from the narrator that the reluctant final sentence is wrung.

W HEN I first knew him, Lev was first sergeant, hated by everybody except the sergeants who played cards with him. He was a faraway deity in his orderly room, and at company formations. He was a Jew, and looked like one, with a hooked nose that seemed all hard bone down to its very tip, but only once did I know anyone to call him Jew in anger, and that time was a victory for Lev, as things turned out.

It happened at Camp Kilmer when we were on our way overseas. A quarrelsome Southerner in my platoon, a private first class named Duval, returning late one evening from a pass to New York City, came across Lev and his cronies at a game of Hearts in the day room. Duval was drunk, and so he dared to ask for a place in the game, which was going along comfortably with four players. There was a silence. I looked up from my letter, and half a dozen others grew quite still over magazines.

"We're playing partners," Lev said after a moment, raising his large, unblinking eyes from his hand. He was quite firm; it was known that he and his friends never played any game with partners.

"Come on, Sarge, le'me sit in," Duval said. "I know that game. I'm a good Hearts player." He was leaning forward a little, a light-heavyweight approximately, known to have sought fights in bars, and respected for his strength and recklessness. "Don't hard-ass me, Sarge," he added. "Ain't we goin' overseas to fight the war together?"

Gravely Lev looked at the members of the game, each in turn shaking his head in response. Then Lev looked up again and said: "We don't want you in the game, Duval. We only play with the first three grades here—staff sergeants and up, that is."

From *Heroic Love*. © 1960 by Edward Loomis and Nicholas Ray. Reprinted by permission of Alfred A. Knopf, Inc.

Again there was a silence, and after a moment, as it became apparent that Duval would not leave, I saw that something more was coming.
Lev began dealing the cards; his lips were drawn back a little from his
teeth, and for an instant his tongue appeared, licking his lower lip in a
gesture which reminded me of a cat just come in from the out-of-doors.

The edge was all to Lev, for he was at home amid the trappings of
his power. In the next room his clerk was laboring over the company
papers. In the barracks most of his company was asleep within reach of
his care, and at each side of the table were his friends expecting him to
defend the privileges of the noncommissioned officer. The man at Lev's
left said something about the Queen of Spades, and Lev responded with
a little chuckle, saying: "He wants to know where the Bitch is, and
nobody'll tell him." There was a laugh, and its effect was to seal the
game into its ritual.

Duval's face grew red. He lifted his right hand and looked at it intently, and then said quickly: "That ain't no way to treat a man." He
was stubborn; now he proved it. "You didn't have to say it that way,
Sarge."

"I'll say it again if I want to!" Lev said sharply, not even looking up
this time. "And don't point your finger at me."

By this time there was a look of helpless rage in Duval's face. "I ain't
leaving," he said. "I'll be damned if I will. You don't give a man hardly
a chance, Sarge!"

"If you don't lay off, I'll give you something, though!" Lev said, and
laughed boisterously. "Oh, I'll give it to you!" He raised his head and
stared insolently at Duval, secure in his high place: who could be more
at home than a first sergeant in his own company day room?

"The hell with you, then," Duval said. He paused, and took courage
from the thing already said. "God damn it, Sarge!"

"All right," Lev said. "All right—all right!"

"With you, Sergeant Lev. *First* Sergeant Lev, by God." Growing
bolder, Duval looked around the room, smiling at the men he knew in
order to claim their support. "Lev?" he said. "What kind of a name is
that, anyway? God damn it, I know what kind of name it is. It's a Yid
name, ain't it? Sure it is." Again he looked at the others in the room, to
rally their approval to his cause. "Come to think of it, there ain't no
reason why a white man would want into a Yid card game anyway."

Lev, without scraping his chair against the floor, and without making
any kind of stir with his feet, had risen; and there he was. He moved
out away from the table, walking straight up, with his hands at his sides,
the fingers closed enough to be hooklike and alert for seizing. "Okay,
Duval," he said. "It's a Yid name, all right. Watch yourself. I'm coming
at you." A little skip appeared in his gait, and suddenly he was no
longer quite walking. His right hand, still open, came up to his right

cheek, where it hovered, and his left arm, weaving a little, like the head of an angry snake, extended itself in front of him.

Square and solid, Duval awaited him, scowling, and so for perhaps three seconds there was the prospect of a fight in the company day room; but there really was no fight. Lev had the movements of a fighter, the strength, and the willingness to commit himself, and he had these qualities with such intensity that as they happened they quite extinguished our sense of a combat.

Duval did not strike a blow, and was himself hit perhaps two dozen times in the space of twenty seconds. He was hit first in the nose by a swinging hook, and there was the sound of the nose breaking like a cracked board; then he was hit in the belly and over the heart, in a flurry of punches, so that he was doubled over on himself, like a man bending down to tie a shoelace; and then he was hit twice on the jaw, once on the left, once on the right, and from these blows he began to fall; but since he was a tough, strong man he straightened up first, so that he toppled slowly, and then he was hit once more, by a sliding, dropping right-hand punch that sliced open his left eyebrow as a razor might slice open a ripe tomato.

At the end he was sitting dumped awkwardly on his hams, with his legs sprawled out crookedly, as if they did not quite belong to him. He was conscious; his right eye stared waveringly up and down at nothing, while blood streamed down the sightless pit of his left eye and spread out across his cheek and into the corner of his mouth, that now was opening and closing rhythmically, like the mouth of a hurt fish.

"All right," Lev said. "All right, then, all right." He stood scowling down for a moment, his lips drawn back from his glittering teeth, his tongue working busily across his upper lip, as if he might be thinking about tasting the blood of his fallen enemy. For perhaps a minute he stood so, looking as I might imagine a veteran gladiator to look after surrounding the armored man with his net and finding his life with the barbed trident, while the crowd roars, and the Emperor, pleased a little, reaches out to touch the pearly thigh of a favorite boy.

Then Lev nodded once, approving, and turned to me his large bold eyes. "Go up to my room and get the little leather bag—it's like a suitcase—out of my green barracks bag. And hurry, God damn it, before this kid bleeds to death on our goddamned floor."

I hurried, and returned quickly, having experienced a curious sensation of guilt on rummaging through the belongings of such an exalted personage. The bag was like the cases that doctors used to carry on calls, and in it, so we all discovered when Lev opened it on the day-room floor, were several kinds of hospital equipment, including a little steel case of scalpels. One of these Lev used to touch up the cut over Duval's eye, and then, with a large needle and something which looked like a coarse thread, he sewed up the cut, using a complicated sewing stroke that I could hardly follow. After that, he cleaned out the left eye with a glass eye-cup and delicate touches with a little cylinder of rolled-up gauze, and washed Duval's face, with an economical tenderness of movement startling in that atmosphere of ancient hate.

When he was done, he had two of the watchers take Duval up to the barracks, leading him like a blind cripple, and then, clearly pleased with himself, and feeling rich, as any man might after such a scene, he returned to the game. For a moment he stood above his chair, appreciating it, and, I think, appreciating the opportunity for pleasure which would soon be laid out before him once again. "Good enough," he said, and sat down.

He composed himself, arched his back, and slowly rotated his head, eyes hooded but glittering above his hawk's nose; and then he spoke once quite clearly to the whole room. "I'm a Yid, all right," he said. "But I'm the kind that always runs to a fight, and that's the worst kind, men. Whose deal is it?"

Then he bent to the game; and that was the man he was in those days.

How much more he might have been I could not know for certain, but nowadays, thinking back, I have the feeling that there was a great deal to know. Certainly he was an imposing first sergeant—and we were proud of him, in spite of our hating him as all first sergeants must be hated. He was a possession we could mention knowingly to men of other companies in the battalion, and they had heard of him, usually, or at least heard rumors about him. He was an elegant marcher and a master of the manual at arms; when he gave the drill, he caused a precision in the movements of men who under other voices tended to slackness; and of course he was proud of what he could make us do. He liked his job, and clearly liked his company, though he was never heard to say so. According to our rosters, his full name was Murray B. Lev, though there was a rumor that his best friends were allowed to call him Moe, on occasion. He was one of those powerful, middle-sized men who seem to summarize the physical intensities of the male principle; he was hairy, with dense black curls matted over his chest and back, and fine silky hairs lying flat on the backs of his hands; his cheeks had a bluish tinge, and he shaved regularly twice a day, even after we entered the combat zone. He had a solid body neatly rigged, and could hardly move without suggesting grace and competence. He carried himself alertly, and his cold brown eyes took note of everything that happened in his little world. He seemed always ready to take advantage of an opportunity, and ready also to design an opportunity if that ever became necessary.

There were women to please him everywhere he went, it was said, but he was close-mouthed in such matters, and not even his best friends among the sergeants were allowed to follow him when he left camp on his Class A Pass, to be gone until reveille the next morning. Twice at our camp in Colorado he brought a pretty blonde girl to watch a parade, but I never saw him with a woman at any other time. He was a skillful lover, surely, but, like most men of that breed, he traveled by darkness, covering his tracks, and never took the same route twice in succession.

His past was not quite a mystery. He was from Chicago, and since he was in his early thirties when he was first sergeant, it was certain that he had lived variously in that dark city before he entered the army. He admitted owning what he called "an interest" in a bar on East 63rd Street, so I was told, and said he had "an income" from a hand laundry on 53rd Street. He did not talk about his civilian jobs, but he would admit earning money with golf at Jackson Park, and that seemed reasonable. He was a fine athlete; he was the shortstop on the regimental baseball team that won the division championship, and in our last season before we went to Europe he batted .419 in twenty-seven games.

He could play golf, I'll venture. Had he lived through the war, he might even now be standing in the shade of a palm tree on the practice green of a resort course in Florida. He would be amiable in the bright, watery light reflected off the Gulf; he would be available for a game, certainly, and he would bet if challenged, and win by a stroke on the last hole, to take all the money. After that, he might buy the drinks and listen modestly to the conversation about the major-league baseball team training at a nearby town.

He was a natural citizen of twilight worlds; it was inevitable that someone should suggest, after seeing his doctor's case at Camp Kilmer, that he had probably been an abortionist in Chicago. He talked sometimes about Barney Ross, the Jewish welterweight champion from Chicago, and once, so it was said, refused to deny that he had worked as a corner-man for some of Ross's opponents. There was a tradition among those of us who cared about sports that Lev's father had been a friend to Abe Attell, the marvelous old-time bantamweight champion from San Francisco, who, growing soft, and aging, had represented the gamblers to the Black Sox of 1919.

Nowadays, as I think back, it seems entirely possible that Lev might have gone the way of Attell if he had lived long enough: Attell, who carried himself unmarked and unbeaten through hundreds of fights, and finally came around to secret meetings with Gandil and Jackson and Cicotte in a Chicago hotel room. We must guess that Attell was a friend to the gambler Arnold Rothstein, who was soft and fat and clever, and and so might Lev have become a friend to a fat and clever man.

I think it could not have been otherwise, had there been no war. Lev had talents, and so he was bound to use them. But the war came to provide a new ground for those talents, and so he became a wonderful soldier, famed for bravery and ferocity, and known for his extreme devotion to his company.

In fact, he was happy as a soldier, there can be no doubt of it. He was proud of his uniform, and had many, so that he was able to change twice and sometimes even three times a day. He was proud of his soldier's skills, and it was nothing to him that he was hated, for that was part of the job.

The chief symptom of his happy life in the war came in the curious nature of some of the friendships he made; and particularly in his friendship with a nineteen-year-old Oklahoma boy named Jim Bob Allison. This was a slender, sturdy boy who had lived most of his life in a town called Cedar Springs. He was innocent, goodhearted, and intelligent, just what a boy from a country town is supposed to be in America. His face might not have looked out of place under a Boy Scout hat, and he had the appearance of one who could make fire with a wooden disk, a stick, and a bow.

He was no athlete, being a little awkward and too long in the leg, but he had a face which was just about right for the skinny end on the high-school football team. His face was squarish, with a narrow bony jaw that might in time take on a formidable curve; his mouth was full but firm, the lips always lying close together, with a faint suggestion of coming maturity, and he had a straight nose which, with his clear blue eyes, gave him an attractive look as of a boy whom any girl's mother would be willing to trust on sight.

He often talked humorously about women, wanting them, but he was bashful and unasking. In Cedar Springs he had sometimes been in the vicinity of girls at ice-cream socials and picnics given by the Kiwanis Club, but he admitted freely that he had been one of those boys who make an uneasy group on the outskirts, hooting the well-combed boys who dare to approach the girls. He was a boy for the out-of-doors, and it was true that he had fished for catfish in the Canadian River where it passes through Hardin County, and had killed his first deer at the age of sixteen, in one of the southern counties of the state, on a trip with his father and two uncles from Ponca City. He was a boy for the straw hat and bib overalls, and he had worn these, and gone barefoot too, of course, moving through his boy's life like some wise man's memory of Huckleberry Finn.

And this boy became a close friend to Moe Lev in the heterogeneous complexity of the American army, where seeing them together became a normal sight, touching somehow, and faintly alarming, for each had much to learn from the other. They were thrown together initially by the fact that Jim Bob was for a while the company commander's runner, and so spent most of his time near company headquarters, where Lev ruled. Jim Bob was noticed, but of course he was not close to Lev so long

as we were in training, for Lev would not befriend a mere private first
class at a time when he was teaching discipline. Jim Bob was willing to
learn, however, and, like many boys of that army, he became startlingly
professional in the way he regarded the army and his duties in it, largely
because he had never known another job; it was the only life he had
ever had away from home, and so he felt for it the respect and admiration
which boys properly reserve for their first major commitment. He read
the manuals, he drilled carefully, and he was a good marksman; thus he
was available for Lev's regard when the time came.

That time came gradually, after we reached France. It was not long
before Lev ceased to be hated in the company, this being a normal
phenomenon in most armies, I suspect. Once the shooting started, his
harshness during training could be seen to have its uses, and his tough-
ness was clearly valuable when there was a town to be attacked or a river
to be crossed. He risked dangers he did not have to risk, and so in time,
after we had moved up out of northern France and Belgium to the
border of Holland, we came to have a strong feeling of respect for him.

Jim Bob became one of his most outspoken admirers, and learned to
say judiciously: "Sure I like him. You goddamn right I like him. Ain't
he the bravest man in the battalion? Everybody knows that." He would
speak of Lev's exploits as if he were speaking of an honored brother or a
hardy, loving father. "Do you remember when he set off the TNT
against the wall of that stone barn on the Belgian border?" he would say,
and wait for his audience to recall whatever images they might have of
that time, when Lev, under fire from a nearby house and from two
snipers in an adjoining wood, had blown an enormous hole in the wall
of a stone barn, so that one of the rifle platoons could attack the Germans
hidden in the barn. "Yes, indeedy," Jim Bob would continue. "We *all*
remember that time, I *guess*. And how about when he led the charge
against that Panther tank in the woods last week? 'A course there was
some others went with him then, but most of them went because old
Lev was there to say 'Come on, let's go get that son-of-a-bitch!' " It had
been a notable triumph: Lev had taken a group of eight men and destroyed a Panther tank and five German infantrymen who had been
accompanying it, with no losses to his group.

There were other exploits, and Jim Bob made the most of them, and
made no secret of his admiration, so that Lev came to be in a position
where it was difficult for him not to like Jim Bob. Lev became a famous
soldier in the regiment, and in due course was awarded both the Bronze
Star and the Silver Star. Furthermore, he was a stable and consistent
man, a soldier to be admired by his fellow soldiers. We had our share of
heroes, there in our north European war, but only a few, like Lev, were
truly sound. The others tended to be brave with a certain desperation
for a few weeks or a few months, goaded into risk by some eccentricity

in their motivations. Such men could be violent and effective, but they often wore themselves out with their violence, growing tired and fretful and even fearful sometimes.

When that happened, the hero became a normal soldier or a psychological casualty, while Lev continued as he had been, expressing the deepest and truest bent of his life; and, naturally enough, affecting those around him, altering them sometimes in a quite startling fashion. Jim Bob, for example, being a hero-worshipper, taught himself war rather quickly, and then, more slowly, emulating Lev, taught himself a fine hardness of intention. Lev did not believe that a proper soldier should surrender unless he was wounded in such a way that he could no longer fight; and so Jim Bob accepted this belief, and one night proved his acceptance in action.

We had reached Germany in late November, and were engaged east of Aachen in the heaviest fighting we had yet seen. Jim Bob was sent with a message to a rifle platoon besieged in a factory, and was present during the German attack which broke the platoon's resistance. There was a Tiger tank to push the door in, and there was a large force of SS infantry. Our platoon leader and platoon sergeant were killed, along with half a dozen others, and of the remainder some ran away and some allowed themselves to be captured; but Jim Bob hid himself under a heap of waste rags, keeping his rifle ready, and stayed there for almost twelve hours, until the factory was retaken by another of our platoons. He stood up then, dusty and begrimed, and I remember how he looked. He was tired, his eyelids were heavy, but his eyes were bright; he was leaning on his rifle, and with his free hand, the left, he was making brushing movements at his jacket and pants. He looked a boy, but a boy precocious in a hard world, and he was not at all dismayed.

Naturally, Lev was pleased. It became known that he had a special regard for Jim Bob, and the two of them began to be seen together rather frequently. They shared rations out of boxes and cans; they sat together when we had a meal from our own kitchen; and many times they dug holes together, sharing the narrow earthen walls. They talked, of course, with Lev telling stories of big-city adventure, and Jim Bob explaining country ways of fishing and hunting; and these conversations came to be a part of the company's legend about itself.

And through all this Lev's instruction continued. Jim Bob acquired a willingness never to stop fighting, and the knowledge that there always came a time when decisive action was necessary. "Somewhere in a fight there's a time when a man has got to do something, and then he'd better do it," so Lev said, and demonstrated in his actions. Thus, when Jim Bob happened to be surprised on a message-carrying mission by a stray German rifleman somehow left behind in the general retreat to the Rhine River, he took care of himself very nicely. He had been caught in the open, with no cover; the German was hidden behind a tree, lying down with almost the whole of his body protected; but Jim Bob moved rapidly to his right on the open ground, rising, running, and falling to fire a shot, and then doing it again, until finally he had got far enough to the German's flank to have a clear shot at him; and then he killed with a bullet through the neck, afterwards like a hunter dipping his fingers in the blood from the wound, for it was first blood.

It was a rare thing, that individual combat, in a war of running and hiding and big guns fired from far away, and the news of it spread rapidly. Again Lev was pleased, and for several days he spoke admiringly of Jim Bob's exploit, returning Jim Bob's compliments. His favorite remark was, simply: "The kid's got that old ticker, men. If he had the built, he'd of made a hell of a fighter, that kid would."

High praise; and of course it came back to Jim Bob multiplied and rhetorically enforced. He became, over a period of time, what Lev wanted all of us to be, a soldier who would not run, and who was capable of fierceness, and he had his reward one day in the outskirts of Cologne, when Lev took the trouble to save his life. Jim Bob, returning from one of the platoon leaders, whom he had visited with a message, was knocked down and stunned by a mortar shell exploding close to him. It was an accidental barrage, a piece of guesswork by German gunners trying to do their best with an impossible situation; and none of us knew how long the barrage might last.

Lev, in the first let-up, ran out to Jim Bob and picked him up, put the limp body on his shoulder, and trotted to the safety of the house where the company command post was hidden in a cellar. There Jim Bob revived; he opened his clear blue eyes like one born again, while outside the barrage resumed with greater intensity than before.

"Look at the kid," Lev said. "The kid's all right. He don't look it with that baby face, but he can't fool the old man. I knew plenty of tough fighters that had a baby face—sure, they were even the kind that liked to see blood!"

Jim Bob sat up, greatly moved, and, after a few moments of getting up his determination, said: "Then you must have brought me in. I don't remember what happened after. . . ."

"Sure I brought you in," Lev said.

"Then you're a brave, good man, Sergeant Lev! I want to say—" But he did not really know what he wanted to say, and so he paused, resting in what he had already said.

And that was the way things were when we reached the Rhine, where the character of the war began to change. We had a few days of rest in Cologne, during which Lev was awarded a commission as second lieutenant and given my platoon, which had lost its platoon leader just west of the city in the last of our attacks there. It had been apparent for a

long time that Lev would have to accept this honor, though he had been
heard to protest against the possibility. I was by then a squad leader,
having moved up through the ranks as one squad leader after another
had fallen or died, and of course I was glad to have Lev control my
future, for he was known to be careful with his men. I was further
pleased that Lev brought with him, to take over another of the platoon's
squads, Jim Bob, newly promoted to staff sergeant for the occasion. By
this time they were close friends of the wartime sort, having shared
enough intense experience in a few months so that they would never
run out of matter for talk so long as the war lasted.

There was a chance of awkwardness in the fact that Duval, once
Lev's victim in the famous fight, had become the platoon sergeant, and
in fact there were a few difficult moments in Cologne, before we returned to the fighting. We were quartered in two big houses whose
owners had stripped them to the walls, and we were not comfortable
there; our footsteps had a flat, vicious sound on the polished floors. We
were caged by the barren walls, and thus it was impossible for Lev not
to make his presence heavily felt when he arrived with his bright new
insignia of rank. He spoke his requests in the normal style of the combat
zone, of course, which was a friendly sound, but it was difficult for him
to use a friendly sound on Duval without seeming apologetic. "We'll
have to find a time to talk to those two new men," he would say, and
look perplexed, while Duval guardedly watched him. Or: "I'll have to
go up to the Company CP for a briefing, Duval. I ought to be back
soon."

The whole platoon was close at hand; there was no chance of privacy
in which the two might parse their differences. During the first day
Lev turned rather frequently to me, as to a neutral observer; we had
been coming closer together during the months just past, and he had
several times allowed himself to talk to me at some length, but now he
let me feel that he was somehow dependent on me. That I liked, for it
was an achievement to be of use to such a man. I understood that I was
expected to serve as a mediator, and so I tried to make up conversations
to include both lieutenant and sergeant.

There was not much I could do, though I intimated to each man in
turn that the other was willing to forget the bitter quarrel in their past;
and this may have helped. Duval, who had lived in both Alabama and
Georgia, was a proud Southerner, a farmer, a man who had kept coon
dogs; he would never understand Lev, and certainly he would never be
able to ask for a reconciliation. But he was a good soldier and an honest
man; he could hold a grudge, but by that time I am sure he recognized
something wrong in his speech to Lev before their fight; he had been
driven to words he might not have found in other circumstances. He was
not inflexible; he may even have admired Lev's skill with his hard brown

fists. Toward the end of Lev's second day with us we were all happy to notice an easing of tension, a softening of official courtesy.

After three days of fighting in the Remagen bridgehead to the south, all old differences had been forgotten, and Lev and Duval were close and friendly as if the past had never been. Certainly there had existed a great violence to hold them apart in other days, in that other world where there was no war, but a greater violence bound them together in a time of combat.

In fact, there were only a few of us who could know that old time on the American shore, for of the twenty-five men in the platoon at the time Lev took it over, only seven had been in the company when we left Camp Kilmer to come to Europe: Lev, Jim Bob, Duval, and myself, with three others. We were the old-timers, and that fact was a bond.

Within ten days of Lev's arrival in the platoon we even had a game of Hearts, the four of us, Lev, Duval, Jim Bob, and I, lions and lambs all squatting together in a hole in the ground. It was daytime, of course, the front having moved out ahead of us for several miles, under the attacks of our armor; over us, a blue sky, and all around the smell of sap running in the trees, and the sound of wind in the first leaves. We played for perhaps two hours in the middle of the afternoon, with Lev a little more quiet than he normally was, and Duval carrying himself quite delicately, like a young man on probation in the family of a new girl friend. Jim Bob and I, being spectators at the formal making of a peace, were able to be a little more loud than the principals, and a little more obviously joyous.

The newly cut earthen walls smelled damply of spring, and a little later of cigar smoke, when Lev distributed the last of his little stock. At the end of the game we all sat back comfortably smoking.

"This is nice," Lev said. "This is all right," nodding his head emphatically, his guard down, his face gently smiling like that of a father at the head of his family table.

"Why, it is," Jim Bob said. "I never smoked a cigar before."

"It's a damn good cigar," Duval said. "A good, free-drawing cigar, by God."

Things began to go very well in our platoon after that, with our organization firm and the men well hardened; but of course it was not long before the character of the war changed most dramatically. Within a week of the breakthrough from the Remagen bridgehead it was apparent to all of us that the war was coming to an end. We had very few fights, though some of them were bitter; for the most part, we traveled to the east like explorers, riding on trucks or tanks sometimes, but mostly marching. We were in a green and pleasant land, and we lived on the fat of it. In little villages of the Rhineland we found eggs, and hams, and fragrant country breads, which we enjoyed on the spot where we found them. We stole fat chickens, after the immemorial style of soldiers, and carried them to our night resting places, where a way could always be found to roast or broil them. There began to be women available to the more resourceful men among us, and surely we must have left some swelling bellies in the wake of our advance.

The war eased off on us, and then, quite naturally, it happened that our own army began to oppress us once again. There came an order from regimental headquarters that all men were to shave at least once a day, and that irregularities of uniform were not to be tolerated; there was an order, very fiercely phrased, which forbade any soldier or officer to fraternize with any German civilian. To these exactions Lev surprisingly paid no attention. "That stuff was all right before. We don't need it now," he said, and we remained comfortable.

And once when a young officer from battalion headquarters attempted to reassert the old power system by driving my squad from an attractive house in a Thuringian village, Lev appeared to stop him. It was a fine evening in late March; above us was a pale sky, all that was left of a great arching day; in the air was a little smell of cooking, and the cheerful voices of men settling down for a night of rest. I was busy with my squad in the front room when the neatly uniformed first lieutenant arrived. We had a goose cooking in the kitchen, and a case of Rhine wine open on the floor of the front room, and we were as cheerful as infantry soldiers can ever be.

"Who's in charge here?" the lieutenant said from the door. He was young; he was wearing a little mustache, and he carried his automatic pistol in a flamboyant shoulder holster. "You men!" he said. "I'm afraid I'll have to commandeer this house for Battalion S–2! You hear? I'm sorry—"

He moved a little to the side as Lev came in from outside; and then Lev, seeming almost clumsy in his movements, as if he did not intend them, eased the young officer out the door, not touching him, but rather suggesting direction and force.

"Ah, Lieutenant Lev," the officer said gratefully. "You see, I've got orders from the boss—" and he waved his right arm gaily. "You know how it is!"

"Of course," Lev said. "You want the house for yourself."

"Well, yes," the officer said, in a tone which suggested that gentlemen could agree without worrying themselves over what the men might think.

"It's a nice house," Lev said mildly.

"Why, yes, it's all right," the officer agreed, not quite so comfortable.

"But you can't have it," Lev said. "These men got here first. Their company captured the goddamned town! And we lost a man here too. So you think of something."

Lev sounded quite cheerful, but not very reasonable, not quite open to argument.

"I don't see, Lieutenant . . ." the other began. "After all, Lieutenant, I outrank you. . . ."

"You do, at that. I can see it."

"And so by regulations. . . ."

"Regulations?" Lev said. "Regulations?" He laughed harshly, stepped back, and seized his crotch, in an old city gesture of derision. "Here's your goddamn regulations, you son-of-a-bitch!" Lev was an officer, all right, but no gentleman, and so there was no way for the young battalion officer to reach him; but he tried.

"I want the house," he said, keeping his voice steady.

"Sure you do!"

"I mean it, Lieutenant. I want the house!"

"Then take it, kid. But let me tell you I'll fight you for it, and not with my hands either. So go ahead—so think of something!"

It was a challenge to a duel, though I have no idea whether Lev would have fought it. But he did not have to fight, for it was not long before the young officer backed off, growling fitfully, and even swearing.

It was a clear victory for us over all others, for Lev over battalion headquarters, and so we celebrated it that night by getting drunk down to the last man.

The incident became an emblem for us of the coming end of the war. There were not many Germans left to fight, and so Lev fought the tyranny which came from above us in our own army. He arranged a magnificent theft of liquor from a stock which was being reserved for officers of the regimental headquarters, and he himself led the raid. He stole rations and bargained for them with the bright intensity he had formerly shown in battle. Day after day he committed exploits of loving care.

He was fully committed to us, that was the fact, and acknowledged no other duties. He might have been a father passionately raising children, and certainly he needed us as much as we needed him. Toward the end, in fact, it seemed that he could not do without us. Once a German tank hit a house he was in with an 88-millimeter shell and knocked a wall over on him, but when he rose from the rubble, dizzy and sick, he refused the offer of hospitalization which was made to him by the company commander.

He came up smelling of the damp interior of that ancient wall; he was whitened with a light dust of plaster, and his nose was stopped up, so that he had to breathe hoarsely and with effort, like an asthmatic when the fit is on. He was dizzy from near-suffocation, and he was sick several times, crawling about in this misery like an old dog with infirm bowels, but even at this time, before he had fully come to his senses, he shouted: "I'm all right! Leave me alone! I'm going to stay right where I am! I got to stay!"

He had not been too badly hurt, in fact, though he had a cough from that moment which he was never to lose; a memory his body preserved, I think, of the cold, pulverous silence under the wall, like the silence of earth in a grave. He was shaken, but when I asked him later why he had been so anxious not to be evacuated to the comforts of hospitals, he had little to say. He seemed perplexed, faintly ill at ease, even a little unhappy. We were standing on the bank of a small river, near the ruins of a bridge the Germans had blown up in their retreat; a short way behind us was the house where the wall had fallen. Lev was leaning against an elm tree, his strong body at ease but not sagging against the finely combed black bark. Delicate prongs of pale green were showing in the branches above his head, and there was a smell of greenery, of cut hay, of flowers in the soft air. The Germans had already left that valley, with the tank which had given us trouble, and so we had the brilliant peace of a battle's end. The day was clear, and the sun so bright and mild that I could almost smell the warmth of it.

"Ah, well, comes the summer and the war'll be over," Lev said. "Back in Chicago, the White Sox will be playing at Comiskey Park, even!"

His face was cold and resolved beneath his steel helmet, and there was something statuelike in his expression, as if he were remembering an ancient tribal image of King David—the old King, the warrior remembering battles and feats of love.

"I'm sad to see the war ending, kid," Lev said. "You know? Why couldn't the war go on forever? I wish the war would go on and never stop!"

And then we moved on, as we had to, until toward the middle of April we reached the Harz Mountains, where for a little while we had again the sharp battles of the old lively war. In those small green mountains a considerable force of miscellaneous German troops had gathered, and they were ready to fight. How did they feel about things, I wonder, as they waited in the hills, in the greening forest? Below them on the plain was a vast army of enemies; behind them only the hills, and, for some of them perhaps, an ancient German memory of Druid priests at work in a leafy darkness, of warriors wearing helmets armed with the horns of bulls.

They were desperate, certainly, and they fought hard. In our first battle with them, which happened at the very edge of the hills, we lost five riflemen and an officer. The next day, in a town which lay enclosed in a canyon, we had even greater losses, and in fact had the last serious losses of the war: there we lost the last remnants of our innocence.

It was a pretty town, and might have been a resort, I think. There were several big inns; there was a hospital with a solarium on the south

wing; perhaps that was a town famous for healing waters. On the square
there were fine old chestnut trees in stately rows, each tree established
in a masonwork pit filled with black earth. There were iron benches,
and there was a bandstand, with rosebushes dependent from its latticed
sides.

Spring was blooming in the square, and we would have been happy
to stay there; but we—Lev's platoon and a machine-gun squad—were
obliged to leave the town and ascend the canyon toward a force of German infantry supposed to be waiting there. There was a zone of gardens
on the edge of town; each garden had its board fence. Then there was
a little meadow, with a brook running through it. The grass was stiff
and high, a purplish green. A milk cow—a bright pastel tan—stood
heavily in the grass, her teats brushing against the grass tops. It happened that I passed close to her, and got a smell of the warm, rank odor
of her, and of her breath, invisibly staining the heavy spring air.

Then we were in a forest of black fir, a darkness with ferns swaying
in it, that sunlight riddled. Suddenly the air was cool; icy currents bil-
lowed down from the heights, which in those small mountains could
not have been very far away, and certainly from the bluish plateaus we
had dimly seen from the valley—lifted horizons of wavy line and watery
surface. Slowly, almost gently, we made our way, in open order. Jim Bob
was to my left with his squad; Lev and Duval were to the right with the
third squad; I was in the middle with the six men remaining to me. We
were scattered out, fearing snipers, but we were ready for almost anything.

The first problem was to find the enemy, and we were lucky in that.
As we began climbing out of the canyon, we came across signs of German troops: a helmet, shiny, black, brand new; two grenades stuck in
the crotch of a fir tree. There was a smell of people about, interrupting
the dense eddies of forest smells. In a little while the climb began to
seem ominous, and we found the enemy at about the time I began to
sweat with the effort of climbing.

A burst from a German machine gun ripped its way down through
the shady silence of the hillside. The fight was on; there was a sound of
rifle fire as we answered the challenge that came down upon us. I was
in cover behind the trunk of a tree—what kind of tree I will never know,
for I was only concerned that it be thick—and I was trying to make out
the contours of the little battle. That was difficult; near me were two
men of my squad, but I could see no one else. I had a sense of heavy fire
from the invisible Germans; it sounded serious this time, seeming to
swarm and rise through the thickets. Now and then a bullet clipped a
bough from a fir tree, and then that bough would settle to the ground
with a faint, sighing flutter, gentle as falling snow.

Then from my right, where Lev was at work, someone called quite clearly: "Go on up the hill. Lev says everybody go on up the hill."

That was reassuring word, suggesting that we had nothing unusual ahead of us. I called my squad to move up, and began making my way; that meant running and falling. I caught sight of Jim Bob, not far to my left, and perceived that he had already got the message; he was on his way. And so we proceeded, and for a while I had the feeling that we would simply ascend the hill and there kill or capture the people who had offered us battle thus late in the war. I was not hoping trustfully; I was only expecting what I had a right to expect. The war was coming to an end, and everybody knew it—even the Germans knew it, who had been coming sadly into our lines for a long time, tired, reluctant, bemused.

Then, as I was moving from one tree to another, a bullet shattered the stock of my rifle. The shock did not quite twist the rifle from my hand, but it brought me up, and made me angry and resentful. I paused, hiding behind the tree trunk, and inspected the damage. The stock was gone, from about two inches behind the trigger guard; there was only a jagged stump, still quivering. "Son of a bitch!" I said. I hefted the rifle, and it felt crazily new and strange; it did not feel like a rifle at all, and suddenly I felt defenseless, there in that handsome forest.

I became reluctant to move on, and so I took time to look about me and listen; and then I heard, from the left, where Jim Bob had his squad, a dim cry of "Medic, Medic!" and from the right, where Lev and Duval were, a cry, a mere susurrus that proposed: "I'm hurt, I'm hurt, I'm really hurt."

"Hold up, second squad," I called, feeling guilty, and began searching carefully through the area to my right, trying to find a sign from the source of authority; and so I saw a man down, not far from me. He was lying on his back, and appeared to be trying to turn over; his body made spasmodic flopping movements, like a beached fish. I looked a little closer and saw that he was covering his face with his hands. In fact, he was clutching his face, as if to hold it against slipping. His hands were clawlike, grasping, and suddenly one of the hands went red with blood.

"I got to go there," I said, and began crawling; but that was slow, and so I got up and raced for him, so that I brought up on the ground at his side. I was winded, and scared, now. I looked down fearfully and saw that the hurt creature under the hands was Platoon Sergeant Duval, struck down in what would surely be the last month of the war. For a moment I paused, thinking what to do. Then, as I was resolving to look at the wound, I heard Lev's voice calling my name. The voice was whispering fiercely, and it said: "Who is it? Who is it? Is it Duval? He was over there."

I nodded, and whispered: "Yes, Duval. He's hit, bad."

I looked again to my right and saw Lev rise up, square and firm and very soldierly, and start running toward me; he was beautifully balanced on the steep slope, and he carried his carbine as an ancient savage might carry his spear. He came fast, and dropped lightly to the ground on the other side of Duval. He had his carbine up in firing position; he took aim carefully and then fired twice. I looked to see what he was shooting at, but could see no target; you understand, I did not expect to. As I looked up the steep hill, I saw the light-spotted shade of the forest; I had a sense of trees, bushes, garlands of fern, but I could see no enemy. It was rare in that war to see a live enemy during a battle, for the great infantry tactic of both sides was to stay hidden, to keep close to the dark.

"There," Lev said. "This isn't going right. It's like the old war. It's a battle. Hey, you got your rifle busted! Well, take Duval's—he won't be needing it for a while."

Lev was looking at me over Duval's slowly writhing body, and Lev's face was intent, concentrated, as if he were aiming a gun. The lines of the face were clearly drawn: the big nose, the harsh jaw, the powerfully controlled stare of the eyes, unblinking and bright as a snake's. The mouth was cruel; the face was calm, and Lev was no more disturbed or upset than he might have been during a training maneuver. So it seemed at that moment; and so it was, I believe, though change was imminent, already setting in like a sunset against bright day.

"You're okay, kid," Lev said to me. "Now, how's old Duval?" He looked down, and instantly there was a change in his expression. He was startled; his lips came apart slowly, and then his tongue appeared, uncertainly touching his upper lip. "Uh-oh," he said. "Hey, Duval, how you makin' it, kid? It's Lev. It's your corner."

Duval's right hand was oily with blood. I touched it, hoping he might lift his hand so that I could see the wound. His body jerked; his hips lifted convulsively, like a hooked fish splashing at the surface just out of reach of the boat. There was a great pool of blood under his head, and its margin, smoothly spreading, had begun to reach my left elbow. "Well, it's no joke, then," Lev said. "Let's get the bandage out. Duval— old buddy?—I'm going to bandage you up, and run a tourniquet if I have to. Hey, it's Lev, it's the old cut man. I fixed you up before, I can do it again. Sure I can!" His fingers went to work—they were spindly and lean, with tufts of black hair between the knuckles; and the fingers were crooked—oddly bent, and that must have been a result of the prize ring, in old Chicago times. Lev was crouching now, exposing the arch of his body to the enemy fire, if it should happen to come that way. His body seemed merely to preside over his nimble hands; his body was something for the arms and hands to hang from.

Then Duval spoke, in a voice absolutely unchanged from his normal voice. "That you, Sarge?" he said. "Lieutenant, I mean. Shoot, ah've had it." The voice stopped eccentrically; there seemed no principle for either stopping or continuing.

"Just take it easy," Lev said. "I'm with you, kid."

"Ah've had it, Sarge," Duval said, and now both his hands were bloody. "In the face. In the neck too. You can't see it. It's awright, Sarge. Ah done my best, comin' up here. You send my stuff to my wife, will you, now? And write her? Hush! Ah can't see! It must of been in the eyes too." He moaned, and viciously his body bucked; this time he turned himself onto his right side, facing me with his mask of red hands, and spilling blood—pouring it, as from a basin—onto my sleeve. Lev moved over, continuing his work, and now had the bandage out; it was the packaged dressing we used to wear at our belts. He held it poised. "Here it is," he said quickly. "I got it right here, kid. I'm right with you—"

Then there was a change in Duval; what was that change? I could not mark its happening, though I noticed a momentary tremor in leg and arm. His blood still warm upon me, he died, and his hands stayed at his face. "Hold on, kid!" Lev shouted. "Don't think about that blood. I'm a cut man, I'll fix it!" Then Lev took Duval's left hand, moved it away from the face, and slipped his fingers over the wrist; and that was to take the pulse, surely, though at that moment, being confused, I could not understand what he intended. Then he dropped the wrist, and there was a look of dismay on his face. "No!" he said. "Why, hell, the war's ending—" Then he bent suddenly over the body and put his helmeted head to the still chest; his face, turned sidewise, looked up at me, the eyes dazed and staring. Then a grimace of disgust came over the face, followed instantly by a look of wrenching sorrow. That strong face came away from all its conventions to look so. "Oh, no!" he said, and raised himself so that he could look down at the body.

"Come on back," he said. "You don't have to die. Don't die! You got the stuff, kid—come on through! Hey, this is Lev! We had a fight, remember! You showed how you could take it! No," he concluded aimlessly.

He raised his face to me, now purged of its old fierceness. He held out his hands, palms up, the white bandage in his right hand like some mysterious piece of clothing, swaddling for a creature no longer available. "He was my friend," he said. "I didn't have so many. You, hey. You listen to his heart and tell me— No! No good in that." He bent his head and lowered his hands, though the hand holding the bandage continued to rise and fall; and that was a futile gesture, the skilled hand reaching out toward something that skill could never reach. Lev began to cry; and so he was a strong man abandoning the conventions of his strength. His powerful body was kneeling now; a devotional posture had erected itself within that massive back and delicately curved those heavy arms. "Come back," he said, "come back. I want you to come back. See if you can't make it. Go ahead, try."

I looked away, rolled over and looked back toward my squad, and saw, not ten feet away, the face of Jim Bob Allison intently watching. He was crouching behind a tree; his face was white, horror-stricken. I turned over once again so that I could look at the ground, and for some time I stared, atomizing the rich black dirt and stones and leaves. I watched the vein of a leaf. I watched a spider—the long-legged breed—ascend with stately elegance a little stack of leaves, and there pause. Lev was crying; I could hear him, and I continued hearing him for a long time after he stopped.

The battle had grown quieter, lacking Lev's purpose to make it happen; and suddenly the forest grew still, as if no battle had been there. I raised my head and looked at Lev, who now was squatting beside Duval, but facing the slope. He was looking up the hill, and his face was once again the familiar face of the warrior, the leader in battle. A speculative look was in his eyes as he turned to me, and he looked gentle. "Well," he said, "what we gonna do? I know."

He picked up his carbine and cleared the bolt; he looked down and inspected the chamber, casually running his little finger along the face of the bolt. "Look to your piece," he said. "I mean Duval's—there." He waited while I took up the rifle. "Well, check it," he said. "It's had a fall, it may have gotten dirty." He watched while I inspected the rifle, and then he said: "Good work, kid. Now we've got to get at it again. Stay here a minute. I'm going to start this battle again." He rose; he paused for a moment, standing at the side of his fallen comrade, and then slowly walked to a nearby tree; he stood behind it, not behind the trunk but only behind the green skirt of spreading boughs. He stood for a moment carelessly, and then, like a bugler preparing to sound a call, he drew his body up and straightened himself. He took the position of the soldier at attention.

"Well," he muttered, and then, in his old parade-ground voice that I had not heard for many months, he called: "Third p'atoon, tench-hut! Hear me, third p'atoon! Come alive! This is Lev! You know me! Get ready now, and I'll give the word!" Then, casually, he relaxed and looked down at me. "Just like an old first sergeant, eh, kid? Well, that's about all there is to it. You ready to go? I want to give the boys a chance to get ready, 'cause we're going up this hill. Huh! The fact is, I can't stand the war to end. You know, that Barney Ross, that fighter—champion he was!—he used to say that a body feint was a good thing, but sometimes you just had to take a shot to give one, and go on in. Well, that's what I'm going to do. I've got to do something." He turned away, almost indifferently, and again set himself in his position of command; and again his electrifying cry rang out along the hillside: "Third p'atoon,

tench-hut! Ready, now! come out shooting! Now's the time. *Ee-yahh!*"
That was a battle shout, and the real David might have roared something like it as he lightly stepped into the deep shadow of Goliath.

Lev moved out from behind the tree, his carbine at his hip; he fired
twice up the hill and began running. "Charge, third platoon," he
shouted. "Charge, God damn it! Let's git those sons-of-bitches!"

There was firing all along our line; we were moving; the surge was
rising! And in a little while there came an answering fire, sweeping down
the hill; the battle was alive! We charged, and charged successfully. Up
we went, and even now I can remember something of the ardor that
thickened in my legs and back as I pounded up that hill. It is the joy of
life that respires in a tired body at such times, when death is near; and
sweat is a sign of noble striving. Lovers ascending a peak of feeling are
not more passionate than men when the spirit finds a precise expression
in brute movement; complex motives running into a simple result—making a fury, melting the bonds of normal possibility.

We assaulted the hill, and there are good American army precedents
for that. Some years after the war I read about Sheridan's gesture at the
foot of Missionary Ridge in the Tennessee mountains; and perhaps Lev
was not so vastly different from that illustrious soldier, who had a fierce
mustache and a dark face, and said "Here's how!" drained his half-pint
flask of whisky, and started up through the rocks toward the Confederate
rifle pits.

For myself, I forgot my surroundings and went shouting up the hill.
I fell once, but otherwise did not stop, for I felt that others were with
me; I hoped that Lev was not too far ahead, and I expected that Jim Bob,
somewhere to my left, was already beyond me. I fired my rifle now and
then, but only in a formal military fashion; there was a battle, and firearms were being carried; it was only right that they should be discharged
now and then. For some time the charge was an exhilaration of movement, a very pure joy, and then, as it reached the German positions,
there began to be fighting, though I saw only a little of it.

Just to my left I saw two German soldiers suddenly rise up out of
their holes with their arms held high in the gesture of surrender. They
were quite close to me; their faces were blurred, mask-like, childish
somehow in their anticipation; they were white, scared faces of boys,
wanting to surrender; but the moment of surrender is a delicate moment
which fate governs, and their fate was to die that day, and so they went
down as if swept by wind—shot from somewhere to the left of me. I myself stepped on a wounded German as I crashed over his hole; and he
only bent down closer to earth, crouching, covering his helmeted head
with crossed hands—and his smell of an earth-bound animal, rank and
fetid, came up to me. Later I saw him marching in the little column of
prisoners we took down the mountain.

The charge ended for me in a gradual slowing-down as I beat my way through a thicket. I became aware of a cobweb; I felt it distinctly, and that was how I knew the charge was over. It came to me that there was no more German small-arms fire; and, a little later, no more fire of any sort, as the after-battle stillness began reaching out from its sources, from the dead, and the hurt, and the suddenly exhausted survivors. I stopped. Bemused, I looked about me, and noticed the details of the forest with a new precision. I even bent down to look at a fern, for I was feeling quiet and content, ready to consider a new thing. I touched it; the underside was waxy, and the upper surfaces had a kindling green feel that was like some essence of life, guessed at but never before touched. I turned around and wandered back toward the German line; I walked cautiously, for in those days I never walked any other way; thus I came upon the battle's end with a certain measure of mental coolness returned. I was already having reservations about the battle, like a newly successful lover considering the obligations his victory has fastened to him. There is an aftertaste of pleasure to such moments, which yields readily to darker feelings, by a process of conversion in the normal irony of change. I was ready to be sad; I felt pale and wan, in a preliminary way, for I was beginning to be afraid about the battle's cost.

Thus I was almost able to accept the news I had from my comrades that the battle had been costly indeed; that seemed right. Seven men had been killed outright, including Lev, who had not gone thirty feet before he took a bullet dead center in the heart; and there were many wounded, so that our platoon—the third platoon—had almost destroyed itself on that little hill. But that was the way the charge happened, and I can remember imagining how, as Lev began his charge, some still-unfrightened German rifleman had carefully taken aim, waiting for his chance as the leader of the enemy came up the slope. I considered how it must have been, the German concentrating, his eye squinting, trying to stay calm so that he could squeeze off his shot. For Lev there must have been a numbing shock and, perhaps, a dim sensation of falling; and then he was down for good, who had once walked boldly on the bleak sidewalks of Chicago.

There were some little matters to tend to then. Prisoners had to be guarded, and there were six of these. The wounded had to be looked to, and this was done by calling in another platoon for assistance; and the dead had to be taken down the hill to the town, and this we did ourselves. Jim Bob it was who carried Lev, and I carried Duval, and the burden was heavy. Duval was a big man, and his body seemed to drive itself into my shoulder, as if it were really seeking the earth. I have never carried a heavier burden, but I was not unhappy, for I wanted something to do, and wanted to do the right thing. It happened that we met stretcher-bearers at the foot of the hill, and then we were able to turn over our burdens to them.

Jim Bob and I, with what was left of the platoon, some eleven men, counting ourselves, went on back into the town, seeking the square. We were tired; that was sure. We were looking for liquor, and looking for a place to sleep; and when we reached the square we found that the company commander had arranged to give us a little rest. We were set free and told to find quarters and something to eat, but we were not quite ready for such things. We got liquor and wine, and I began to drink wine, standing with Jim Bob in the shadow of the bandstand in the little square. After a time he wandered off, carrying a bottle of wine, and I settled down to the business of conceiving a drunkenness; I managed a thin, clear intoxication that worked only in my head and left my legs firm. I walked about in the square; I approached the budding roses, and smelled the grainy roughness of the bark of chestnut trees. What else could I do? I wondered about Jim Bob, and grew angry at the sun, glowing across every surface of the pretty little square.

Toward five thirty I saw Jim Bob, walking meditatively on his high, skinny legs; he was across the square, and he was looking down at a body—Lev's body, so I guessed—that had been laid out on a stretcher under somebody's blanket. Lev was gone, assuredly; he had been approaching this end for a long time, and come away from the nearness of it so often that there was a kind of justice in his being touched by it at last. I did not look at the body—that little hooded and narrow thing; I watched Jim Bob, who was having his struggles. After a while two men from another platoon marched a group of eight prisoners into the square, stopped them, and then stood leaning on their rifles, awaiting orders. In the group of prisoners I thought I recognized some of those who had surrendered after killing my friends; and I began to feel resentment and even hate.

The town was quiet. A pale bluish light was dying above the canyon, and the hills were irregularly tipped with fir trees growing thickly; it was a time when there was nothing to say. I sat on one of the iron benches, with liquor in my head, heavy and stupid, unable to move. Such quiet is not far from death, I think, with the mind intact but ineffective. I got up once and found a little branch from a rosebush on the bandstand; I took it to the bench, and there played with it, as if there might be contained in it some principle of dignified regret for the death of old friends. The leaves had not yet come, but the thorns were left from other seasons, and I let them catch at the skin of my hands.

I was all alone, surely, just as Jim Bob was all alone, but he was at least capable of action; and perhaps that defines him. In that dim evening light he looked a boy, but he could move and change of his own power; he could accept his fate as if he were choosing it, and that is a rare gift. He got up. I could see him quite clearly. He went to the two riflemen guarding the prisoners, and talked with them. Their heads inclined to him, and they nodded. They stood patiently, servants to a just intention grown corrupt in its happening; they were careless and blind, and now, if they are still alive, perhaps they have quite forgotten that day.

A faint sibilance in the air was all I could hear of that talk, but of course I knew what was being said. How could I not? I understood that Jim Bob was selecting the prisoner he thought had killed his friend Lev; and Jim Bob was preparing a revenge.

Then it was decided. Jim Bob unsheathed his bayonet and fixed it to his rifle. With the bayonet point he picked out one of the prisoners and began marching him out of the square. Slowly the figures of the two men merged in the distance. As the day weakened, they went out of sight, into an alley perhaps, where there would be the dung of dogs, and scraps of paper blowing on the wind.

Then there came a shot, bursting into the heavy silence. At the shock of it, I drove one of the rose thorns deep into the palm of my right hand, and it seemed a proper thing to do. There was another crash, incredibly loud, and I held the thorn in place, waiting for the little flow of blood which ought to come. There were eight shots in all, but it was almost fifteen minutes between the first and the last. Truly, Jim Bob was in no hurry. He was not submitting to an accident; he intended every blow of the little copper-jacketed bullets. Thin and harsh, he must have stood with the rifle held firmly, counting the rounds, and watching the effect of them.

When it was over, I sat sweating and exhausted on my bench. I threw away my sprig of rose; death had been done, and long before Jim Bob returned, I had begun the process of recovery. I was an expert on recoveries, and still am. When Jim Bob stood before me, his rifle slung over his right shoulder, I was ready for him.

"You know where I've been," he said. "I saw you watching me. The truth is—damn it, it's so!—I loved that man, and now he's dead. Dead, I wouldn't have believed it." His boy's face was shadowy under his helmet; only his outline was clear, drawn against the last light of day, and it was a dense, formal darkness in the shape of an armed man. "Well, I got even," he said. "You know."

I nodded, and he leaned forward a little before continuing; he was still on the attack. "But it was funny what happened," he said. "Up there on the hill, I mean. Who'd ever think he'd feel that bad about Duval? And that's what made him charge like that, I guess."

I shook my head, keeping silence, for I thought I understood why Lev had felt that bad about Duval. Once again I could not help thinking that war is not all bad; and to that thought I cling now, though it is a belief hard to cherish and impossible to defend in a peaceful society.

And then Jim Bob changed the subject, saying: "But I got even with the bastard that killed him—or with some one of the bastards. Yes I did!" Tears of rage appeared in his eyes and ran untended down his cheeks. "Bastard, coming in to surrender after shooting us up! Don't you ever think I didn't get something back, though, up there in the alley with that German son-of-a-bitch! It was close range—" And here Jim Bob raised his free hand and clenched it into a fist. "Close range. I could see the bullets hit him—I never saw that before. A bullet punches a man, and you miss that when you pot him at long range. By God, a bullet fairly knocks the life out of a man—it's like stomping him to death! And I took my time about it, you know that. And learned something about life, I reckon. You bet I did! And old Lev was the man who taught me how to be that way!" Then he went away victorious, a fierce boy who had done what he wanted to do, and he will have that as long as he lives.

But the next day it was plain that his hair had begun to turn gray during the night, and three weeks later, with the war all but over, his hair was streaked with broad silvery bands. His face had not changed much; it was still a boy's face, but for the white hair, which darkened the features into something resembling an image of fallen man; a handsome face, and hard-eyed, that had been quite undistinguished in other days.

For a long time I ignored this oddity, out of politeness and respect, but of course in the end we had to talk about it, if only to arrange mutually friendly attitudes toward it. I mentioned the white hair, and Jim Bob said: "It scares me. I don't know what to think about it. But maybe it'll be all right. Maybe it'll help me look older, so I can get a woman back in the States. And then it reminds me of old Lev, and how we used to play Hearts together, and I like that. Though, God damn it, he was a bad influence on me, making me mean like I am. Wasn't he? Why, he may have made a killer out of me!

"But I like to remember him. I want to remember him. He was a good man, wasn't he? The best I ever knew in all my life. Wasn't he?"

"He was a good man," I said. "Sure he was."

Frank O'Connor (1903–   )

GUESTS OF THE NATION

The theme is not, as in the previous story, friendship passing into violence but good fellowship counterpointed against it. Consider whether at the heart of the story there lies anything but a wretched turn of fate. Is its meaning in the events, or in the situation out of which the events arise?

— 1 —

At dusk the big Englishman Belcher would shift his long legs out of the ashes and ask, "Well, chums, what about it?" and Noble or me would say, "As you please, chum" (for we had picked up some of their curious expressions), and the little Englishman 'Awkins would light the lamp and produce the cards. Sometime Jeremiah Donovan would come up of an evening and supervise the play, and grow excited over 'Awkin's cards (which he always played badly), and shout at him as if he was one of our own, "Ach, you divil you, why didn't you play the trey?" But, ordinarily, Jeremiah was a sober and contented poor devil like the big Englishman Belcher, and was looked up to at all only because he was a fair hand at documents, though slow enough at these, I vow. He wore a small cloth hat, and big gaiters over his long pants, and seldom did I perceive his hands outside the pockets of that pants. He reddened when you talked to him, tilting from toe to heel and back and looking down all the while at his big farmer's feet. His uncommon broad accent was a great source of jest to me, I being from the town, as you may recognize.

I couldn't at the time see the point of me and Noble being with Belcher and 'Awkins at all, for it was and is my fixed belief you could have planted that pair in any untended spot from this to Claregalway and they'd have stayed put and flourished like a native weed. I never seen in my short experience two men that took to the country as they did.

They were handed on to us by the Second Battalion to keep when the search for them became too hot, and Noble and myself, being young, took charge with a natural feeling of responsibility. But little 'Awkins made us look right fools when he displayed he knew the countryside as well as we did and something more. "You're the bloke they calls Bonaparte?" he said to me. "Well, Bonaparte, Mary Brigid Ho'Connell was arskin' abaout you and said 'ow you'd a pair of socks belonging to 'er young brother." For it seemed, as they explained it, that the Second used to have little evenings of their own, and some of the girls of the neighborhood would turn in, and, seeing they were such decent fellows, our lads couldn't well ignore the two Englishmen, but invited them in and were hail-fellow-well-met with them. 'Awkins told me he learned to dance "The Walls of Limerick" and "The Siege of Ennis" and "The Waves of Tory" in a night or two, though naturally he could not return the compliment, because our lads at that time did not dance foreign dances on principle.

So whatever privileges and favors Belcher and 'Awkins had with the Second they duly took with us, and after the first evening we gave up all pretence of keeping a close eye on their behavior. Not that they could have got far, for they had a notable accent and wore khaki tunics and overcoats with civilian pants and boots. But it's my belief they never had an idea of escaping and were quite contented with their lot.

Now, it was a treat to see how Belcher got off with the old woman of the house we were staying in. She was a great warrant to scold, and crotchety even with us, but before ever she had a chance of giving our guests, as I may call them, a lick of her tongue, Belcher had made her his friend for life. She was breaking sticks at the time, and Belcher, who hadn't been in the house for more than ten minutes, jumped up out of his seat and went across to her.

"Allow me, madam," he says, smiling his queer little smile; "please allow me," and takes the hatchet from her hand. She was struck too parlatic to speak, and ever after Belcher would be at her heels carrying a bucket, or basket, or load of turf, as the case might be. As Noble wittily remarked, he got into looking before she lept, and hot water or any little thing she wanted Belcher would have it ready before her. For such a huge man (and though I am five foot ten myself I had to look up to him) he had an uncommon shortness—or should I say lack—of speech. It took us some time to get used to him walking in and out like a ghost, without a syllable out of him. Especially because 'Awkins talked enough for a platoon, it was strange to hear big Belcher with his toes in the ashes come out with a solitary "Excuse me, chum," or "That's right, chum." His one and only abiding passion was cards, and I will say for him he was a good card player. He could have fleeced me and Noble many a time; only if we lost to him, 'Awkins lost to us, and 'Awkins played with the money Belcher gave him.

'Awkins lost to us because he talked too much, and I think now we lost to Belcher for the same reason. 'Awkins and Noble would spit at one another about religion into the early hours of the morning; the little Englishman as you could see worrying the soul out of young Noble (whose brother was a priest) with a string of questions that would puzzle a cardinal. And to make it worse, even in treating of these holy subjects, 'Awkins had a deplorable tongue; I never in all my career struck across a man who could mix such a variety of cursing and bad language into the simplest topic. Oh, a terrible man was little 'Awkins, and a fright to argue! He never did a stroke of work, and when he had no one else to talk to he fixed his claws into the old woman.

I am glad to say that in her he met his match, for one day when he tried to get her to complain profanely of the drought she gave him a great comedown by blaming the drought upon Jupiter Pluvius (a deity neither 'Awkins nor I had ever heard of, though Noble said among the pagans he was held to have something to do with rain). And another day the same 'Awkins was swearing at the capitalists for starting the German war, when the old dame laid down her iron, puckered up her little crab's mouth and said, "Mr. 'Awkins, you can say what you please about the war, thinking to deceive me because I'm an ignorant old woman, but I know well what started the war. It was that Italian count that stole the heathen divinity out of the temple in Japan, for believe me, Mr. 'Awkins, nothing but sorrow and want follows them that disturbs the hidden powers!" Oh, a queer old dame, as you remark!

— 2 —

So one evening we had our tea together, and 'Awkins lit the lamp and we all sat into cards. Jeremiah Donovan came in too, and sat down and watched us for a while. Though he was a shy man and didn't speak much, it was easy to see he had no great love for the two Englishmen, and I was surprised it hadn't struck me so clearly before. Well, like that in the story, a terrible dispute blew up late in the evening between 'Awkins and Noble, about capitalists and priests and love for your own country.

"The capitalists," says 'Awkins, with an angry gulp, "the capitalists pays the priests to tell you all abaout the next world, so's you awon't notice what they do in this!"

"Nonsense, man," says Noble, losing his temper, "before ever a capitalist was thought of people believed in the next world."

'Awkins stood up as if he was preaching a sermon. "Oh, they did, did they?" he says with a sneer. "They believed all the things you believed, that's what you mean? And you believe that God created Hadam and

Hadam created Shem and Shem created Jehosophat? You believe all
the silly hold fairy-tale abaout Heve and Heden and the happle? Well,
listen to me, chum. If you're entitled to 'old to a silly belief like that,
I'm entitled to 'old to my own silly belief—which is, that the fust thing
your God created was a bleedin' capitalist with mirality and Rolls Royce
complete. Am I right, chum?" he says then to Belcher.

"You're right, chum," says Belcher, with his queer smile, and gets up
from the table to stretch his long legs into the fire and stroke his moustache. So, seeing that Jeremiah Donovan was going, and there was no
knowing when the conversation about religion would be over, I took my
hat and went out with him. We strolled down towards the village together, and then he suddenly stopped, and blushing and mumbling, and
shifting, as his way was, from toe to heel, he said I ought to be behind
keeping guard on the prisoners. And I, having it put to me so suddenly,
asked him what the hell he wanted a guard on the prisoners at all for,
and said that so far as Noble and me were concerned we had talked it
over and would rather be out with a column. "What use is that pair to
us?" I asked him.

He looked at me for a spell and said, "I thought you knew we were
keeping them as hostages." "Hostages—?" says I, not quite understanding. "The enemy," he says in his heavy way, "have prisoners belong' to
us, and now they talk of shooting them. If they shoot our prisoners we'll
shoot theirs, and serve them right." "Shoot them?" said I, the possibility
just beginning to dawn on me. "Shoot them, exactly," said he. "Now,"
said I, "wasn't it very unforeseen of you not to tell me and Noble that?"
"How so?" he asks. "Seeing that we were acting as guards upon them, of
course." "And hadn't you reason enough to guess that much?" "We had
not, Jeremiah Donovan, we had not. How were we to know when the
men were on our hands so long?" "And what difference does it make?
The enemy have our prisoners as long or longer, haven't they?" "It makes
a great difference," said I. "How so?" said he sharply; but I couldn't tell
him the difference it made, for I was struck too silly to speak. "And
when may we expect to be released from this anyway?" said I. "You may
expect it tonight," says he. "Or tomorrow or the next day at latest. So if
it's hanging round here that worries you, you'll be free soon enough."

I cannot explain it even now, how sad I felt, but I went back to the
cottage a miserable man. When I arrived the discussion was still on,
'Awkins holding forth to all and sundry that there was no next world
at all and Noble answering in his best canonical style that there was.
But I saw 'Awkins was after having the best of it. "Do you know what,
chum?" he was saying, with his saucy smile, "I think you're jest as big
a bleedin' hunbeliever as I am. You say you believe in the next world
and you know jest as much abaout the next world as I do, which is sweet
damn-all. What's 'Eaven? You dunno. Where's 'Eaven? You dunno.

Who's in 'Eaven? You dunno. You know sweet damn-all! I arsk you again, do they wear wings?"

"Very well then," says Noble, "they do; is that enough for you? They do wear wings." "Where do they get them then? Who makes them? 'Ave they a fact'ry for wings? 'Ave they a sort of store where you 'ands in your chit and tikes your bleedin' wings? Answer me that."

"Oh, you're an impossible man to argue with," says Noble. "Now listen to me—." And off the pair of them went again.

It was long after midnight when we locked up the Englishmen and went to bed ourselves. As I blew out the candle I told Noble what Jeremiah Donovan had told me. Noble took it very quietly. After we had been in bed about an hour he asked me did I think we ought to tell the Englishmen. I having thought of the same thing myself (among many others) said no, because it was more than likely the English wouldn't shoot our men, and anyhow it wasn't to be supposed the Brigade who were always up and down with the second battalion and knew the Englishmen well would be likely to want them bumped off. "I think so," says Noble. "It would be sort of cruelty to put the wind up them now." "It was very unforeseen of Jeremiah Donovan anyhow," says I, and by Noble's silence I realized he took my meaning.

So I lay there half the night, and thought and thought, and picturing myself and young Noble trying to prevent the Brigade from shooting 'Awkins and Belcher sent a cold sweat out through me. Because there were men on the Brigade you daren't let nor hinder without a gun in your hand, and at any rate, in those days disunion between brothers seemed to me an awful crime. I knew better after.

It was next morning we found it so hard to face Belcher and 'Awkins with a smile. We went about the house all day scarcely saying a word. Belcher didn't mind us much; he was stretched into the ashes as usual with his usual look of waiting in quietness for something unforeseen to happen, but little 'Awkins gave us a bad time with his audacious gibing and questioning. He was disgusted at Noble's not answering him back. "Why can't you tike your beating like a man, chum?" he says. "You with your Hadam and Heve! I'm a Communist—or an Anarchist. An Anarchist, that's what I am." And for hours after he went round the house, mumbling when the fit took him "Hadam and Heve! Hadam and Heve!"

— 3 —

I don't know clearly how we got over that day, but get over it we did, and a great relief it was when the tea things were cleared away and Belcher said in his peaceable manner, "Well, chums, what about it?"

So we all sat round the table and 'Awkins produced the cards, and at that moment I heard Jeremiah Donovan's footsteps up the path, and a dark presentiment crossed my mind. I rose quietly from the table and laid my hand on him before he reached the door. "What do you want?" I asked him. "I want those two soldier friends of yours," he says reddening. "Is that the way it is, Jeremiah Donovan?" I ask. "That's the way. There were four of our lads went west this morning, one of them a boy of sixteen." "That's bad, Jeremiah," says I.

At that moment Noble came out, and we walked down the path together talking in whispers. Feeney, the local intelligence officer, was standing by the gate. "What are you going to do about it?" I asked Jeremiah Donovan. "I want you and Noble to bring them out: you can tell them they're being shifted again; that'll be the quietest way." "Leave me out of that," says Noble suddenly. Jeremiah Donovan looked at him hard for a minute or two. "All right so," he said peaceably. "You and Feeney collect a few tools from the shed and dig a hole by the far end of the bog. Bonaparte and I'll be after you in about twenty minutes. But whatever else you do, don't let anyone see you with the tools. No one must know but the four of ourselves."

We saw Feeney and Noble go round to the houseen where the tools were kept, and sidled in. Everything if I can so express myself was tottering before my eyes, and I left Jeremiah Donovan to do the explaining as best he could, while I took a seat and said nothing. He told them they were to go back to the Second. 'Awkins let a mouthful of curses out of him at that, and it was plain that Belcher, though he said nothing, was duly perturbed. The old woman was for having them stay in spite of us, and she did not shut her mouth until Jeremiah Donovan lost his temper and said some nasty things to her. Within the house by this time it was pitch dark, but no one thought of lighting the lamp, and in the darkness the two Englishmen fetched their khaki topcoats and said good-bye to the woman of the house. "Just as a man mikes a 'ome of a bleedin' place," mumbles 'Awkins shaking her by the hand, "some bastard at headquarters thinks you're too cushy and shunts you off." Belcher shakes her hand very hearty. "A thousand thanks, madam," he says, "a thousand thanks for everything . . ." as though he'd made it all up.

We go round to the back of the house and down towards the fatal bog. Then Jeremiah Donovan comes out with what is in his mind. "There were four of our lads shot by your fellows this morning so now you're to be bumped off." "Cut that stuff out," says 'Awkins flaring up. "It's bad enough to be mucked about such as we are without you plying at soldiers." "It's true," says Jeremiah Donovan. "I'm sorry, 'Awkins, but 'tis true," and comes out with the usual rigamarole about our duty and obeying our superiors. "Cut it out," says 'Awkins irritably, "cut it out!"

Then, when Donovan sees he is not being believed he turns to me.

"Ask Bonaparte here," he says. "I don't need to arsk Bonaparte. Me and Bonaparte are chums." "Isn't it true, Bonaparte?" says Jeremiah Donovan solemnly to me. "It is," I say sadly, "it is." 'Awkins stops. "Now, for Christ's sike. . . ." "I mean it, chum," I say. "You daon't saound as if you mean it. You knaow well you don't mean it." "Well, if he don't I do," says Jeremiah Donovan. "Why the 'ell sh'd you want to shoot me, Jeremiah Donovan?" "Why the hell should your people take out four prisoners and shoot them in cold blood upon a barrack square?" I perceive Jeremiah Donovan is trying to encourage himself with hot words.

Anyway, he took little 'Awkins by the arm and dragged him on, but it was impossible to make him understand that we were in earnest. From which you will perceive how difficult it was for me, as I kept feeling my Smith and Wesson and thinking what I would do if they happened to put up a fight or ran for it, and wishing in my heart they would. I knew if only they ran I would never fire on them. "Was Noble in this?" 'Awkins wanted to know, and we said yes. He laughed. But why should Noble want to shoot him? Why should we want to shoot him? What had he done to us? Weren't we chums (the word lingers painfully in my memory)? Weren't we? Didn't we understand him and didn't he understand us? Did either of us imagine for an instant that he'd shoot us for all the so-and-so brigadiers in the so-and-so British Army? By this time I began to perceive in the dusk the desolate edges of the bog that was to be their last earthly bed, and, so great a sadness overtook my mind, I could not answer him. We walked along the edge of it in the darkness, and every now and then 'Awkins would call a halt and begin again, just as if he was wound up, about us being chums, and I was in despair that nothing but the cold and open grave made ready for his presence would convince him that we meant it all. But all the same, if you can understand, I didn't want him to be bumped off.

— 4 —

At last we saw the unsteady glint of a lantern in the distance and made towards it. Noble was carrying it, and Feeney stood somewhere in the darkness behind, and somehow the picture of the two of them so silent in the boglands was like the pain of death in my heart. Belcher, on recognizing Noble, said "'Allo, chum" in his usual peaceable way, but 'Awkins flew at the poor boy immediately, and the dispute began all over again, only that Noble hadn't a word to say for himself, and stood there with the swaying lantern between his gaitered legs.

It was Jeremiah Donovan who did the answering. 'Awkins asked for the twentieth time (for it seemed to haunt his mind) if anybody thought he'd shoot Noble. "You would," says Jeremiah Donovan shortly. "I wouldn't, damn you!" "You would if you knew you'd be shot for not doing it." "I wouldn't, not if I was to be shot twenty times over; he's my chum. And Belcher wouldn't—isn't that right, Belcher?" "That's right, chum," says Belcher peaceably. "Damned if I would. Anyway, who says Noble'd be shot if I wasn't bumped off? What d'you think I'd do if I was in Noble's place and we were out in the middle of a blasted bog?" "What would you do?" "I'd go with him wherever he was going. I'd share my last bob with him and stick by 'im through thick and thin."

"We've had enough of this," says Jeremiah Donovan, cocking his revolver. "Is there any message you want to send before I fire?" "No, there isn't but. . . ." "Do you want to say your prayers?" 'Awkins came out with a cold-blooded remark that shocked even me and turned to Noble again. "Listen to me, Noble," he said. "You and me are chums. You won't come over to my side, so I'll come over to your side. Is that fair? Just you give me a rifle and I'll go with you wherever you want."

Nobody answered him.

"Do you understand?" he said. "I'm through with it all. I'm a deserter or anything else you like, but from this on I'm one of you. Does that prove to you that I mean what I say?" Noble raised his head, but as Donovan began to speak he lowered it again without answering. "For the last time have you any messages to send?" says Donovan in a cold and excited voice.

"Ah, shut up, you, Donovan; you don't understand me, but these fellows do. They're my chums; they stand by me and I stand by them. We're not the capitalist tools you seem to think us."

I alone of the crowd saw Donovan raise his Webley to the back of 'Awkins's neck, and as he did so I shut my eyes and tried to say a prayer. 'Awkins had begun to say something else when Donovan let fly, and, as I opened my eyes at the bang, I saw him stagger at the knees and lie out flat at Noble's feet, slowly, and as quiet as a child, with the lantern-light falling sadly upon his lean legs and bright farmer's boots. We all stood very still for a while watching him settle out in the last agony.

Then Belcher quietly takes out a handkerchief, and begins to tie it about his own eyes (for in our excitement we had forgotten to offer the same to 'Awkins), and, seeing it is not big enough, turns and asks for a loan of mine. I give it to him and as he knots the two together he points with his foot at 'Awkins. "'E's not quite dead," he says, "better give 'im another." Sure enough 'Awkins's left knee as we see it under the lantern is rising again. I bend down and put my gun to his ear; then, recollecting myself and the company of Belcher, I stand up again with a few hasty words. Belcher understands what is in my mind. "Give 'im 'is first," he says. "I don't mind. Poor bastard, we dunno what's 'appening to 'im now." As by this time I am beyond all feeling I kneel down again and skilfully give 'Awkins the last shot so as to put him forever out of pain.

Belcher, who is fumbling a bit awkwardly with the handkerchief, comes out with a laugh when he hears the shot. It is the first time I have heard him laugh, and it sends a shiver down my spine, coming as it does so inappropriately upon the tragic death of his old friend. "Poor blighter," he says quietly, "and last night he was so curious abaout it all. It's very queer, chums, I always think. Naow, 'e knows as much abaout it as they'll ever let 'im know, and last night 'e was all in the dark."

Donovan helps him to tie the handkerchiefs about his eyes. "Thanks, chum," he says. Donovan asks him if there are any messages he would like to send. "Naow, chum," he says, "none for me. If any of you likes to write to 'Awkins's mother you'll find a letter from 'er in 'is pocket. But my missus left me eight years ago. Went away with another fellow and took the kid with her. I likes the feelin' of a 'ome (as you may 'ave noticed) but I couldn't start again after that."

We stand around like fools now that he can no longer see us. Donovan looks at Noble and Noble shakes his head. Then Donovan raises his Webley again and just at that moment Belcher laughs his queer nervous laugh again. He must think we are talking of him; anyway, Donovan lowers his gun. "'Scuse me, chums," says Belcher, "I feel I'm talking the 'ell of a lot . . . and so silly . . . abaout me being so 'andy abaout a 'ouse. But this thing come on me so sudden. You'll forgive me, I'm sure." "You don't want to say a prayer?" asks Jeremiah Donovan. "No, chum," he replies, "I don't think that'd 'elp. I'm ready if you want to get it over." "You understand," says Jeremiah Donovan, "it's not so much our doing. It's our duty, so to speak." Belcher's head is raised like a real blind man's, so that you can only see his nose and chin in the lamplight. "I never could make out what duty was myself," he said, "but I think you're all good lads, if that's what you mean. I'm not complaining." Noble, with a look of desperation, signals to Donovan, and in a flash Donovan raises his gun and fires. The big man goes over like a sack of meal, and this time there is no need of a second shot.

I don't remember much about the burying, but that it was worse than all the rest, because we had to carry the warm corpses a few yards before we sunk them in the windy bog. It was all mad lonely, with only a bit of lantern between ourselves and the pitch blackness, and birds hooting and screeching all round disturbed by the guns. Noble had to search 'Awkins first to get the letter from his mother. Then having smoothed all signs of the grave away, Noble and I collected our tools, said good-bye to the others, and went back along the desolate edge of the treacherous bog without a word. We put the tools in the houeseen and went into the house. The kitchen was pitch black and cold, just as we left it, and the old woman was sitting over the hearth telling her beads. We walked past her into the room, and Noble struck a match to light the lamp. Just then she rose quietly and came to the doorway, being not at all so bold or crabbed as usual.

"What did ye do with them?" she says in a sort of whisper, and Noble took such a mortal start the match quenched in his trembling hand. "What's that?" he asks without turning round. "I heard ye," she said. "What did you hear?" asks Noble, but sure he wouldn't deceive a child the way he said it. "I heard ye. Do you think I wasn't listening to ye putting the things back in the houseen?" Noble struck another match and this time the lamp lit for him. "Was that what ye did with them?" she said, and Noble said nothing—after all what could he say?

So then, by God, she fell on her two knees by the door, and began telling her beads, and after a minute or two Noble went on his knees by the fireplace, so I pushed my way out past her, and stood at the door, watching the stars and listening to the damned shrieking of the birds. It is so strange what you feel at such moments, and not to be written afterwards. Noble says he felt he seen everything ten times as big, perceiving nothing around him but the little patch of black bog with the two Englishmen stiffening into it; but with me it was the other way, as though the patch of bog where the two Englishmen were was a thousand miles away from me, and even Noble mumbling just behind me and the old woman and the birds and the bloody stars were all far away, and I was somehow very small and very lonely. And anything that ever happened to me after I never felt the same about again.

William Carlos Williams (1883–1963)

THE USE OF FORCE

The doctor's training provides for impersonal violence, but between persons nothing can be impersonal. Does the relationship of writer and reader (who are persons also) change as the narrative progresses?

THEY were new patients to me, all I had was the name, Olson. Please come down as soon as you can, my daughter is very sick.

When I arrived I was met by the mother, a big startled looking woman, very clean and apologetic who merely said, Is this the doctor? and let me in. In the back, she added. You must excuse us, doctor, we have her in the kitchen where it is warm. It is very damp here sometimes.

The child was fully dressed and sitting on her father's lap near the kitchen table. He tried to get up, but I motioned for him not to bother, took off my overcoat and started to look things over. I could see that they were all very nervous, eyeing me up and down distrustfully. As often, in such cases, they weren't telling me more than they had to, it was up to me to tell them; that's why they were spending three dollars on me.

The child was fairly eating me up with her cold, steady eyes, and no expression to her face whatever. She did not move and seemed, inwardly, quiet; an unusually attractive little thing, and as strong as a heifer in appearance. But her face was flushed, she was breathing rapidly, and I realized that she had a high fever. She had magnificent blonde hair, in profusion. One of those picture children often reproduced in advertising leaflets and the photogravure sections of the Sunday papers.

She's had a fever for three days, began the father, and we don't know what it comes from. My wife has given her things, you know, like people do, but it don't do no good. And there's been a lot of sickness around. So we tho't you'd better look her over and tell us what is the matter.

As doctors often do I took a trial shot at it as a point of departure. Has she had a sore throat?

From *The Farmers' Daughters: The Collected Stories of William Carlos Williams.* © 1961 by New Directions. Reprinted by permission of New Directions.

Both parents answered me together, No . . . No, she says her throat don't hurt her.

Does your throat hurt you? added the mother to the child. But the little girl's expression didn't change, nor did she move her eyes from my face.

Have you looked?

I tried to, said the mother, but I couldn't see.

As it happens, we had been having a number of cases of diphtheria in the school to which this child went during that month and we were all, quite apparently, thinking of that, though no one had as yet spoken of the thing.

Well, I said, suppose we take a look at the throat first. I smiled in my best professional manner and asking for the child's first name I said, come on, Mathilda, open your mouth and let's take a look at your throat.

Nothing doing.

Aw, come on, I coaxed, just open your mouth wide and let me take a look. Look, I said opening both hands wide, I haven't anything in my hands. Just open up and let me see.

Such a nice man, put in the mother. Look how kind he is to you. Come on, do what he tells you to. He won't hurt you.

At that I ground my teeth in disgust. If only they wouldn't use the word "hurt" I might be able to get somewhere. But I did not allow myself to be hurried or disturbed, but speaking quietly and slowly I approached the child again.

As I moved my chair a little nearer, suddenly with one catlike movement both her hands clawed instinctively for my eyes and she almost reached them too. In fact she knocked my glasses flying and they fell, though unbroken, several feet away from me on the kitchen floor.

Both the mother and father almost turned themselves inside out in embarrassment and apology. You bad girl, said the mother, taking her and shaking her by one arm. Look what you've done. The nice man. . . .

For heaven's sake, I broke in. Don't call me a nice man to her. I'm here to look at her throat on the chance that she might have diphtheria and possibly die of it. But that's nothing to her. Look here, I said to the child, we're going to look at your throat. You're old enough to understand what I'm saying. Will you open it now by yourself or shall we have to open it for you?

Not a move. Even her expression hadn't changed. Her breaths however were coming faster and faster. Then the battle began. I had to do it. I had to have a throat culture for her own protection. But first I told the parents that it was entirely up to them. I explained the danger but said that I would not insist on a throat examination so long as they would take the responsibility.

If you don't do what the doctor says you'll have to go to the hospital, the mother admonished her severely.

Oh yeah? I had to smile to myself. After all, I had already fallen in love with the savage brat, the parents were contemptible to me. In the ensuing struggle they grew more and more abject, crushed, exhausted while she surely rose to magnificent heights of insane fury of effort bred of her terror of me.

The father tried his best, and he was a big man but the fact that she was his daughter, his shame at her behavior and his dread of hurting her made him release her just at the critical moment several times when I had almost achieved success, till I wanted to kill him. But his dread also that she might have diphtheria made him tell me to go on, go on though he himself was almost fainting, while the mother moved back and forth behind us raising and lowering her hands in an agony of apprehension.

Put her in front of you on your lap, I ordered, and hold both her wrists.

But as soon as he did the child let out a scream. Don't, you're hurting me. Let go of my hands. Let them go I tell you. Then she shrieked terrifyingly, hysterically. Stop it! Stop it! You're killing me!

Do you think she can stand it, doctor! said the mother.

You get out, said the husband to his wife. Do you want her to die of diphtheria?

Come on now, hold her, I said.

Then I grasped the child's head with my left hand and tried to get the wooden tongue depressor between her teeth. She fought, with clenched teeth, desperately! But now I also had grown furious—at a child. I tried to hold myself down but I couldn't. I know how to expose a throat for inspection. And I did my best. When finally I got the wooden spatula behind the last teeth and just the point of it into the mouth cavity, she opened up for an instant but before I could see anything she came down again and gripping the wooden blade between her molars she reduced it to splinters before I could get it out again.

Aren't you ashamed, the mother yelled at her. Aren't you ashamed to act like that in front of the doctor?

Get me a smooth-handled spoon of some sort, I told the mother. We're going through with this. The child's mouth was already bleeding. Her tongue was cut and she was screaming in wild hysterical shrieks. Perhaps I should have desisted and come back in an hour or more. No doubt it would have been better. But I have seen at least two children lying dead in bed of neglect in such cases, and feeling that I must get a diagnosis now or never I went at it again. But the worst of it was that I too had got beyond reason. I could have torn the child apart in my own fury and enjoyed it. It was a pleasure to attack her. My face was burning with it.

The damned little brat must be protected against her own idiocy, one says to one's self at such times. Others must be protected against her. It is social necessity. And all these things are true. But a blind fury, a feeling of adult shame, bred of a longing for muscular release are the operatives. One goes on to the end.

In a final unreasoning assault I overpowered the child's neck and jaws. I forced the heavy silver spoon back of her teeth and down her throat till she gagged. And there it was—both tonsils covered with membrane. She had fought valiantly to keep me from knowing her secret. She had been hiding that sore throat for three days at least and lying to her parents in order to escape just such an outcome as this.

Now truly she *was* furious. She had been on the defensive before but now she attacked. Tried to get off her father's lap and fly at me while tears of defeat blinded her eyes.

James Joyce (1882–1941)

ARABY

"At last she spoke to me. . . . She asked me was I going to Araby."
The indirect discourse, deliberately graceless in phrasing, counter-
points the exoticism of Araby. The story is built out of just such
counterpoints. "The Use of Force" is by contrast a piece of report-
ing. What is "After the Storm"? How many detailed contrasts be-
tween sordidness and expectancy can you find in the story? Five?
Twenty? Fifty? Is the narrator identical with the boy protagonist?

NORTH Richmond Street, being blind, was a quiet street except at the hour when the Christian Brothers' School set the boys free. An uninhabited house of two storys stood at the blind end, detached from its neighbors in a square ground. The other houses of the street, conscious of decent lives within them, gazed at one another with brown imperturbable faces.

The former tenant of our house, a priest, had died in the back drawing room. Air, musty from having been long enclosed, hung in all the rooms, and the waste room behind the kitchen was littered with old useless papers. Among these I found a few paper-covered books, the pages of which were curled and damp: *The Abbot,* by Walter Scott, *The Devout Communicant,* and *The Memoirs of Vidocq.* I liked the last best because its leaves were yellow. The wild garden behind the house contained a central apple tree and a few straggling bushes, under one of which I found the late tenant's rusty bicycle pump. He had been a very charitable priest; in his will he had left all his money to institutions and the furniture of his house to his sister.

When the short days of winter came dusk fell before we had well eaten our dinners. When we met in the street the houses had grown sombre. The space of sky above us was the color of ever-changing violet and towards it the lamps of the street lifted their feeble lanterns. The cold air stung us and we played till our bodies glowed. Our shouts echoed

From *Dubliners.* Originally published by B. W. Huebsch in 1916. Reprinted by permission of The Viking Press, Inc.

in the silent street. The career of our play brought us through the dark muddy lanes behind the houses where we ran the gauntlet of the rough tribes from the cottages, to the back doors of the dark dripping gardens where odors arose from the ashpits, to the dark odorous stables where a coachman smoothed and combed the horse or shook music from the buckled harness. When we returned to the street light from the kitchen windows had filled the areas. If my uncle was seen turning the corner we hid in the shadow until we had seen him safely housed. Or if Mangan's sister came out on the doorstep to call her brother in to his tea we watched her from our shadow peer up and down the street. We waited to see whether she would remain or go in and, if she remained, we left our shadow and walked up to Mangan's steps resignedly. She was waiting for us, her figure defined by the light from the half-opened door. Her brother always teased her before he obeyed and I stood by the railings looking at her. Her dress swung as she moved her body and the soft rope of her hair tossed from side to side.

Every morning I lay on the floor in the front parlor watching her door. The blind was pulled down to within an inch of the sash so that I could not be seen. When she came out on the doorstep my heart leaped. I ran to the hall, seized my books and followed her. I kept her brown figure always in my eye and, when we came near the point at which our ways diverged, I quickened my pace and passed her. This happened morning after morning. I had never spoken to her, except for a few casual words, and yet her name was like a summons to all my foolish blood.

Her image accompanied me even in places the most hostile to romance. On Saturday evenings when my aunt went marketing I had to go to carry some of the parcels. We walked through the flaring streets, jostled by drunken men and bargaining women, amid the curses of laborers, the shrill litanies of shop boys who stood on guard by the barrels of pigs' cheeks, the nasal chanting of street singers, who sang a *come-all-you* about O'Donovan Rossa, or a ballad about the troubles in our native land. These noises converged in a single sensation of life for me: I imagined that I bore my chalice safely through a throng of foes. Her name sprang to my lips at moments in strange prayers and praises which I myself did not understand. My eyes were often full of tears (I could not tell why) and at times a flood from my heart seemed to pour itself out into my bosom. I thought little of the future. I did not know whether I would ever speak to her or not or, if I spoke to her, how I could tell her of my confused adoration. But my body was like a harp and her words and gestures were like fingers running upon the wires.

One evening I went into the back drawing room in which the priest had died. It was a dark rainy evening and there was no sound in the house. Through one of the broken panes I heard the rain impinge upon the earth, the fine incessant needles of water playing in the sodden beds. Some distant lamp or lighted window gleamed below me. I was thankful that I could see so little. All my senses seemed to desire to veil themselves and, feeling that I was about to slip from them, I pressed the palms of my hands together until they trembled, murmuring: *"O love! O love!"* many times.

At last she spoke to me. When she addressed the first words to me I was so confused that I did not know what to answer. She asked me was I going to *Araby*. I forgot whether I answered yes or no. It would be a splendid bazaar, she said she would love to go.

"And why can't you?" I asked.

While she spoke she turned a silver bracelet round and round her wrist. She could not go, she said, because there would be a retreat that week in her convent. Her brother and two other boys were fighting for their caps and I was alone at the railings. She held one of the spikes, bowing her head towards me. The light from the lamp opposite our door caught the white curve of her neck, lit up her hair that rested there and, falling, lit up the hand upon the railing. It fell over one side of her dress and caught the white border of a petticoat, just visible as she stood at ease.

"It's well for you," she said.

"If I go," I said, "I will bring you something."

What innumerable follies laid waste my waking and sleeping thoughts after that evening! I wished to annihilate the tedious intervening days. I chafed against the work of school. At night in my bedroom and by day in the classroom her image came between me and the page I strove to read. The syllables of the word *Araby* were called to me through the silence in which my soul luxuriated and cast an Eastern enchantment over me. I asked for leave to go to the bazaar on Saturday night. My aunt was surprised and hoped it was not some Freemason affair. I answered few questions in class. I watched my master's face pass from amiability to sternness; he hoped I was not beginning to idle. I could not call my wandering thoughts together. I had hardly any patience with the serious work of life which, now that it stood between me and my desire, seemed to me child's play, ugly monotonous child's play.

On Saturday morning I reminded my uncle that I wished to go to the bazaar in the evening. He was fussing at the hallstand, looking for the hat brush, and answered me curtly:

"Yes, boy, I know."

As he was in the hall I could not go into the front parlor and lie at the window. I left the house in bad humor and walked slowly towards the school. The air was pitilessly raw and already my heart misgave me.

When I came home to dinner my uncle had not yet been home. Still it was early. I sat staring at the clock for some time and, when its ticking began to irritate me, I left the room. I mounted the staircase and gained the upper part of the house. The high cold empty gloomy rooms liberated me and I went from room to room singing. From the front window I saw my companions playing below in the street. Their cries reached me weakened and indistinct and, leaning my forehead against the cool glass, I looked over at the dark house where she lived. I may have stood there for an hour, seeing nothing but the brown-clad figure cast by my imagination, touched discreetly by the lamplight at the curved neck, at the hand upon the railings and at the border below the dress.

When I came downstairs again I found Mrs. Mercer sitting at the fire. She was an old garrulous woman, a pawnbroker's widow, who collected used stamps for some pious purpose. I had to endure the gossip of the tea table. The meal was prolonged beyond an hour and still my uncle did not come. Mrs. Mercer stood up to go: she was sorry she couldn't wait any longer, but it was after eight o'clock and she did not like to be out late, as the night air was bad for her. When she had gone I began to walk up and down the room, clenching my fists. My aunt said:

"I'm afraid you may put off your bazaar for this night of Our Lord."

At nine o'clock I heard my uncle's latchkey in the halldoor. I heard him talking to himself and heard the hallstand rocking when it had received the weight of his overcoat. I could interpret these signs. When he was midway through his dinner I asked him to give me the money to go to the bazaar. He had forgotten.

"The people are in bed and after their first sleep now," he said.

I did not smile. My aunt said to him energetically:

"Can't you give him the money and let him go? You've kept him late enough as it is."

My uncle said he was very sorry he had forgotten. He said he believed in the old saying: "All work and no play makes Jack a dull boy." He asked me where I was going and, when I had told him a second time he asked me did I know *The Arab's Farewell to His Steed*. When I left the kitchen he was about to recite the opening lines of the piece to my aunt.

I held a florin tightly in my hand as I strode down Buckingham Street towards the station. The sight of the streets thronged with buyers and glaring with gas recalled to me the purpose of my journey. I took my seat in a third-class carriage of a deserted train. After an intolerable delay the train moved out of the station slowly. It crept onward among ruinous houses and over the twinkling river. At Westland Row Station a crowd of people pressed to the carriage doors; but the porters moved them back, saying that it was a special train for the bazaar. I remained alone in the bare carriage. In a few minutes the train drew up beside an improvised wooden platform. I passed out on to the road and saw by the lighted dial of a clock that it was ten minutes to ten. In front of me was a large building which displayed the magical name.

I could not find any sixpenny entrance and, fearing that the bazaar would be closed, I passed in quickly through a turnstile, handing a shilling to a weary-looking man. I found myself in a big hall girdled at half its height by a gallery. Nearly all the stalls were closed and the greater part of the hall was in darkness. I recognized a silence like that which pervades a church after a service. I walked into the center of the bazaar timidly. A few people were gathered about the stalls which were still open. Before a curtain, over which the words *Café Chantant* were written in colored lamps, two men were counting money on a salver. I listened to the fall of the coins.

Remembering with difficulty why I had come I went over to one of the stalls and examined porcelain vases and flowered tea sets. At the door of the stall a young lady was talking and laughing with two young gentlemen. I remarked their English accents and listened vaguely to their conversation.

"O, I never said such a thing!"

"O, but you did!"

"O, but I didn't!"

"Didn't she say that?"

"Yes. I heard her."

"O, there's a . . . fib!"

Observing me the young lady came over and asked me did I wish to buy anything. The tone of her voice was not encouraging; she seemed to have spoken to me out of a sense of duty. I looked humbly at the great jars that stood like eastern guards at either side of the dark entrance to the stall and murmured:

"No, thank you."

The young lady changed the position of one of the vases and went back to the two young men. They began to talk of the same subject. Once or twice the young lady glanced at me over her shoulder.

I lingered before her stall, though I knew my stay was useless, to make my interest in her wares seem the more real. Then I turned away slowly and walked down the middle of the bazaar. I allowed the two pennies to fall against the sixpence in my pocket. I heard a voice call from one end of the gallery that the light was out. The upper part of the hall was now completely dark.

Gazing up into the darkness I saw myself as a creature driven and derided by vanity; and my eyes burned with anguish and anger.

Ernest Hemingway (1898–1961)

AFTER THE STORM

Like a meticulous still-life painting, Hemingway's naturalism pro-
duces effects of dreamlike stillness. Note the circumstances in which
the only spoken words in the story occur. The sunken liner "as big
as the whole world," with its dead woman floating wordlessly under
the porthole, not only is but represents an order of existence from
which the narrator is excluded. Compare the story with "Araby" for
its management of an event which is both itself and the symbol of
something more than itself. Does the narrator understand the full im-
plications of the story? Does the narrator of "Araby"?

IT wasn't about anything, something about making punch, and then
we started fighting and I slipped and he had me down kneeling on my
chest and choking me with both hands like he was trying to kill me and
all the time I was trying to get the knife out of my pocket to cut him
loose. Everybody was too drunk to pull him off me. He was choking me
and hammering my head on the floor and I got the knife out and opened
it up; and I cut the muscle right across his arm and he let go of me. He
couldn't have held on if he wanted to. Then he rolled and hung onto
that arm and started to cry and I said:
"What the hell you want to choke me for?"
I'd have killed him. I couldn't swallow for a week. He hurt my throat
bad.
Well, I went out of there and there were plenty of them with him
and some come out after me and I made a turn and was down by the
docks and I met a fellow and he said somebody killed a man up the
street. I said "Who killed him?" and he said "I don't know who killed
him but he's dead all right," and it was dark and there was water standing in the street and no lights and windows broke and boats all up in
the town and trees blown down and everything all blown and I got a

skiff and went out and found my boat where I had her inside of Mango Key and she was all right only she was full of water. So I bailed her out and pumped her out and there was a moon but plenty of clouds and still plenty rough and I took it down along; and when it was daylight I was off Eastern Harbor.

Brother, that was some storm. I was the first boat out and you never saw water like that was. It was just as white as a lye barrel and coming from Eastern Harbor to Sou'west Key you couldn't recognize the shore. There was a big channel blown right out through the middle of the beach. Trees and all blown out and a channel cut through and all the water white as chalk and everything on it; branches and whole trees and dead birds, and all floating. Inside the keys were all the pelicans in the world and all kinds of birds flying. They must have gone inside there when they knew it was coming.

I lay at Sou'west Key a day and nobody came after me. I was the first boat out and I seen a spar floating and I knew there must be a wreck and I started out to look for her. I found her. She was a three-masted schooner and I could just see the stumps of her spars out of water. She was in too deep water and I didn't get anything off of her. So I went on looking for something else. I had the start on all of them and I knew I ought to get whatever there was. I went on down over the sand bars from where I left that three-masted schooner and I didn't find anything and I went on a long way. I was way out toward the quicksands and I didn't find anything so I went on. Then when I was in sight of the Rebecca Light I saw all kinds of birds making over something and I headed over for them to see what it was and there was a cloud of birds all right.

I could see something looked like a spar up out of the water and when I got over close the birds all went up in the air and stayed all around me. The water was clear out there and there was a spar of some kind sticking out just above the water and when I come up close to it I saw it was all dark under water like a long shadow and I came right over it and there under water was a liner; just lying there all under water as big as the whole world. I drifted over her in the boat. She lay on her side and the stern was deep down. The portholes were all shut tight and I could see the glass shine in the water and the whole of her; the biggest boat I ever saw in my life laying there and I went along the whole length of her and then I went over and anchored and I had the skiff on the deck forward and I shoved it down into the water and sculled over with the birds all around me.

I had a water glass like we use sponging and my hand shook so I could hardly hold it. All the portholes were shut that you could see going along over her but way down below near the bottom something must have been open because there were pieces of things floating out all the time. You couldn't tell what they were. Just pieces. That's what the birds were after. You never saw so many birds. They were all around me; crazy yelling.

I could see everything sharp and clear. I could see her rounded over and she looked a mile long under the water. She was lying on a clear white bank of sand and the spar was a sort of foremast or some sort of tackle that slanted out of water the way she was laying on her side. Her bow wasn't very far under. I could stand on the letters of her name on her bow and my head was just out of water. But the nearest porthole was twelve feet down. I could just reach it with the grains pole and I tried to break it with that but I couldn't. The glass was too stout. So I sculled back to the boat and got a wrench and lashed it to the end of the grains pole and I couldn't break it. There I was looking down through the glass at that liner with everything in her and I was the first one to her and I couldn't get into her. She must have had five million dollars worth in her.

It made me shaky to think how much she must have in her. Inside the porthole that was closest I could see something but I couldn't make it out through the water glass. I couldn't do any good with the grains pole and I took off my clothes and stood and took a couple of deep breaths and dove over off the stern with the wrench in my hand and swam down. I could hold on for a second to the edge of the porthole and I could see in and there was a woman inside with her hair floating all out. I could see her floating plain and I hit the glass twice with the wrench hard and I heard the noise clink in my ears but it wouldn't break and I had to come up.

I hung onto the dinghy and got my breath and then I climbed in and took a couple of breaths and dove again. I swam down and took hold of the edge of the porthole with my fingers and held it and hit the glass as hard as I could with the wrench. I could see the woman floated in the water through the glass. Her hair was tied once close to her head and it floated all out in the water. I could see the rings on one of her hands. She was right up close to the porthole and I hit the glass twice and I didn't even crack it. When I came up I thought I wouldn't make it to the top before I'd have to breathe.

I went down once more and I cracked the glass, only cracked it, and when I came up my nose was bleeding and I stood on the bow of the liner with my bare feet on the letters of her name and my head just out and rested there and then I swam over to the skiff and pulled up into it and sat there waiting for my head to stop aching and looking down into the water glass, but I bled so I had to wash out the water glass. Then I lay back in the skiff and held my hand under my nose to stop it and I lay there with my head back looking up and there was a million birds above and all around.

When I quit bleeding I took another look through the glass and then I sculled over to the boat to try and find something heavier than the wrench but I couldn't find a thing; not even a sponge hook. I went back and the water was clearer all the time and you could see everything that floated out over that white bank of sand. I looked for sharks but there weren't any. You could have seen a shark a long way away. The water was so clear and the sand white. There was a grapple for an anchor on the skiff and I cut it off and went overboard and down with it. It carried me right down and past the porthole and I grabbed and couldn't hold anything and went on down and down, sliding along the curved side of her. I had to let go of the grapple. I heard it bump once and it seemed like a year before I came up through to the top of the water. The skiff was floated away with the tide and I swam over to her with my nose bleeding in the water while I swam and I was plenty glad there weren't sharks; but I was tired.

My head felt cracked open and I lay in the skiff and rested and then I sculled back. It was getting along in the afternoon. I went down once more with the wrench and it didn't do any good. That wrench was too light. It wasn't any good diving unless you had a big hammer or something heavy enough to do good. Then I lashed the wrench to the grains pole again and I watched through the water glass and pounded on the glass and hammered until the wrench came off and I saw it in the glass, clear and sharp, go sliding down along her and then off and down to the quicksand and go in. Then I couldn't do a thing. The wrench was gone and I'd lost the grapple so I sculled back to the boat. I was too tired to get the skiff aboard and the sun was pretty low. The birds were all pulling out and leaving her and I headed for Sou'west Key towing the skiff and the birds going on ahead of me and behind me. I was plenty tired.

That night it came on to blow and it blew for a week. You couldn't get out to her. They come out from town and told me the fellow I'd had to cut was all right except for his arm and I went back to town and they put me under five hundred dollar bond. It came out all right because some of them, friends of mine, swore he was after me with an ax, but by the time we got back out to her the Greeks had blown her open and cleaned her out. They got the safe out with dynamite. Nobody ever knows how much they got. She carried gold and they got it all. They stripped her clean. I found her and I never got a nickel out of her.

It was a hell of a thing all right. They say she was just outside of Havana harbor when the hurricane hit and she couldn't get in or the owners wouldn't let the captain chance coming in; they say he wanted to try; so she had to go with it and in the dark they were running with it trying to go through the gulf between Rebecca and Tortugas when she struck on the quicksands. Maybe her rudder was carried away. Maybe they weren't even steering. But anyway they couldn't have known they

were quicksands and when she struck the captain must have ordered
them to open up the ballast tanks so she'd lay solid. But it was quicksand
she'd hit and when they opened the tanks she went in stern first and
then over on her beam ends. There were four hundred and fifty passengers and the crew on board of her and they must all have been aboard
of her when I found her. They must have opened the tanks as soon as
she struck and the minute she settled on it the quicksands took her
down. Then her boilers must have burst and that must have been what
made those pieces that came out. It was funny there weren't any sharks
though. There wasn't a fish. I could have seen them on that clear white
sand.

Plenty of fish now though; jewfish, the biggest kind. The biggest part
of her's under the sand now but they live inside of her; the biggest kind
of jewfish. Some weigh three to four hundred pounds. Sometime we'll go
out and get some. You can see the Rebecca light from where she is.
They've got a buoy on her now. She's right at the end of the quicksand
right at the edge of the gulf. She only missed going through by about a
hundred yards. In the dark in the storm they just missed it; raining the
way it was they couldn't have seen the Rebecca. Then they're not used
to that sort of thing. The captain of a liner isn't used to scudding that
way. They have a course and they tell me they set some sort of a compass and it steers itself. They probably didn't know where they were
when they ran with that blow but they come close to making it. Maybe
they'd lost the rudder though. Anyway there wasn't another thing for
them to hit till they'd get to Mexico once they were in that gulf. Must
have been something though when they struck in that rain and wind
and he told them to open her tanks. Nobody could have been on deck
in that blow and rain. Everybody must have been below. They couldn't
have lived on deck. There must have been some scenes inside all right
because you know she settled fast. I saw that wrench go into the sand.
The captain couldn't have known it was quicksand when she struck unless he knew these waters. He just knew it wasn't rock. He must have
seen it all up in the bridge. He must have known what it was about
when she settled. I wonder how fast she made it. I wonder if the mate
was there with him. Do you think they stayed inside the bridge or do you
think they took it outside? They never found any bodies. Not a one.
Nobody floating. They float a long way with life belts too. They must
have took it inside. Well, the Greeks got it all. Everything. They must
have come fast all right. They picked her clean. First there was the
birds, then me, then the Greeks, and even the birds got more out of her
than I did.

Franz Kafka (1883–1924)

THE HUNTER GRACCHUS

*Careful comparison of this story with "After the Storm" can yield
considerable understanding of the nature and principles of symbolism.
Like the seeming irrelevance of the episodes in Hemingway's story,
the seeming implausibility of the action in Kafka's sends us in quest
of a viewpoint from which the whole will cohere. Yet the stories
differ profoundly in nature, as well as in method and meaning.*

Two boys were sitting on the harbor wall playing with dice. A man
was reading a newspaper on the steps of the monument, resting in the
shadow of a hero who was flourishing his sword on high. A girl was filling her bucket at the fountain. A fruit-seller was lying beside his scales,
staring out to sea. Through the vacant window and door openings of a
café one could see two men quite at the back drinking their wine. The
proprietor was sitting at a table in front and dozing. A bark was silently
making for the little harbor, as if borne by invisible means over the water.
A man in a blue blouse climbed ashore and drew the rope through a
ring. Behind the boatman two other men in dark coats with silver buttons carried a bier, on which, beneath a great flower-patterned tasseled
silk cloth, a man was apparently lying.

Nobody on the quay troubled about the newcomers; even when they
lowered the bier to wait for the boatman, who was still occupied with his
rope, nobody went nearer, nobody asked them a question, nobody accorded them an inquisitive glance.

The pilot was still further detained by a woman who, a child at her
breast, now appeared with loosened hair on the deck of the boat. Then
he advanced and indicated a yellowish two-storied house that rose
abruptly on the left beside the sea; the bearers took up their burden and
bore it to the low but gracefully pillared door. A little boy opened a window just in time to see the party vanishing into the house, then hastily
shut the window again. The door too was now shut; it was of black oak,

From *The Great Wall of China*. Translated by Willa and Edwin Muir. Copyright
1936, 1937 by Heinr Mercy Sohn, Prague. Copyright 1946, 1948 by Schocken Books,
Inc., New York. Reprinted by permission of Schocken Books, Inc.

and very strongly made. A flock of doves which had been flying round
the belfry alighted in the street before the house. As if their food were
stored within, they assembled in front of the door. One of them flew up
to the first story and pecked at the windowpane. They were bright-hued,
well-tended, beautiful birds. The woman on the boat flung grain to them
in a wide sweep; they ate it up and flew across to the woman.

A man in a top hat tied with a band of crêpe now descended one of
the narrow and very steep lanes that led to the harbor. He glanced round
vigilantly, everything seemed to displease him, his mouth twisted at the
sight of some offal in a corner. Fruit skins were lying on the steps of the
monument; he swept them off in passing with his stick. He rapped at
the house door, at the same time taking his top hat from his head with
his black-gloved hand. The door was opened at once, and some fifty little
boys appeared in two rows in the long entry hall, and bowed to him.

The boatman descended the stairs, greeted the gentleman in black,
conducted him up to the first story, led him round the bright and elegant
loggia which encircled the courtyard, and both of them entered, while
the boys pressed after them at a respectful distance, a cool spacious room
looking towards the back, from whose window no habitation, but only a
bare, blackish grey rocky wall was to be seen. The bearers were busied
in setting up and lighting several long candles at the head of the bier,
yet these did not give light, but only scared away the shadows which had
been immobile till then, and made them flicker over the walls. The cloth
covering the bier had been thrown back. Lying on it was a man with
wildly matted hair, who looked somewhat like a hunter. He lay without
motion and, it seemed, without breathing, his eyes closed; yet only his
trappings indicated that this man was probably dead.

The gentleman stepped up to the bier, laid his hand on the brow of
the man lying upon it, then kneeled down and prayed. The boatman
made a sign to the bearers to leave the room; they went out, drove away
the boys who had gathered outside, and shut the door. But even that did
not seem to satify the gentleman, he glanced at the boatman; the boatman understood, and vanished through a side door into the next room.
At once the man on the bier opened his eyes, turned his face painfully
towards the gentleman, and said: "Who are you?" Without any mark of
surprise the gentleman rose from his kneeling posture and answered:
"The Burgomaster of Riva."

The man on the bier nodded, indicated a chair with a feeble movement of his arm, and said, after the Burgomaster had accepted his invitation: "I knew that, of course, Burgomaster, but in the first moments of
returning consciousness I always forget, everything goes round before
my eyes, and it is best to ask about anything even if I know. You too
probably know that I am the hunter Gracchus."

"Certainly," said the Burgomaster. "Your arrival was announced to me during the night. We had been asleep for a good while. Then towards midnight my wife cried: 'Salvatore'—that's my name—'look at that dove at the window.' It was really a dove, but as big as a cock. It flew over me and said in my ear: 'Tomorrow the dead hunter Gracchus is coming; receive him in the name of the city.'"

The hunter nodded and licked his lips with the tip of his tongue: "Yes, the doves flew here before me. But do you believe, Burgomaster, that I shall remain in Riva?"

"I cannot say that yet," replied the Burgomaster. "Are you dead?"

"Yes," said the hunter, "as you see. Many years ago, yes, it must be a great many years ago, I fell from a precipice in the Black Forest—that is in Germany—when I was hunting a chamois. Since then I have been dead."

"But you are alive too," said the Burgomaster.

"In a certain sense," said the hunter, "in a certain sense I am alive too. My death ship lost its way; a wrong turn of the wheel, a moment's abscence of mind on the pilot's part, a longing to turn aside towards my lovely native country, I cannot tell what it was; I only know this, that I remained on earth and that ever since my ship has sailed earthly waters. So I, who asked for nothing better than to live among my mountains, travel after my death through all the lands of the earth."

"And you have no part in the other world?" asked the Burgomaster, knitting his brow.

"I am forever," replied the hunter, "on the great stair that leads up to it. On that infinitely wide and spacious stair I clamber about, sometimes up, sometimes down, sometimes on the right, sometimes on the left, always in motion. The hunter has been turned into a butterfly. Do not laugh."

"I am not laughing," said the Burgomaster in self-defense.

"That is very good of you," said the hunter. "I am always in motion. But when I make a supreme flight and see the gate actually shining before me I awaken presently on my old ship, still stranded forlornly in some earthly sea or other. The fundamental error of my one-time death grins at me as I lie in my cabin. Julia, the wife of the pilot, knocks at the door and brings me on my bier the morning drink of the land whose coasts we chance to be passing. I lie on a wooden pallet, I wear—it cannot be a pleasure to look at me—a filthy winding sheet, my hair and beard, black tinged with grey, have grown together inextricably, my limbs are covered with a great flower-patterned woman's shawl with long fringes. A sacramental candle stands at my head and lights me. On the wall opposite me is a little picture, evidently of a Bushman who is aiming his spear at me and taking cover as best he can behind a beautifully painted shield. On shipboard one is often a prey to stupid imaginations, but that is the stupidest of them all. Otherwise my wooden case is quite empty. Through a hole in the side wall come in the warm airs of the southern night, and I hear the water slapping against the old boat.

"I have lain here ever since the time when, as the hunter Gracchus living in the Black Forest, I followed a chamois and fell from a precipice. Everything happened in good order. I pursued, I fell, bled to death in a ravine, died, and this ship should have conveyed me to the next world. I can still remember how gladly I stretched myself out on this pallet for the first time. Never did the mountains listen to such songs from me as these shadowy walls did then.

"I had been glad to live and I was glad to die. Before I stepped aboard, I joyfully flung away my wretched load of ammunition, my knapsack, my hunting rifle that I had always been proud to carry, and I slipped into my winding sheet like a girl into her marriage dress. I lay and waited. Then came the mishap."

"A terrible fate," said the Burgomaster, raising his hand defensively. "And you bear no blame for it?"

"None," said the hunter. "I was a hunter; was there any sin in that? I following my calling as a hunter in the Black Forest, where there were still wolves in those days. I lay in ambush, shot, hit my mark, flayed the skins from my victims: was there any sin in that? My labors were blessed. 'The great hunter of the Black Forest' was the name I was given. Was there any sin in that?"

"I am not called upon to decide that," said the Burgomaster, "but to me also there seems to be no sin in such things. But, then whose is the guilt?"

"The boatman's," said the hunter. "Nobody will read what I say here, no one will come to help me; even if all the people were commanded to help me, every door and window would remain shut, everybody would take to bed and draw the bedclothes over his head, the whole earth would become an inn for the night. And there is sense in that, for no-body knows of me, and if anyone knew he would not know where I could be found, and if he knew where I could be found, he would not know how to deal with me, he would not know how to help me. The thought of helping me is an illness that has to be cured by taking to one's bed.

"I know that, and so I do not shout to summon help, even though at moments—when I lose control over myself, as I have done just now, for instance—I think seriously of it. But to drive out such thoughts I need only look round me and verify where I am, and—I can safely assert—have been for hundreds of years."

"Extraordinary," said the Burgomaster, "extraordinary—and now do you think of staying here in Riva with us?"

"I think not," said the hunter with a smile, and, to excuse himself, he laid his hand on the Burgomaster's knee. "I am here, more than that I do not know, further than that I cannot go. My ship has no rudder, and it is driven by the wind that blows in the undermost regions of death."

Nathaniel Hawthorne (1804–1864)

YOUNG GOODMAN BROWN

Why he is called Goodman and why his wife is called Faith no one will need to be told; yet Faith is a common name for a woman, and "Goodman" was a form of address like our "Mr." Hawthorne's allegory constantly blends with his facts, which he imagines as facts rather than transcribes from a symbolic scheme. Thus there is wind in the forest, and cold dew on the hanging twig, and genuine panic in young Goodman's heart. What difference would it make to the story if details of this kind were edited out?

Young Goodman Brown came forth at sunset into the street at Salem village; but put his head back, after crossing the threshold, to exchange a parting kiss with his young wife. And Faith, as the wife was aptly named, thrust her own pretty head into the street, letting the wind play with the pink ribbons of her cap while she called to Goodman Brown.

"Dearest heart," whispered she, softly and rather sadly, when her lips were close to his ear, "prithee put off your journey until sunrise and sleep in your own bed tonight. A lone woman is troubled with such dreams and such thoughts that she's afeard of herself sometimes. Pray tarry with me this night, dear husband, of all nights in the year."

"My love and my Faith," replied young Goodman Brown, "of all nights in the year, this one night must I tarry away from thee. My journey, as thou callest it, forth and back again, must needs be done 'twixt now and sunrise. What, my sweet, pretty wife, dost thou doubt me already, and we but three months married?"

"Then God bless you!" said Faith, with the pink ribbons; "and may you find all well when you come back."

"Amen!" cried Goodman Brown. "Say thy prayers, dear Faith, and go to bed at dusk, and no harm will come to thee."

So they parted; and the young man pursued his way until, being about to turn the corner by the meetinghouse, he looked back and saw

From *Mosses from an Old Manse* (1846).

the head of Faith still peeping after him with a melancholy air, in spite of her pink ribbons.

"Poor little Faith!" thought he, for his heart smote him. "What a wretch am I to leave her on such an errand! She talks of dreams, too. Methought as she spoke there was trouble in her face, as if a dream had warned her what work is to be done tonight. But no, no; 't would kill her to think it. Well, she's a blessed angel on earth; and after this one night I'll cling to her skirts and follow her to heaven."

With this excellent resolve for the future, Goodman Brown felt himself justified in making more haste on his present evil purpose. He had taken a dreary road, darkened by all the gloomiest trees of the forest, which barely stood aside to let the narrow path creep through, and closed immediately behind. It was all as lonely as could be; and there is this peculiarity in such a solitude, that the traveler knows not who may be concealed by the innumerable trunks and the thick boughs overhead; so that with lonely footsteps he may yet be passing through an unseen multitude.

"There may be a devilish Indian behind every tree," said Goodman Brown to himself; and he glanced fearfully behind him as he added, "What if the devil himself should be at my very elbow!"

His head being turned back, he passed a crook of the road, and, looking forward again, beheld the figure of a man, in grave and decent attire, seated at the foot of an old tree. He arose at Goodman Brown's approach and walked onward side by side with him.

"You are late, Goodman Brown," said he. "The clock of the Old South was striking as I came through Boston, and that is full fifteen minutes agone."

"Faith kept me back a while," replied the young man, with a tremor in his voice, caused by the sudden appearance of his companion, though not wholly unexpected.

It was now deep dusk in the forest, and deepest in that part of it where these two were journeying. As nearly as could be discerned, the second traveler was about fifty years old, apparently in the same rank of life as Goodman Brown, and bearing a considerable resemblance to him, though perhaps more in expression than features. Still they might have been taken for father and son. And yet, though the elder person was as simply clad as the younger, and as simple in manner too, he had an indescribable air of one who knew the world, and who would not have felt abashed at the governor's dinner table or in King William's court, were it possible that his affairs should call him thither. But the only thing about him that could be fixed upon as remarkable was his staff, which bore the likeness of a great black snake, so curiously wrought that it might almost be seen to twist and wriggle itself like a living serpent. This, of course, must have been an ocular deception, assisted by the uncertain light.

"Come, Goodman Brown," cried his fellow-traveler, "this is a dull pace for the beginning of a journey. Take my staff, if you are so soon weary."

"Friend," said the other, exchanging his slow pace for a full stop, "having kept covenant by meeting thee here, it is my purpose now to return whence I came. I have scruples touching the matter thou wot'st of."

"Sayest thou so?" replied he of the serpent, smiling apart. "Let us walk on, nevertheless, reasoning as we go; and if I convince thee not thou shalt turn back. We are but a little way in the forest yet."

"Too far! too far!" exclaimed the goodman, unconsciously resuming his walk. "My father never went into the woods on such an errand, nor his father before him. We have been a race of honest men and good Christians since the days of the martyrs; and shall I be the first of the name of Brown that ever took this path and kept—"

"Such company, thou wouldst say," observed the elder person, inter-preting his pause. "Well said, Goodman Brown! I have been as well acquainted with your family as with ever a one among the Puritans; and that's no trifle to say. I helped your grandfather, the constable, when he lashed the Quaker woman so smartly through the streets of Salem; and it was I that brought your father a pitch-pine knot, kindled at my own hearth, to set fire to an Indian village, in King Philip's war. They were my good friends, both; and many a pleasant walk have we had along this path, and returned merrily after midnight. I would fain be friends with you for their sake."

"If it be as thou sayest," replied Goodman Brown, "I marvel they never spoke of these matters; or, verily, I marvel not, seeing that the least rumor of the sort would have driven them from New England. We are a people of prayer, and good works to boot, and abide no such wickedness."

"Wickedness or not," said the traveler with the twisted staff, "I have a very general acquaintance here in New England. The deacons of many a church have drunk the communion wine with me; the selectmen of divers towns make me their chairman; and a majority of the Great and General Court are firm supporters of my interest. The governor and I, too— But these are state secrets."

"Can this be so?" cried Goodman Brown, with a stare of amazement at his undisturbed companion. "Howbeit, I have nothing to do with the governor and council; they have their own ways, and are no rule for a simple husbandman like me. But, were I to go on with thee, how should I meet the eye of that good old man, our minister, at Salem village? Oh, his voice would make me tremble both Sabbath day and lecture day."

Thus far the elder traveler had listened with due gravity; but now burst into a fit of irrepressible mirth, shaking himself so violently that his snakelike staff actually seemed to wriggle in sympathy.

"Ha! ha! ha!" shouted he again and again; then composing himself, "Well, go on, Goodman Brown, go on; but, prithee, don't kill me with laughing."

"Well, then, to end the matter at once," said Goodman Brown, considerably nettled, "there is my wife, Faith. It would break her dear little heart; and I'd rather break my own."

"Nay, if that be the case," answered the other, "e'en go thy ways, Goodman Brown. I would not for twenty old women like the one hobbling before us that Faith should come to any harm."

As he spoke he pointed his staff at a female figure on the path, in whom Goodman Brown recognized a very pious and exemplary dame, who had taught him his catechism in youth, and was still his moral and spiritual adviser, jointly with the minister and Deacon Gookin.

"A marvel, truly, that Goody Cloyse should be so far in the wilderness at nightfall," said he. "But with your leave, friend, I shall take a cut through the woods until we have left this Christian woman behind. Being a stranger to you, she might ask whom I was consorting with and whither I was going."

"Be it so," said his fellow-traveler. "Betake you the woods, and let me keep the path."

Accordingly the young man turned aside, but took care to watch his companion, who advanced softly along the road until he had come within a staff's length of the old dame. She, meanwhile, was making the best of her way, with singular speed for so aged a woman, and mumbling some indistinct words—a prayer, doubtless—as she went. The traveler put forth his staff and touched her withered neck with what seemed the serpent's tail.

"The devil!" screamed the pious old lady.

"Then Goody Cloyse knows her old friend?" observed the traveler, confronting her and leaning on his writhing stick.

"Ah, forsooth, and is it your worship indeed?" cried the good dame. "Yea, truly is it, and in the very image of my old gossip, Goodman Brown, the grandfather of the silly fellow that now is. But—would your worship believe it?—my broomstick hath strangely disappeared, stolen, as I suspect, by that unhanged witch, Goody Cory, and that, too, when I was all anointed with the juice of smallage, and cinquefoil, and wolf's bane—"

"Mingled with fine wheat and the fat of a newborn babe," said the shape of old Goodman Brown.

"Ah, your worship knows the recipe," cried the old lady, cackling aloud. "So, as I was saying, being all ready for the meeting, and no horse to ride on, I made up my mind to foot it; for they tell me there is a nice young man to be taken into communion tonight. But now your good worship will lend me your arm, and we shall be there in a twinkling."

"That can hardly be," answered her friend. "I may not spare you my arm, Goody Cloyse; but here is my staff, if you will."

So saying, he threw it down at her feet, where, perhaps, it assumed life, being one of the rods which its owner had formerly lent to the Egyptian magi. Of this fact, however, Goodman Brown could not take cognizance. He had cast up his eyes in astonishment, and, looking down again, beheld neither Goody Cloyse nor the serpentine staff, but his fellow-traveler alone, who waited for him as calmly as if nothing had happened.

"That old woman taught me my catechism," said the young man; and there was a world of meaning in this simple comment.

They continued to walk onward, while the elder traveler exhorted his companion to make good speed and persevere in the path, discoursing so aptly that his arguments seemed rather to spring up in the bosom of his auditor than to be suggested by himself. As they went, he plucked a branch of maple to serve for a walking stick, and began to strip it of the twigs and little boughs, which were wet with evening dew. The moment his fingers touched them they became strangely withered and dried up as with a week's sunshine. Thus the pair proceeded, at a good free pace, until suddenly, in a gloomy hollow of the road, Goodman Brown sat himself down on the stump of a tree and refused to go any farther.

"Friend," said he, stubbornly, "my mind is made up. Not another step will I budge on this errand. What if a wretched old woman do choose to go to the devil when I thought she was going to heaven: is that any reason why I should quit my dear Faith and go after her?"

"You will think better of this by and by," said his acquaintance, composedly. "Sit here and rest yourself a while; and when you feel like moving again, there is my staff to help you along."

Without more words, he threw his companion the maple stick, and was as speedily out of sight as if he had vanished into the deepening gloom. The young man sat a few moments by the roadside, applauding himself greatly, and thinking with how clear a conscience he should meet the minister in his morning walk, nor shrink from the eye of good old Deacon Gookin. And what calm sleep would be his that very night, which was to have been spent so wickedly, but so purely and sweetly now, in the arms of Faith! Amidst these pleasant and praiseworthy meditations, Goodman Brown heard the tramp of horses along the road, and deemed it advisable to conceal himself within the verge of the forest, conscious of the guilty purpose that had brought him thither, though now so happily turned from it.

On came the hoof tramps and the voices of the riders, two grave old voices, conversing soberly as they drew near. These mingled sounds appeared to pass along the road, within a few yards of the young man's hiding place; but, owing doubtless to the depth of the gloom at that particular spot, neither the travelers nor their steeds were visible. Though their figures brushed the small boughs by the wayside, it could not be seen that they intercepted, even for a moment, the faint gleam from the strip of bright sky athwart which they must have passed. Goodman Brown alternately crouched and stood on tiptoe, pulling aside the branches and thrusting forth his head as far as he durst without discerning so much as a shadow. It vexed him the more, because he could have sworn, were such a thing possible, that he recognized the voices of the minister and Deacon Gookin, jogging along quietly, as they were wont to do, when bound to some ordination or ecclesiastical council. While yet within hearing, one of the riders stopped to pluck a switch.

"Of the two, reverend sir," said the voice like the deacon's, "I had rather miss an ordination dinner than tonight's meeting. They tell me that some of our community are to be here from Falmouth and beyond, and others from Connecticut and Rhode Island, besides several of the Indian powwows, who, after their fashion, know almost as much deviltry as the best of us. Moreover, there is a goodly young woman to be taken into communion."

"Mighty well, Deacon Gookin!" replied the solemn old tones of the minister. "Spur up, or we shall be late. Nothing can be done, you know, until I get on the ground."

The hoofs clattered again; and the voices, talking so strangely in the empty air, passed on through the forest, where no church had ever been gathered or solitary Christian prayed. Whither, then, could these holy men be journeying so deep into the heathen wilderness? Young Goodman Brown caught hold of a tree for support, being ready to sink down on the ground, faint and overburdened with the heavy sickness of his heart. He looked up to the sky, doubting whether there really was a heaven above him. Yet there was the blue arch, and the stars brightening in it.

"With heaven above and Faith below, I will yet stand firm against the devil!" cried Goodman Brown.

While he still gazed upward into the deep arch of the firmament and had lifted his hands to pray, a cloud, though no wind was stirring, hurried across the zenith and hid the brightening stars. The blue sky was still visible, except directly overhead, where this black mass of cloud was sweeping swiftly northward. Aloft in the air, as if from the depths of the cloud, came a confused and doubtful sound of voices. Once the listener fancied that he could distinguish the accents of townspeople of his own, men and women, both pious and ungodly, many of whom he had met at the communion table, and had seen others rioting at the tavern. The next moment, so indistinct were the sounds, he doubted whether he had heard aught but the murmur of the old forest, whispering without a wind. Then came a stronger swell of those familiar tones, heard daily in the sunshine at Salem village, but never until now from a cloud of night. There was one voice, of a young woman, uttering lamentations, yet with an uncertain sorrow, and entreating for some favor, which, perhaps, it would grieve her to obtain; and all the unseen multitude, both saints and sinners, seemed to encourage her onward. .

"Faith!" shouted Goodman Brown, in a voice of agony and desperation; and the echoes of the forest mocked him, crying, "Faith! Faith!" as if bewildered wretches were seeking her all through the wilderness.

The cry of grief, rage, and terror was yet piercing the night, when the unhappy husband held his breath for a response. There was a scream, drowned immediately in a louder murmur of voices, fading into far-off laughter, as the dark cloud swept away, leaving the clear and silent sky above Goodman Brown. But something fluttered lightly down through the air and caught on the branch of a tree. The young man seized it, and beheld a pink ribbon.

"My Faith is gone!" cried he, after one stupefied moment. "There is no good on earth; and sin is but a name. Come, devil; for to thee is this world given."

And, maddened with despair, so that he laughed loud and long, did Goodman Brown grasp his staff and set forth again, at such a rate that he seemed to fly along the forest path rather than to walk or run. The road grew wilder and drearier and more faintly traced, and vanished at length, leaving him in the heart of the dark wilderness, still rushing onward with the instinct that guides mortal man to evil. The whole forest was peopled with frightful sounds—the creaking of the trees, the howling of wild beasts, and the yell of Indians; while sometimes the wind tolled like a distant church bell, and sometimes gave a broad roar around the traveler, as if all Nature were laughing him to scorn. But he was himself the chief horror of the scene, and shrank not from its other horrors.

"Ha! ha! ha!" roared Goodman Brown when the wind laughed at him. "Let us hear which will laugh loudest. Think not to frighten me with your deviltry. Come witch, come wizard, come Indian powwow, come devil himself, and here comes Goodman Brown. You may as well fear him as he fear you."

In truth, all through the haunted forest there could be nothing more frightful than the figure of Goodman Brown. On he flew among the black pines, brandishing his staff with frenzied gestures, now giving vent to an inspiration of horrid blasphemy, and now shouting forth such laughter as set all the echoes of the forest laughing like demons around him. The fiend in his own shape is less hideous than when he rages in the breast of man. Thus sped the demoniac on his course, until, quiver-

ing among the trees, he saw a red light before him, as when the felled
trunks and branches of a clearing have been set on fire, and throw up
their lurid blaze against the sky, at the hour of midnight. He paused, in
a lull of the tempest that had driven him onward, and heard the swell of
what seemed a hymn, rolling solemnly from a distance with the weight
of many voices. He knew the tune; it was a familiar one in the choir of
the village meetinghouse. The verse died heavily away, and was length-
ened by a chorus, not of human voices, but of all the sounds of the
benighted wilderness pealing in awful harmony together. Goodman
Brown cried out, and his cry was lost to his own ear by its unison with
the cry of the desert.

In the interval of silence he stole forward until the light glared full
upon his eyes. At one extremity of an open space, hemmed in by the
dark wall of the forest, arose a rock, bearing some rude, natural resemblance either to an altar or a pulpit, and surrounded by four blazing
pines, their tops aflame, their stems untouched, like candles at an evening meeting. The mass of foliage that had overgrown the summit of
the rock was all on fire, blazing high into the night and fitfully illuminating the whole field. Each pendent twig and leafy festoon was in a
blaze. As the red light arose and fell, a numerous congregation alternately shone forth, then disappeared in shadow, and again grew, as it
were, out of the darkness, peopling the heart of the solitary woods at
once.

"A grave and dark-clad company," quoth Goodman Brown.

In truth they were such. Among them, quivering to and fro between
gloom and splendor, appeared faces that would be seen next day at the
council board of the province, and others which, Sabbath after Sabbath,
looked devoutly heavenward, and benignantly over the crowded pews,
from the holiest pulpits in the land. Some affirm that the lady of the
governor was there. At least there were high dames well known to her,
and wives of honored husbands, and widows, a great multitude, and
ancient maidens, all of excellent repute, and fair young girls, who
trembled lest their mothers should espy them. Either the sudden gleams
of light flashing over the obscure field bedazzled Goodman Brown, or he
recognized a score of the church members of Salem village famous for
their especial sancity. Good old Deacon Gookin had arrived, and waited
at the skirts of that venerable saint, his revered pastor. But, irreverently
consorting with these grave, reputable, and pious people, these elders of
the church, these chaste dames and dewy virgins, there were men of dis-
solute lives and women of spotted fame, wretches given over to all mean
and filthy vice, and suspected even of horrid crimes. It was strange to see
that the good shrank not from the wicked, nor were the sinners abashed
by the saints. Scattered also among their pale-faced enemies were the
Indian priests, or powwows, who had often scared their native forest

with more hideous incantations than any known to English witchcraft.

"But where is Faith?" thought Goodman Brown; and, as hope came into his heart, he trembled.

Another verse of the hymn arose, a slow and mournful strain, such as the pious love, but joined to words which expressed all that our nature can conceive of sin, and darkly hinted at far more. Unfathomable to mere mortals is the lore of fiends. Verse after verse was sung; and still the chorus of the desert swelled between like the deepest tone of a mighty organ; and with the final peal of that dreadful anthem there came a sound, as if the roaring wind, the rushing streams, the howling beasts, and every other voice of the unconcerted wilderness were mingling and according with the voice of guilty man in homage to the prince of all. The four blazing pines threw up a loftier flame, and obscurely discovered shapes and visages of horror on the smoke wreaths above the impious assembly. At the same moment the fire on the rock shot redly forth and formed a glowing arch above its base, where now appeared a figure. With reverence be it spoken, the figure bore no slight similitude, both in garb and manner, to some grave divine of the New England churches.

"Bring forth the converts!" cried a voice that echoed through the field and rolled into the forest.

At the word, Goodman Brown stepped forth from the shadow of the trees and approached the congregation, with whom he felt a loathful brotherhood by the sympathy of all that was wicked in his heart. He could have well-nigh sworn that the shape of his own dead father beckoned him to advance, looking downward from a smoke wreath, while a woman, with dim features of despair, threw out her hand to warn him back. Was it his mother? But he had no power to retreat one step, nor to resist, even in thought, when the minister and good old Deacon Gookin seized his arms and led him to the blazing rock. Thither came also the slender form of a veiled female, led between Goody Cloyse, that pious teacher of the catechism, and Martha Carrier, who had received the devil's promise to be queen of hell. A rampant hag was she. And there stood the proselytes beneath the canopy of fire.

"Welcome, my children," said the dark figure, "to the communion of your race. Ye have found thus young your nature and your destiny. My children, look behind you!"

They turned; and flashing forth, as it were, in a sheet of flame, the fiend worshippers were seen; the smile of welcome gleamed darkly on every visage.

"There," resumed the sable form, "are all whom ye have reverenced from youth. Ye deemed them holier than yourselves, and shrank from your own sin, contrasting it with their lives of righteousness and prayerful aspirations heavenward. Yet here are they all in my worshipping assembly. This night it shall be granted you to know their secret deeds: how hoary-bearded elders of the church have whispered wanton words to the young maids of their households; how many a woman, eager for widows' weeds, has given her husband a drink at bedtime and let him sleep his last sleep in her bosom; how beardless youths have made haste to inherit their fathers' wealth; and how fair damsels—blush not, sweet ones—have dug little graves in the garden, and bidden me, the sole guest, to an infant's funeral. By the sympathy of your human hearts for sin ye shall scent out all the places—whether in church, bed-chamber, street, field, or forest—where crime has been committed, and shall exult to behold the whole earth one stain of guilt, one mighty blood spot. Far more than this. It shall be yours to penetrate, in every bosom, the deep mystery of sin, the fountain of all wicked arts, and which inexhaustibly supplies more evil impulses than human power—than my power at its utmost—can make manifest in deeds. And now, my children, look upon each other."

They did so; and, by the blaze of the hell-kindled torches, the wretched man beheld his Faith, and the wife her husband, trembling before that unhallowed altar.

"Lo, there ye stand, my children," said the figure, in a deep and solemn tone, almost sad with its despairing awfulness, as if his once angelic nature could yet mourn for our miserable race. "Depending upon one another's hearts, ye had still hoped that virtue were not all a dream. Now are ye undeceived. Evil is the nature of mankind. Evil must be your only happiness. Welcome again, my children, to the communion of your race."

"Welcome," repeated the fiend worshippers, in one cry of despair and triumph.

And there they stood, the only pair, as it seemed, who were yet hesitating on the verge of wickedness in this dark world. A basin was hollowed, naturally, in the rock. Did it contain water, reddened by the lurid light? or was it blood? or, perchance, a liquid flame? Herein did the shape of evil dip his hand and prepare to lay the mark of baptism upon their foreheads, that they might be partakers of the mystery of sin, more conscious of the secret guilt of others, both in deed and thought, than they could now be of their own. The husband cast one look at his pale wife, and Faith at him. What polluted wretches would the next glance show them to each other, shuddering alike at what they disclosed and what they saw!

"Faith! Faith!" cried the husband, "look up to heaven, and resist the wicked one."

Whether Faith obeyed he knew not. Hardly had he spoken when he found himself amid calm night and solitude, listening to a roar of the wind which died heavily away through the forest. He staggered against the rock, and felt it chill and damp; while a hanging twig, that had been all on fire, besprinkled his cheek with the coldest dew.

The next morning young Goodman Brown came slowly into the street of Salem village, staring around him like a bewildered man. The good old minister was taking a walk along the graveyard to get an appetite for breakfast and meditate his sermon, and bestowed a blessing, as he passed, on Goodman Brown. He shrank from the venerable saint as if to avoid an anathema. Old Deacon Gookin was at domestic worship, and the holy words of his prayer were heard through the open window. "What God doth the wizard pray to?" quoth Goodman Brown. Goody Cloyse, that excellent old Christian, stood in the early sunshine at her own lattice, catechizing a little girl who had brought her a pint of morning's milk. Goodman Brown snatched away the child as from the grasp of the fiend himself. Turning the corner by the meetinghouse, he spied the head of Faith, with the pink ribbons, gazing anxiously forth, and bursting into such joy at sight of him that she skipped along the street and almost kissed her husband before the whole village. But Goodman Brown looked sternly and sadly into her face, and passed on without a greeting.

Had Goodman Brown fallen asleep in the forest and only dreamed a wild dream of a witch-meeting?

Be it so if you will; but, alas! it was a dream of evil omen for young Goodman Brown. A stern, a sad, a darkly meditative, a distrustful, if not a desperate man did he become from the night of that fearful dream. On the Sabbath day, when the congregation were singing a holy psalm, he could not listen because an anthem of sin rushed loudly upon his ear and drowned all the blessed strain. When the minister spoke from the pulpit with power and fervid eloquence, and, with his hand on the open Bible, of the sacred truths of our religion, and of saintlike lives and triumphant deaths, and of future bliss or misery unutterable, then did Goodman Brown turn pale, dreading lest the roof should thunder down upon the gray blasphemer and his hearers. Often, awaking suddenly at midnight, he shrank from the bosom of Faith; and at morning or eventide, when the family knelt down at prayer, he scowled and muttered to himself, and gazed sternly at his wife, and turned away. And when he had lived long, and was borne to his grave a hoary corpse, followed by Faith, an aged woman, and children and grandchildren, a goodly procession, besides neighbors not a few, they carved no hopeful verse upon his tombstone, for his dying hour was gloom.

Edgar Allan Poe (1809–1849)

THE TELL-TALE HEART

Compare this story with "Young Goodman Brown." Poe's story mixes morbid psychology, as Hawthorne's mixes theological allegory, with an order of psychic truth that does not depend on our agreement with the opinions of either author.

TRUE!—nervous—very, very dreadfully nervous I had been and am; but why *will* you say that I am mad? The disease had sharpened my senses—not destroyed—not dulled them. Above all was the sense of hearing acute. I heard all things in the heaven and in the earth. I heard many things in hell. How, then, am I mad? Hearken! and observe how healthily—how calmly I can tell you the whole story.

It is impossible to say how first the idea entered my brain; but once conceived, it haunted me day and night. Object there was none. Passion there was none. I loved the old man. He had never wronged me. He had never given me insult. For his gold I had no desire. I think it was his eye! yes, it was this! He had the eye of a vulture—a pale blue eye, with a film over it. Whenever it fell upon me, my blood ran cold; and so by degrees—very gradually—I made up my mind to take the life of the old man, and thus rid myself of the eye forever.

Now this is the point. You fancy me mad. Madmen know nothing. But you should have seen *me*. You should have seen how wisely I proceeded—with what caution—with what foresight—with what dissimulation I went to work! I was never kinder to the old man than during the whole week before I killed him. And every night, about midnight, I turned the latch of his door and opened it—oh so gently! And then, when I had made an opening sufficient for my head, I put in a dark lantern, all closed, closed, so that no light shone out, and then I thrust in my head. Oh, you would have laughed to see how cunningly I thrust it in! I moved it slowly—very, very slowly, so that I might not disturb the old man's sleep. It took me an hour to place my whole head within the open-

First published in *The Pioneer* (1843).

195

ing so far that I could see him as he lay upon his bed. Ha!—would a madman have been so wise as this? And then, when my head was well in the room, I undid the lantern cautiously—oh, so cautiously—cautiously (for the hinges creaked)—I undid it just so much that a single thin ray fell upon the vulture eye. And this I did for seven long nights—every night just at midnight—but I found the eye always closed; and so it was impossible to do the work; for it was not the old man who vexed me, but his Evil Eye. And every morning, when the day broke, I went boldly into the chamber, and spoke courageously to him, calling him by name in a hearty tone, and inquiring how he had passed the night. So you see he would have been a very profound old man, indeed, to suspect that every night, just at twelve, I looked in upon him while he slept.

Upon the eighth night I was more than usually cautious in opening the door. A watch's minute hand moves more quickly than did mine. Never before that night, had I *felt* the extent of my own powers—of my sagacity. I could scarcely contain my feelings of triumph. To think that there I was, opening the door, little by little, and he not even to dream of my secret deeds or thoughts. I fairly chuckled at the idea; and perhaps he heard me; for he moved on the bed suddenly, as if startled. Now you may think that I drew back—but no. His room was as black as pitch with the thick darkness (for the shutters were close fastened, through fear of robbers), and so I knew that he could not see the opening of the door, and I kept pushing it on steadily, steadily.

I had my head in, and was about to open the lantern, when my thumb slipped upon the tin fastening, and the old man sprang up in bed, crying out—"Who's there?"

I kept quite still and said nothing. For a whole hour I did not move a muscle, and in the meantime I did not hear him lie down. He was still sitting up in the bed listening—just as I have done, night after night, hearkening to the death watches in the wall.

Presently I heard a slight groan, and I knew it was the groan of mortal terror. It was not a groan of pain or of grief—oh, no!—it was the low stifled sound that arises from the bottom of the soul when overcharged with awe. I knew the sound well. Many a night, just at midnight, when all the world slept, it has welled up from my own bosom, deepening, with its dreadful echo, the terrors that distracted me. I say I knew it well. I knew what the old man felt, and pitied him, although I chuckled at heart. I knew that he had been lying awake ever since the first slight noise, when he had turned in the bed. His fears had been ever since growing upon him. He had been trying to fancy them causeless, but could not. He had been saying to himself—"It is nothing but the wind in the chimney—it is only a mouse crossing the floor," or "it is merely a cricket which has made a single chirp." Yes, he had been trying to comfort himself with these suppositions: but he had found all in vain. *All in vain;* because Death, in approaching him had stalked with his black shadow before him, and enveloped the victim. And it was the mournful influence of the unperceived shadow that caused him to feel—although he neither saw nor heard—to *feel* the presence of my head within the room.

When I had waited a long time, very patiently, without hearing him lie down, I resolved to open a little—a very, very little crevice in the lantern. So I opened it—you cannot imagine how stealthily, stealthily—until, at length, a simple dim ray, like the thread of the spider, shot from out the crevice and fell full upon the vulture eye.

It was open—wide, wide open—and I grew furious as I gazed upon it. I saw it with perfect distinctness—all a dull blue, with a hideous veil over it that chilled the very marrow in my bones; but I could see nothing else of the old man's face or person: for I had directed the ray as if by instinct, precisely upon the damned spot.

And have I not told you that what you mistake for madness is but overacuteness of the senses?—now, I say, there came to my ears a low, dull, quick sound, such as a watch makes when enveloped in cotton. I knew *that* sound well, too. It was the beating of the old man's heart. It increased my fury, as the beating of a drum stimulates the soldier into courage.

But even yet I refrained and kept still. I scarcely breathed. I held the lantern motionless. I tried how steadily I could maintain the ray upon the eye. Meantime the hellish tattoo of the heart increased. It grew quicker and quicker, and louder and louder every instant. The old man's terror *must* have been extreme! It grew louder, I say, louder every moment!—do you mark me well? I have told you that I am nervous: so I am. And now at the dead hour of the night, amid the dreadful silence of that old house, so strange a noise as this excited me to uncontrollable terror. Yet, for some minutes longer I refrained and stood still. But the beating grew louder, louder! I thought the heart must burst. And now a new anxiety seized me—the sound would be heard by a neighbor! The old man's hour had come! With a loud yell, I threw open the lantern and leaped into the room. He shrieked once—once only. In an instant I dragged him to the floor, and pulled the heavy bed over him. I then smiled gaily, to find the deed so far done. But, for many minutes, the heart beat on with a muffled sound. This, however, did not vex me; it would not be heard through the wall. At length it ceased. The old man was dead. I removed the bed and examined the corpse. Yes, he was stone, stone dead. I placed my hand upon the heart and held it there many minutes. There was no pulsation. He was stone dead. His eye would trouble me no more.

If still you think me mad, you will think so no longer when I describe the wise precautions I took for the concealment of the body. The night waned, and I worked hastily, but in silence. First of all I dismembered the corpse. I cut off the head and the arms and the legs.

I then took up three planks from the flooring of the chamber, and deposited all between the scantlings. I then replaced the boards so cleverly, so cunningly, that no human eye—not even *his*—could have detected anything wrong. There was nothing to wash out—no stain of any kind—no blood spot whatever. I had been too wary for that. A tub had caught all—ha! ha!

When I had made an end of these labors, it was four o'clock—still dark as midnight. As the bell sounded the hour, there came a knocking at the street door. I went down to open it with a light heart, for what had I *now* to fear? There entered three men, who introduced themselves, with perfect suavity, as officers of the police. A shriek had been heard by a neighbor during the night; suspicion of foul play had been aroused; information had been lodged at the police office, and they (the officers) had been deputed to search the premises.

I smiled, for *what* had I to fear? I bade the gentlemen welcome. The shriek, I said, was my own in a dream. The old man, I mentioned, was absent in the country. I took my visitors all over the house. I bade them search—search *well*. I led them, at length, to *his* chamber. I showed them his treasures, secure, undisturbed. In the enthusiasm of my confidence, I brought chairs into the room, and desired them *here* to rest from their fatigues, while I myself, in the wild audacity of my perfect triumph, placed my own seat upon the very spot beneath which reposed the corpse of the victim.

The officers were satisfied. My *manner* had convinced them. I was singularly at ease. They sat, and while I answered cheerily, they chatted of familiar things. But, ere long, I felt myself getting pale and wished them gone. My head ached, and I fancied a ringing in my ears: but still they sat and still chatted. The ringing became more distinct—it continued and became more distinct. I talked more freely to get rid of the feeling, but it continued and gained definiteness—until, at length, I found that the noise was *not* within my ears.

No doubt I now grew *very* pale—but I talked more fluently, and with a heightened voice. Yet the sound increased—and what could I do? It was *a low, dull, quick sound—much such a sound as a watch makes when enveloped in cotton.* I gasped for breath—and yet the officers heard it not. I talked more quickly—more vehemently; but the noise steadily increased. I arose and argued about trifles, in a high key and with violent gesticulations; but the noise steadily increased. Why *would* they not be gone? I paced the floor to and fro with heavy strides, as if excited to fury by the observations of the men—but the noise steadily increased. Oh God! what *could* I do? I foamed—I raved—I swore! I swung the chair upon which I had been sitting, and grated it upon the boards, but the

noise arose over all and continually increased. It grew louder—louder—
louder! And still the men chatted pleasantly, and smiled. Was it possible
they heard not? Almighty God!—no, no! They heard!—they suspected!—
they *knew!*—they were making a mockery of my horror—this I thought,
and this I think. But anything was better than this agony! Anything was
more tolerable than this derision! I could bear those hypocritical smiles
no longer! I felt that I must scream or die! and now—again!—hark!
louder! louder! louder! *louder!*

"Villains!" I shrieked, "dissemble no more! I admit the deed!—tear up
the planks! here, here!—it is the beating of his hideous heart!"

Samuel Beckett (1905–   )

STONES

In this excerpt from his novel Molloy, *Beckett undertakes like a con-
juror to hold our attention with the very minimum of color, rhetoric,
or incident, eliciting problem, complication, passion, resolution, and
coda from nothing more than an elderly fanatic and sixteen stones.
The passions engaged, though seldom touched on by fiction, are by
no means eccentric or fantastic, as anyone knows who has arranged
dishes on a shelf, and Sir Isaac Newton would have read these pages
entranced.*

I took advantage of being at the seaside to lay in a store of sucking
stones. They were pebbles but I call them stones. Yes, on this occasion I
laid in a considerable store. I distributed them equally between my four
pockets, and sucked them turn and turn about. This raised a problem
which I first solved in the following way. I had say sixteen stones, four
in each of my four pockets these being the two pockets of my trousers
and the two pockets of my greatcoat. Taking a stone from the right
pocket of my greatcoat, and putting it in my mouth, I replaced it in the
right pocket of my greatcoat by a stone from the right pocket of my
trousers, which I replaced by a stone from the left pocket of my trousers,
which I replaced by a stone from the left pocket of my greatcoat, which
I replaced by the stone which was in my mouth, as soon as I had finished
sucking it. Thus there were still four stones in each of my four pockets,
but not quite the same stones. And when the desire to suck took hold of
me again, I drew again on the right pocket of my greatcoat, certain of not
taking the same stone as the last time. And while I sucked it I rearranged
the other stones in the way I have just described. And so on. But this
solution did not satisfy me fully. For it did not escape me that, by an
extraordinary hazard, the four stones circulating thus might always be
the same four. In which case, far from sucking the sixteen stones turn

and turn about, I was really only sucking four, always the same, turn and
turn about. But I shuffled them well in my pockets, before I began to
suck, and again, while I sucked, before transferring them, in the hope
of obtaining a more general circulation of the stones from pocket to
pocket. But this was only a makeshift that could not long content a man
like me. So I began to look for something else. And the first thing I hit
upon was that I might do better to transfer the stones four by four, instead of one by one, that is to say, during the sucking, to take the three
stones remaining in the right pocket of my greatcoat and replace them
by the four in the right pocket of my trousers, and these by the four in
the left pocket of my trousers, and these by the four in the left pocket
of my greatcoat, and finally these by the three from the right pocket of
my greatcoat, plus the one, as soon as I had finished sucking it, which
was in my mouth. Yes, it seemed to me at first that by so doing I would
arrive at a better result. But on further reflection I had to change my
mind and confess that the circulation of the stones four by four came to
exactly the same thing as their circulation one by one. For if I was certain of finding each time, in the right pocket of my greatcoat, four stones
totally different from their immediate predecessors, the possibility nevertheless remained of my always chancing on the same stone, within each
group of four, and consequently of my sucking, not the sixteen turn and
turn about as I wished, but in fact four only, always the same, turn and
turn about. So I had to seek elsewhere than in the mode of circulation.
For no matter how I caused the stones to circulate, I always ran the same
risk. It was obvious that by increasing the number of my pockets I was
bound to increase my chances of enjoying my stones in the way I
planned, that is to say one after the other until their number was exhausted. Had I had eight pockets, for example, instead of the four I did
have, then even the most diabolical hazard could not have prevented
me from sucking at least eight of my sixteen stones, turn and turn
about. The truth is I should have needed sixteen pockets in order to be
quite easy in my mind. And for a long time I could see no other conclusion than this, that short of having sixteen pockets, each with its
stone, I could never reach the goal I had set myself, short of an extraordinary hazard. And if at a pinch I could double the number of my
pockets, were it only by dividing each pocket in two, with the help of a
few safety-pins let us say, to quadruple them seemed to be more than
I could manage. And I did not feel inclined to take all that trouble for a
half-measure. For I was beginning to lose all sense of measure, after all
this wrestling and wrangling, and to say, All or nothing. And if I was
tempted for an instant to establish a more equitable proportion between
my stones and my pockets, by reducing the former to the number of the
latter, it was only for an instant. For it would have been an admission of
defeat. And sitting on the shore, before the sea, the sixteen stones spread

out before my eyes, I gazed at them in anger and perplexity. For just as I had difficulty in sitting on a chair, or in an armchair, because of my stiff leg you understand, so I had none in sitting on the ground, because of my stiff leg and my stiffening leg, for it was about this time that my good leg, good in the sense that it was not stiff, began to stiffen. I needed a prop under the ham, you understand, and even under the whole length of the leg, the prop of the earth. And while I gazed thus at my stones, revolving interminable martingales all equally defective, and crushing handfuls of sand, so that the sand ran through my fingers and fell back on the strand, yes, while thus I lulled my mind and part of my body, one day suddenly it dawned on the former, dimly, that I might perhaps achieve my purpose without increasing the number of my pockets, or reducing the number of my stones, but simply by sacrificing the principle of trim. The meaning of this illumination, which suddenly began to sing within me, like a verse of Isaiah, or of Jeremiah, I did not penetrate at once, and notably the word trim, which I had never met with, in this sense, long remained obscure. Finally I seemed to grasp that this word trim could not here mean anything else, anything better, than the distribution of the sixteen stones in four groups of four, one group in each pocket, and that it was my refusal to consider any distribution other than this that had vitiated my calculations until then and rendered the problem literally insoluble. And it was on the basis of this interpretation, whether right or wrong, that I finally reached a solution, inelegant assuredly, but sound, sound. Now I am willing to believe, indeed I firmly believe, that other solutions to this problem might have been found, and indeed may still be found, no less sound, but much more elegant, than the one I shall now describe, if I can. And I believe too that had I been a little more insistent, a little more resistant, I could have found them myself. But I was tired, but I was tired, and I contented myself ingloriously with the first solution that was a solution, to this problem. But not to go over the heartbreaking stages through which I passed before I came to it, here it is, in all its hideousness. All (all!) that was necessary was to put for example, to begin with, six stones in the right pocket of my greatcoat, or supply-pocket, five in the right pocket of my trousers, and five in the left pocket of my trousers, that makes the lot, twice five ten plus six sixteen, and none, for none remained, in the left pocket of my greatcoat, which for the time being remained empty, empty of stones that is, for its usual contents remained, as well as occasional objects. For where do you think I hid my vegetable knife, my silver, my horn and the other things that I have not yet named, perhaps shall never name. Good. Now I can begin to suck. Watch me closely. I take a stone from the right pocket of my greatcoat, suck it, stop sucking it, put it in the left pocket of my greatcoat, the one empty (of stones). I take a second stone from the right pocket of my greatcoat, suck it, put it in the left pocket of my greatcoat. And so on until the right pocket of my greatcoat is empty (apart from its usual and casual contents) and the six stones I have just sucked, one after the other, are all in the left pocket of my greatcoat. Pausing then, and concentrating, so as not to make a balls of it, I transfer to the right pocket of my greatcoat, in which there are no stones left, the five stones in the right pocket of my trousers, which I replace by the five stones in the left pocket of my trousers, which I replace by the six stones in the left pocket of my greatcoat. At this stage then the left pocket of my greatcoat is again empty of stones, while the right pocket of my greatcoat is again supplied, and in the right way, that is to say with other stones than those I have just sucked. These other stones I then begin to suck, one after the other, and to transfer as I go along to the left pocket of my greatcoat, being absolutely certain, as far as one can be in an affair of this kind, that I am not sucking the same stones as a moment before, but others. And when the right pocket of my greatcoat is again empty (of stones), and the five I have just sucked are all without exception in the left pocket of my greatcoat, then I proceed to the same redistribution as a moment before, or a similar redistribution, that is to say I transfer to the right pocket of my greatcoat, now again available, the five stones in the right pocket of my trousers, which I replace by the six stones in the left pocket of my trousers, which I replace by the five stones in the left pocket of my greatcoat. And there I am ready to begin again. Do I have to go on? No, for it is clear that after the next series, of sucks and transfers, I shall be back where I started, that is to say with the first six stones back in the supply pocket, the next five in the right pocket of my stinking old trousers and finally the last five in left pocket of same, and my sixteen stones will have been sucked once at least in impeccable succession, not one sucked twice, not one left unsucked. It is true that the next time I could scarcely hope to suck my stones in the same order as the first time and that the first, seventh and twelfth for example of the first cycle might very well be the sixth, eleventh and sixteenth respectively of the second, if the worst came to the worst. But that was a drawback I could not avoid. And if in the cycles taken together utter confusion was bound to reign, at least within each cycle taken separately I could be easy in my mind, at least as easy as one can be, in a proceeding of this kind. For in order for each cycle to be identical, as to the succession of stones in my mouth, and God knows I had set my heart on it, the only means were numbered stones or sixteen pockets. And rather than make twelve more pockets or number my stones, I preferred to make the best of the comparative peace of mind I enjoyed within each cycle taken separately. For it was not enough to number the stones, but I would have had to remember, every time I put a stone in my mouth, the number I needed and look for it in my pocket. Which would have put me off stone for ever, in a very short time. For I would never have been sure of not making a mistake, unless of course I had kept a kind of register, in which to tick off the stones one by one, as I sucked them. And of this I believed myself incapable. No, the only perfect solution would have been the sixteen pockets, symmetrically disposed, each one with its stone. Then I would have needed neither to number nor to think, but merely, as I sucked a given stone, to move on the fifteen others, each to the next pocket, a delicate business admittedly, but within my power, and to call always on the same pocket when I felt like a suck. This would have freed me from all anxiety, not only within each cycle taken separately, but also for the sum of all cycles, though they went on forever. But however imperfect my own solution was, I was pleased at having found it all alone, yes, quite pleased. And if it was perhaps less sound than I had thought in the first flush of discovery, its inelegance never diminished. And it was above all inelegant in this, to my mind, that the uneven distribution was painful to me, bodily. It is true that a kind of equilibrium was reached, at a given moment, in the early stages of each cycle, namely after the third suck and before the fourth, but it did not last long, and the rest of the time I felt the weight of the stones dragging me now to one side, now to the other. So it was something more than a principle I abandoned, when I abandoned the equal distribution, it was a bodily need. But to suck the stones in the way I have described, not haphazard, but with method, was also I think a bodily need. Here then were two incompatible bodily needs, at loggerheads. Such things happen. But deep down I didn't give a tinker's curse about being off my balance, dragged to the right hand and the left, backwards and forwards. And deep down it was all the same to me whether I sucked a different stone each time or always the same stone, until the end of time. For they all tasted exactly the same. And if I had collected sixteen, it was not in order to ballast myself in such and such a way, or to suck them turn about, but simply to have a little store, so as never to be without. But deep down I didn't give a fiddler's curse about being without, when they were all gone they would be all gone, I wouldn't be any the worse off, or hardly any. And the solution to which I rallied in the end was to throw away all the stones but one, which I kept now in one pocket, now in another, and which of course I soon lost, or threw away, or gave away, or swallowed.

Jorge Luis Borges (1899–   )

TLÖN, UQBAR, ORBIS TERTIUS

*Borges typically exploits in his fiction the sort of integrity with which
we credit both a carefully documented article and its author. Tlön
being more interesting than anything we can imagine taking place
there, he has refrained from the familiar fantasy-writer's gambit of
using it as environment for an adventure story. The story is instead
about the process by which such a world comes to seem credible, a
process to which any reader of fiction or student of history lends himself repeatedly. The reader of the last two paragraphs of the story
should remember, for instance, how Shakespeare's Richard III has
supplanted the "real" one."*

— 1 —

I owe the discovery of Uqbar to the conjunction of a mirror and an
encyclopedia. The mirror troubled the depths of a corridor in a country
house on Gaona Street in Ramos Mejía; the encyclopedia is fallaciously
called *The Anglo-American Cyclopaedia* (New York, 1917) and is a
literal but delinquent reprint of the *Encyclopaedia Britannica* of 1902.
The event took place some five years ago. Bioy Casares had had dinner
with me that evening and we became lengthily engaged in a vast
polemic concerning the composition of a novel in the first person, whose
narrator would omit or disfigure the facts and indulge in various contradictions which would permit a few readers—very few readers—to perceive an atrocious or banal reality. From the remote depths of the corridor, the mirror spied upon us. We discovered (such a discovery is inevitable in the late hours of the night) that mirrors have something
monstrous about them. Then Bioy Casares recalled that one of the
heresiarchs of Uqbar had declared that mirrors and copulation are
abominable, because they increase the number of men. I asked him the
origin of this memorable observation and he answered that it was repro-

From *Labyrinths: Selected Stories & Other Writings of Jorge Luis Borges.* Edited
by Donald A. Yates and James E. Irby (trans.). © 1962 by New Directions. Reprinted
by permission of New Directions.

duced in *The Anglo-American Cyclopaedia,* in its article on Uqbar. The house (which we had rented furnished) had a set of this work. On the last pages of Volume XLVI we found an article on Upsala; on the first pages of Volume XLVII, one on Ural-Altaic Languages, but not a word about Uqbar. Bioy, a bit taken aback, consulted the volumes of the index. In vain he exhausted all of the imaginable spellings: Ukbar, Ucbar, Ooqbar, Ookbar, Oukbahr. Before leaving, he told me that it was a region of Iraq or of Asia Minor. I must confess that I agreed with some discomfort. I conjectured that this undocumented country and its anonymous heresiarch were a fiction devised by Bioy's modesty in order to justify a statement. The fruitless examination of one of Justus Perthes' atlases fortified my doubt.

The following day, Bioy called me from Buenos Aires. He told me he had before him the article on Uqbar, in Volume XLVI of the encyclopedia. The heresiarch's name was not forthcoming, but there was a note on his doctrine, formulated in words almost identical to those he had repeated, though perhaps literarily inferior. He had recalled: *Copulation and mirrors are abominable.* The text of the encyclopedia said: *For one of those gnostics, the visible universe was an illusion or (more precisely) a sophism. Mirrors and fatherhood are abominable because they multiply and disseminate that universe.* I told him, in all truthfulness, that I should like to see that article. A few days later he brought it. This surprised me, since the scupulous cartographical indices of Ritter's *Erdkunde* were plentifully ignorant of the name Uqbar.

The tome Bioy brought was, in fact, Volume XLVI of the *Anglo-American Cyclopaedia.* On the half-title page and the spine, the alphabetical marking (Tor-Ups) was that of our copy, but, instead of 917, it contained 921 pages. These four additional pages made up the article on Uqbar, which (as the reader will have noticed) was not indicated by the alphabetical marking. We later determined that there was no other difference between the volumes. Both of them (as I believe I have indicated) are reprints of the tenth *Encyclopaedia Britannica.* Bioy had acquired his copy at some sale or other.

We read the article with some care. The passage recalled by Bioy was perhaps the only surprising one. The rest of it seemed very plausible, quite in keeping with the general tone of the work and (as is natural) a bit boring. Reading it over again, we discovered beneath its rigorous prose a fundamental vagueness. Of the fourteen names which figured in the geographical part, we only recognized three—Khorasan, Armenia, Erzerum—interpolated in the text in an ambiguous way. Of the historical names, only one: the impostor magician Smerdis, invoked more as a metaphor. The note seemed to fix the boundaries of Uqbar, but its nebulous reference points were rivers and craters and mountain ranges of that same region. We read, for example, that the lowlands of Tsai

Khaldun and the Axa Delta marked the southern frontier and that on the islands of the delta wild horses procreate. All this, on the first part of page 918. In the historical section (page 920) we learned that as a result of the religious persecutions of the thirteen century, the orthodox believers sought refuge on these islands, where to this day their obelisks remain and where it is not uncommon to unearth their stone mirrors. The section on Language and Literature was brief. Only one trait is worthy of recollection: it noted that the literature of Uqbar was one of fantasy and that its epics and legends never referred to reality, but to the two imaginary regions of Mlejnas and Tlön. The bibliography enumerated four volumes which we have not yet found, though the third—Silas Haslam: *History of the Land Called Uqbar*, 1874—figures in the catalogues of Bernard Quaritch's book shop.[1] The first, *Lesbare und lesenswerthe Bemerkungen über das Land Ukkbar in Klein-Asien*, dates from 1641 and is the work of Johannes Valentinus Andreä. This fact is significant; a few years later, I came upon that name in the unsuspected pages of De Quincey (*Writings*, Volume XIII) and learned that it belonged to a German theologian who, in the early seventeenth century, described the imaginary community of Rosae Crucis—a community that others founded later, in imitation of what he had prefigured.

That night we visited the National Library. In vain we exhausted atlases, catalogues, annuals of geographical societies, travelers' and historians' memoirs: no one had ever been in Uqbar. Neither did the general index of Bioy's encyclopedia register that name. The following day, Carlos Mastronardi (to whom I had related the matter) noticed the black and gold covers of the *Anglo-American Cyclopaedia* in a bookshop on Corrientes and Talcahuano. He entered and examined Volume XLVI. Of course, he did not find the slightest indication of Uqbar.

— 2 —

Some limited and waning memory of Herbert Ashe, an engineer of the southern railways, persists in the hotel at Adrogué, amongst the effusive honeysuckles and in the illusory depths of the mirrors. In his lifetime, he suffered from unreality, as do so many Englishmen; once dead, he is not even the ghost he was then. He was tall and listless and his tired rectangular beard had once been red. I understand he was a widower, without children. Every few years he would go to England, to visit (I judge from some photographs he showed us) a sundial and a few oaks. He and my father had entered into one of those close (the adjective is excessive) English friendships that begin by excluding con-

[1] Haslam has also published *A General History of Labyrinths*.

fidences and very soon dispense with dialogue. They used to carry out
an exchange of books and newspapers and engage in taciturn chess
games. I remember him in the hotel corridor, with a mathematics book
in his hand, sometimes looking at the irrecoverable colors of the sky. One
afternoon, we spoke of the duodecimal system of numbering (in which
twelve is written as 10). Ashe said that he was converting some kind of
tables from the duodecimal to the sexagesimal system (in which sixty is
written as 10). He added that the task had been entrusted to him by a
Norwegian, in Rio Grande do Sul. We had known him for eight years
and he had never mentioned his sojourn in that region. We talked of
country life, of the *capangas,* of the Brazilian etymology of the word
gaucho (which some old Uruguayans still pronounce *gaúcho*) and nothing more was said—may God forgive me—of duodecimal functions. In
September of 1937 (we were not at the hotel), Herbert Ashe died of a
ruptured aneurysm. A few days before, he had received a sealed and
certified package from Brazil. It was a book in large octavo. Ashe left it
at the bar, where—months later—I found it. I began to leaf through it
and experienced an astonished and airy feeling of vertigo which I shall
not describe, for this is not the story of my emotions but of Uqbar and
Tlön and Orbis Tertius. On one of the nights of Islam called the Night
of Nights, the secret doors of heaven open wide and the water in the
jars becomes sweeter; if those doors opened, I would not feel what I felt
that afternoon. The book was written in English and contained 1001
pages. On the yellow leather back I read these curious words which were
repeated on the title page: *A First Encyclopaedia of Tlön. Vol. XI. Hlaer
to Jangr.* There was no indication of date or place. On the first page and
on a leaf of silk paper that covered one of the color plates there was
stamped a blue oval with this inscription: *Orbis Tertius.* Two years
before I had discovered, in a volume of a certain pirated encyclopedia,
a superficial description of a nonexistent country; now chance afforded
me something more precious and arduous. Now I held in my hands a
vast methodical fragment of an unknown planet's entire history, with
its architecture and its playing cards, with the dread of its mythologies
and the murmur of its languages, with its emperors and its seas, with its
minerals and its birds and its fish, with its algebra and its fire, with its
theological and metaphysical controversy. And all of it articulated, co-
herent, with no visible doctrinal intent or tone of parody.

In the "Eleventh Volume" which I have mentioned, there are allusions to preceding and succeeding volumes. In an article in the *N. R. F.*
which is now classic, Néstor Ibarra has denied the existence of those
companion volumes; Ezequiel Martínez Estrada and Drieu La Rochelle
have refuted that doubt, perhaps victoriously. The fact is that up to now
the most diligent inquiries have been fruitless. In vain we have upended
the libraries of the two Americas and of Europe. Alfonso Reyes, tired of

these subordinate sleuthing procedures, proposes that we should all undertake the task of reconstructing the many and weighty tomes that are lacking: *ex ungue leonem.* He calculates, half in earnest and half jokingly, that a generation of *tlönistas* should be sufficient. This venturesome computation brings us back to the fundamental problem: Who are the inventors of Tlön? The plural is inevitable, because the hypothesis of a lone inventor—an infinite Leibniz laboring away darkly and modestly—has been unanimously discounted. It is conjectured that this brave new world is the work of a secret society of astronomers, biologists, engineers, metaphysicians, poets, chemists, algebraists, moralists, painters, geometers . . . directed by an obscure man of genius. Individuals mastering these diverse disciplines are abundant, but not so those capable of inventiveness and less so those capable of subordinating that inventiveness to a rigorous and systematic plan. This plan is so vast that each writer's contribution is infinitesimal. At first it was believed that Tlön was a mere chaos, an irresponsible license of the imagination; now it is known that it is a cosmos and that the intimate laws which govern it have been formulated, at least provisionally. Let it suffice for me to recall that the apparent contradictions of the Eleventh Volume are the fundamental basis for the proof that the other volumes exist, so lucid and exact is the order observed in it. The popular magazines, with pardonable excess, have spread news of the zoology and topography of Tlön; I think its transparent tigers and towers of blood perhaps do not merit the continued attention of *all* men. I shall venture to request a few minutes to expound its concept of the universe.

Hume noted for all time that Berkeley's arguments did not admit the slightest refutation, nor did they cause the slightest conviction. This dictum is entirely correct in its application to the earth, but entirely false in Tlön. The nations of this planet are congenitally idealist. Their language and the derivations of their language—religion, letters, metaphysics—all presuppose idealism. The world for them is not a concourse of objects in space; it is a heterogeneous series of independent acts. It is successive and temporal, not spatial. There are no nouns in Tlön's conjectural *Ursprache,* from which the "present" languages and the dialects are derived: there are impersonal verbs, modified by monosyllabic suffixes (or prefixes) with an adverbial value. For example: there is no word corresponding to the word "moon," but there is a verb which in English would be "to moon" or "to moonate." "The moon rose above the river" is *blör u fang axaxaxas mlö,* or literally: "upward behind the onstreaming it mooned."

The preceding applies to the languages of the southern hemisphere. In those of the northern hemisphere (on whose *Ursprache* there is very little data in the Eleventh Volume), the prime unit is not the verb, but the monosyllabic adjective. The noun is formed by an accumulation of adjectives. They do not say "moon," but rather "round airy-light on dark" or "pale-orange-of-the-sky" or any other such combination. In the example selected the mass of adjectives refers to a real object, but this is purely fortuitous. The literature of this hemisphere (like Meinong's subsistent world) abounds in ideal objects, which are convoked and dissolved in a moment, according to poetic needs. At times they are determined by mere simultaneity. There are objects composed of two terms, one of visual and another of auditory character: the color of the rising sun and the faraway cry of a bird. There are objects of many terms: the sun and the water on a swimmer's chest, the vague-tremulous rose color we see with our eyes closed, the sensation of being carried along by a river and also by sleep. These second-degree objects can be combined with others; through the use of certain abbreviations, the process is practically infinite. There are famous poems made up of one enormous word. This word forms a *poetic object* created by the author. The fact that no one believes in the reality of nouns paradoxically causes their number to be unending. The languages of Tlön's northern hemisphere contain all the nouns of the Indo-European languages—and many others as well.

It is no exaggeration to state that the classic culture of Tlön comprises only one discipline: psychology. All others are subordinated to it. I have said that the men of this planet conceive the universe as a series of mental processes which do not develop in space but successively in time. Spinoza ascribes to his inexhaustible divinity the attributes of extension and thought; no one in Tlön would understand the juxtaposition of the first (which is typical only of certain states) and the second—which is a perfect synonym of the cosmos. In other words, they do not conceive that the spatial persists in time. The perception of a cloud of smoke on the horizon and then of the burning field and then of the half-extinguished cigarette that produced the blaze is considered an example of association of ideas.

This monism or complete idealism invalidates all science. If we explain (or judge) a fact, we connect it with another; such linking, in Tlön, is a later state of the subject which cannot affect or illuminate the previous state. Every mental state is irreducible: the mere fact of naming it—that is, of classifying it—implies a falsification. From which it can be deduced that there are no sciences on Tlön, not even reasoning. The paradoxical truth is that they do exist, and in almost uncountable number. The same thing happens with philosophies as happens with nouns in the northern hemisphere. The fact that every philosophy is by definition a dialectical game, a *Philosophie des Als Ob,* has caused them to multiply. There is an abundance of incredible systems of pleasing design or sensational type. The metaphysicians of Tlön do not seek for the truth or even for verisimilitude, but rather for the astounding. They judge that metaphysics is a branch of fantastic literature. They know that a system is nothing more than the subordination of all aspects of the universe to any one such aspect. Even the phrase "all aspects" is rejectable, for it supposes the impossible addition of the present and of all past moments. Neither is it licit to use the plural "past moments," since it supposes another impossible operation. One of the schools of Tlön goes so far as to negate time: it reasons that the present is indefinite, that the future has no reality other than as a present hope, that the past has no reality other than as a present memory.[2] Another school declares that *all time* has already transpired and that our life is only the crepuscular and no doubt falsified and mutilated memory or reflection of an irrecoverable process. Another, that the history of the universe—and in it our lives and the most tenuous detail of our lives—is the scripture produced by a subordinate god in order to communicate with a demon. Another, that the universe is comparable to those cryptographs in which not all the symbols are valid and that only what happens every three hundred nights is true. Another, that while we sleep here, we are awake elsewhere and that in this way every man is two men.

Amongst the doctrines of Tlön, none has merited the scandalous reception accorded to materialism. Some thinkers have formulated it with less clarity than fervor, as one might put forth a paradox. In order to facilitate the comprehension of this inconceivable thesis, a heresiarch of the eleventh century[3] devised the sophism of the nine copper coins, whose scandalous renown is in Tlön equivalent to that of the Eleatic paradoxes. There are many versions of this "specious reasoning," which vary the number of coins and the number of discoveries; the following is the most common:

> On Tuesday, X crosses a deserted road and loses nine copper coins. On Thursday, Y finds in the road four coins, somewhat rusted by Wednesday's rain. On Friday, Z discovers three coins in the road. On Friday morning, X finds two coins in the corridor of his house. The heresiarch would deduce from this story the reality—that is, the continuity—of the nine coins which were recovered. *It is absurd* (he affirmed) *to imagine that four of the coins have not existed between Tuesday and Thursday, three between Tuesday and Friday afternoon, two between Tuesday and Friday morning. It is logical to think that they have existed—at least in some secret way, hidden from the comprehension of men—at every moment of those three periods.*

The language of Tlön resists the formulation of this paradox; most people did not even understand it. The defenders of common sense at

<hr />

[2] Russell (*The Analysis of Mind*, 1921, page 159) supposes that the planet has been created a few minutes ago, furnished with a humanity that "remembers" an illusory past.

[3] A century, according to the duodecimal system, signifies a period of a hundred and forty-four years.

first did no more than negate the veracity of the anecdote. They repeated that it was a verbal fallacy, based on the rash application of two neologisms not authorized by usage and alien to all rigorous thought: the verbs "find" and "lose," which beg the question, because they presuppose the identity of the first and of the last nine coins. They recalled that all nouns (man, coin, Thursday, Wednesday, rain) have only a metaphorical value. They denounced the treacherous circumstance "somewhat rusted by Wednesday's rain," which presupposes what is trying to be demonstrated: the persistence of the four coins from Tuesday to Thursday. They explained that *equality* is one thing and *identity* another, and formulated a kind of *reductio ad absurdum*: the hypothetical case of nine men who on nine successive nights suffer a severe pain. Would it not be ridiculous—they questioned—to pretend that this pain is one and the same?[4] They said that the heresiarch was prompted only by the blasphemous intention of attributing the divine category of *being* to some simple coins and that at times he negated plurality and at other times did not. They argued: if equality implies identity, one would also have to admit that the nine coins are one.

Unbelievably, these refutations were not definitive. A hundred years after the problem was stated, a thinker no less brilliant than the heresiarch but of orthodox tradition formulated a very daring hypothesis. This happy conjecture affirmed that there is only one subject, that this indivisible subject is every being in the universe and that these beings are the organs and masks of the divinity. X is Y and is Z. Z discovers three coins because he remembers that X lost them; X finds two in the corridor because he remembers that the others have been found. The Eleventh Volume suggests that three prime reasons determined the complete victory of this idealist pantheism. The first, its repudiation of solipsism; the second, the possibility of preserving the psychological basis of the sciences; the third, the possibility of preserving the cult of the gods. Schopenhauer (the passionate and lucid Schopenhauer) formulates a very similar doctrine in the first volume of *Parerga und Paralipomena*.

The geometry of Tlön comprises two somewhat different disciplines: the visual and the tactile. The latter corresponds to our own geometry and is subordinated to the first. The basis of visual geometry is the surface, not the point. This geometry disregards parallel lines and declares that man in his movement modifies the forms which surround him. The basis of its arithmetic is the notion of indefinite numbers. They emphasize the importance of the concepts of greater and lesser, which

---

[4] Today, one of the churches of Tlön Platonically maintains that a certain pain, a certain greenish tint of yellow, a certain temperature, a certain sound, are the only reality. All men, in the vertiginous moment of coitus, are the same man. All men who repeat a line from Shakespeare *are* William Shakespeare.

our mathematicians symbolize as > and <. They maintain that the operation of counting modifies quantities and converts them from indefinite into definite sums. The fact that several individuals who count the same quantity should obtain the same result is, for the psychologists, an example of association of ideas or of a good exercise of memory. We already know that in Tlön the subject of knowledge is one and eternal.

In literary practices the idea of a single subject is also all-powerful. It is uncommon for books to be signed. The concept of plagiarism does not exist: it has been established that all works are the creation of one author, who is attemporal and anonymous. The critics often invent authors: they select two dissimilar works—the *Tao Te Ching* and the *1001 Nights,* say—attribute them to the same writer and then determine most scrupulously the psychology of this interesting *homme de letters.*

Their books are also different. Works of fiction contain a single plot, with all its imaginable permutations. Those of a philosophical nature invariably include both the thesis and the antithesis, the rigorous pro and con of a doctrine. A book which does not contain its counterbook is considered incomplete.

Centuries and centuries of idealism have not failed to influence reality. In the most ancient regions of Tlön, the duplication of lost objects is not infrequent. Two persons look for a pencil; the first finds it and says nothing; the second finds a second pencil, no less real, but closer to his expectations. These secondary objects are called *hrönir* and are, though awkward in form, somewhat longer. Until recently, the *hrönir* were the accidental products of distraction and forgetfulness. It seems unbelievable that their methodical production dates back scarcely a hundred years, but this is what the Eleventh Volume tells us. The first efforts were unsuccessful. However, the *modus operandi* merits description. The director of one of the state prisons told his inmates that there were certain tombs in an ancient river bed and promised freedom to whoever might make an important discovery. During the months preceding the excavation the inmates were shown photographs of what they were to find. This first effort proved that expectation and anxiety can be inhibitory; a week's work with pick and shovel did not manage to unearth anything in the way of a *hrön* except a rusty wheel of a period posterior to the experiment. But this was kept in secret and the process was repeated later in four schools. In three of them the failure was almost complete; in the fourth (whose director died accidentally during the first excavations) the students unearthed—or produced—a gold mask, an archaic sword, two or three clay urns and the moldy and mutilated torso of a king whose chest bore an inscription which it has not yet been possible to decipher. Thus was discovered the unreliability of witnesses who knew of the experimental nature of the search. Mass investigations produce contradictory objects; now individual and almost improvised jobs are preferred. The methodical fabrication of *hrönir* (says the Eleventh Volume) has performed prodigious services for archaeologists. It has made possible the interrogation and even the modification of the past, which is now no less plastic and docile than the future. Curiously, the *hrönir* of second and third degree—the *hrönir* derived from another *hrön*, those derived from the *hrön* of a *hrön*—exaggerate the aberrations of the initial one; those of fifth degree are almost uniform; those of ninth degree become confused with those of the second; in those of the eleventh there is a purity of line not found in the original. The process is cyclical: the *hrön* of twelfth degree begins to fall off in quality. Stranger and more pure than any *hrön* is, at times, the *ur*: the object produced through suggestion, educed by hope. The great golden mask I have mentioned is an illustrious example.

Things become duplicated in Tlön; they also tend to become effaced and lose their details when they are forgotten. A classic example is the doorway which survived so long as it was visited by a beggar and disappeared at his death. At times some birds, a horse, have saved the ruins of an amphitheater.

— *3* —

Postscript (1947). I reproduce the preceding article just as it appeared in the *Anthology of Fantastic Literature* (1940), with no omission other than that of a few metaphors and a kind of sarcastic summary which now seems frivolous. So many things have happened since then. I shall do no more than recall them here.

In March of 1941 a letter written by Gunnar Erfjord was discovered in a book by Hinton which had belonged to Herbert Ashe. The envelope bore a cancellation from Ouro Preto; the letter completely elucidated the mystery of Tlön. Its text corroborated the hypotheses of Martínez Estrada. One night in Lucerne or in London, in the early seventeenth century, the splendid history had its beginning. A secret and benevolent society (amongst whose members were Dalgarno and later George Berkeley) arose to invent a country. Its vague initial program included "hermetic studies," philanthropy, and the cabala. From this first period dates the curious book by Andreä. After a few years of secret conclaves and premature syntheses, it was understood that one generation was not sufficient to give articulate form to a country. They resolved that each of the masters should elect a disciple who would continue his work. This hereditary arrangement prevailed; after an interval of two centuries the persecuted fraternity sprang up again in America. In 1824, in Memphis (Tennessee), one of its affiliates conferred with the ascetic millionaire Erza Buckley. The latter, somewhat disdainfully, let him speak—and laughed at the plan's modest scope. He told the agent that in America it was absurd to invent a country and proposed the invention of a planet. To this gigantic idea he added another, a product of his nihilism: [5] that of keeping the enormous enterprise secret. At that time the twenty volumes of the *Encyclopaedia Britannica* were circulating in the United States; Buckley suggested that a methodical encyclopedia of the imaginary planet be written. He was to leave them his mountains of gold, his navigable rivers, his pasture lands roamed by cattle and buffalo, his Negroes, his brothels, and his dollars, on one condition: "The work will make no pact with the impostor Jesus Christ." Buckley did not believe in God, but he wanted to demonstrate to this nonexistent God that mortal man was capable of conceiving a world. Buckley was poisoned in Baton Rouge in 1828; in 1914 the society delivered to its collaborators, some three hundred in number, the last volume of the First Encyclopedia of Tlön. The edition was a secret one; its forty volumes (the vastest undertaking ever carried out by man) would be the basis for another more detailed edition, written not in English but in one of the languages of Tlön. This revision of an illusory world, was called, provisionally, *Orbis Tertius* and one of its modest demiurgi was Herbert Ashe, whether as an agent of Gunnar Erfjord or as an affiliate, I do not know. His having received a copy of the Eleventh Volume would seem to favor the latter assumption. But what about the others?

In 1942 events became more intense. I recall one of the first of these with particular clarity and it seems that I perceived then something of its premonitory character. It happened in an apartment on Laprida Street, facing a high and light balcony which looked out toward the sunset. Princess Faucigny Lucinge had received her silverware from Poitiers. From the vast depths of a box embellished with foreign stamps, delicate immobile objects emerged: silver from Utrecht and Paris covered with hard heraldic fauna, and a samovar. Amongst them—with the perceptible and tenuous tremor of a sleeping bird—a compass vibrated mysteriously. The Princess did not recognize it. Its blue needle longed for magnetic north; its metal case was concave in shape; the letters around its edge corresponded to one of the alphabets of Tlön. Such was the first intrusion of this fantastic world into the world of reality.

I am still troubled by a stroke of chance which made me the witness of the second intrusion as well. It happened some months later, at a country store owned by a Brazilian in Cuchilla Negra. Amorim and I were returning from Sant' Anna. The River Tacuarembó had flooded and we were obliged to sample (and endure) the proprietor's rudimentary hospitality. He provided us with some creaking cots in a large room cluttered with barrels and hides. We went to bed, but were kept from sleeping until dawn by the drunken ravings of an unseen neighbor, who

[5] Buckley was a freethinker, a fatalist, and a defender of slavery.

intermingled inextricable insults with snatches of *milongas*—or rather with snatches of the same *milonga*. As might be supposed, we attributed this insistent uproar to the store owner's fiery cane liquor. By daybreak, the man was dead in the hallway. The roughness of his voice had deceived us: he was only a youth. In his delirium a few coins had fallen from his belt, along with a cone of bright metal, the size of a die. In vain a boy tried to pick up this cone. A man was scarcely able to raise it from the ground. I held it in my hand for a few minutes; I remember that its weight was intolerable and that after it was removed, the feeling of oppressiveness remained. I also remember the exact circle it pressed into my palm. This sensation of a very small and at the same time extremely heavy object produced a disagreeable impression of repugnance and fear. One of the local men suggested we throw it into the swollen river; Amorim acquired it for a few pesos. No one knew anything about the dead man, except that "he came from the border." These small, very heavy cones (made from a metal which is not of this world) are images of the divinity in certain regions of Tlön.

Here I bring the personal part of my narrative to a close. The rest is in the memory (if not in the hopes or fears) of all my readers. Let it suffice for me to recall or mention the following facts, with a mere brevity of words which the reflective recollection of all will enrich or amplify. Around 1944, a person doing research for the newspaper *The American* (of Nashville, Tennessee) brought to light in a Memphis library the forty volumes of the First Encyclopedia of Tlön. Even today there is a controversy over whether this discovery was accidental or whether it was permitted by the directors of the still nebulous *Orbis Tertius*. The latter is most likely. Some of the incredible aspects of the Eleventh Volume (for example, the multiplication of the *hrönir*) have been eliminated or attenuated in the Memphis copies; it is reasonable to imagine that these omissions follow the plan of exhibiting a world which is not too incompatible with the real world. The dissemination of objects from Tlön over different countries would complement this plan.[6] The fact is that the international press infinitely proclaimed the "find." Manuals, anthologies, summaries, literal versions, authorized re-editions and pirated editions of the Greatest Work of Man flooded and still flood the earth. Almost immediately, reality yielded on more than one account. The truth is that it longed to yield. Ten years ago any symmetry with a semblance of order—dialectical materialism, anti-Semitism, Nazism—was sufficient to entrance the minds of men. How could one do other than submit to Tlön, to the minute and vast evidence of an orderly planet? It is useless to answer that reality is also orderly. Perhaps it is, but in accordance with divine laws—I translate: inhuman laws—which

[6] There remains, of course, the problem of the *material* of some objects.

we never quite grasp. Tlön is surely a labyrinth, but it is a labyrinth devised by men, a labyrinth destined to be deciphered by men.

The contact and the habit of Tlön have disintegrated this world. Enchanted by its rigor, humanity forgets over and again that it is a rigor of chess masters, not of angels. Already the schools have been invaded by the (conjectural) "primitive language" of Tlön; already the teaching of its harmonious history (filled with moving episodes) has wiped out the one which governed in my childhood; already a fictitious past occupies in our memories the place of another, a past of which we know nothing with certainty—not even that it is false. Numismatology, pharmacology and archaeology have been reformed. I understand that biology and mathematics also await their avatars. A scattered dynasty of solitary men has changed the face of the world. Their task continues. If our forecasts are not in error, a hundred years from now someone will discover the hundred volumes of the Second Encyclopedia of Tlön.

Then English and French and mere Spanish will disappear from the globe. The world will be Tlön. I pay no attention to all this and go on revising, in the still days at the Adrogué hotel, an uncertain Quevedian translation (which I do not intend to publish) of Browne's *Urn Burial*.

Graham Greene (1904–   )

THE DESTRUCTORS

As much (and as little) a parable as "The Tell-Tale Heart," this story is less sensational only because its narrative assumptions are both quieter and more familiar to us. It can readily be reduced to its central idea: technical resourcefulness, itself amoral, bent with chilling perversity on an act of uncreation. The author's job is to make real this conception so that our moral sense can experience the feel of it. How do these boys differ from the soldiers in "Friendship"?

— *1* —

It was on the eve of August Bank Holiday that the latest recruit became the leader of the Wormsley Common Gang. No one was surprised except Mike, but Mike at the age of nine was surprised by everything. "If you don't shut your mouth," somebody once said to him, "you'll get a frog down it." After that Mike had kept his teeth tightly clamped except when the surprise was too great.

The new recruit had been with the gang since the beginning of the summer holidays, and there were possibilities about his brooding silence that all recognized. He never wasted a word even to tell his name until that was required of him by the rules. When he said "Trevor" it was a statement of fact, not as it would have been with the others a statement of shame or defiance. Nor did anyone laugh except Mike, who finding himself without support and meeting the dark gaze of the newcomer opened his mouth and was quiet again. There was every reason why T., as he was afterwards referred to, should have been an object of mockery —there was his name (and they substituted the initial because otherwise they had no excuse not to laugh at it), the fact that his father, a former architect and present clerk, had "come down in the world" and that his mother considered herself better than the neighbors. What but an odd quality of danger, of the unpredictable, established him in the gang without any ignoble ceremony of initiation?

The gang met every morning in an impromptu car-park, the site of the last bomb of the first blitz. The leader, who was known as Blackie, claimed to have heard it fall, and no one was precise enough in his dates to point out that he would have been one year old and fast asleep on the down platform of Wormsley Common Underground Station. On one side of the car-park leant the first occupied house, No. 3, of the shattered Northwood Terrace—literally leant, for it had suffered from the blast of the bomb and the side walls were supported on wooden struts. A smaller bomb and some incendiaries had fallen beyond, so that the house stuck up like a jagged tooth and carried on the further wall relics of its neighbor, a dado, the remains of a fireplace. T., whose words were almost confined to voting "Yes" or "No" to the plan of operations proposed each day by Blackie, once startled the whole gang by saying broodingly, "Wren built that house, father says."

"Who's Wren?"

"The man who built St. Paul's."

"Who cares?" Blackie said. "It's only old Misery's."

Old Misery—whose real name was Thomas—had once been a builder and decorator. He lived alone in the crippled house, doing for himself. Once a week you could see him coming back across the common with bread and vegetables, and once as the boys played in the car-park he put his head over the smashed wall of his garden and looked at them.

"Been to the loo," one of the boys said, for it was common knowledge that since the bombs fell something had gone wrong with the pipes of the house and Old Misery was too mean to spend money on the property. He could do the redecorating himself at cost price, but he had never learnt plumbing. The loo was a wooden shed at the bottom of the narrow garden with a star-shaped hole in the door: it had escaped the blast which had smashed the house next door and sucked out the window-frames of No. 3.

The next time the gang became aware of Mr. Thomas was more surprising. Blackie, Mike, and a thin yellow boy, who for some reason was called by his surname Summers, met him on the common coming back from the market. Mr. Thomas stopped them. He said glumly, "You belong to the lot that play in the car-park?"

Mike was about to answer when Blackie stopped him. As the leader he had responsibilities. "Suppose we are?" he said ambiguously.

"I got some chocolates," Mr. Thomas said. "Don't like 'em myself. Here you are. Not enough to go round, I don't suppose. There never is," he added with sombre conviction. He handed over three packets of Smarties.

The gang were puzzled and perturbed by this action and tried to explain it away. "Bet someone dropped them and he picked 'em up," somebody suggested.

"Pinched 'em and then got in a bleeding funk," another thought aloud.

"It's a bribe," Summers said. "He wants us to stop bouncing balls on his wall."

"We'll show him we don't take bribes," Blackie said, and they sacrificed the whole morning to the game of bouncing that only Mike was young enough to enjoy. There was no sign from Mr. Thomas.

Next day T. astonished them all. He was late at the rendezvous, and the voting for that day's exploit took place without him. At Blackie's suggestion the gang was to disperse in pairs, take buses at random, and see how many free rides could be snatched from unwary conductors (the operation was to be carried out in pairs to avoid cheating). They were drawing lots for their companions when T. arrived.

"Where you been, T.?" Blackie asked. "You can't vote now. You know the rules."

"I've been *there*," T. said. He looked at ground, as though he had thoughts to hide.

"Where?"

"At Old Misery's." Mike's mouth opened and then hurriedly closed again with a click. He had remembered the frog.

"At Old Misery's?" Blackie said. There was nothing in the rules against it, but he had a sensation that T. was treading on dangerous ground. He asked hopefully, "Did you break in?"

"No. I rang the bell."

"And what did you say?"

"I said I wanted to see his house."

"What did he do?"

"He showed it me."

"Pinch anything?"

"No."

"What did you do it for then?"

The gang had gathered round: it was as though an impromptu court were about to form and to try some case of deviation. T. said, "It's a beautiful house," and still watching the ground, meeting no one's eyes, he licked his lips first one way, then the other.

"What do you mean, a beautiful house?" Blackie asked with scorn.

"It's got a staircase two hundred years old like a corkscrew. Nothing holds it up."

"What do you mean, nothing holds it up. Does it float?"

"It's to do with opposite forces, Old Misery said."

"What else?"

"There's panelling."

"Like in the Blue Boar?"

"Two hundred years old."

"Is Old Misery two hundred years old?"

Mike laughed suddenly and then was quiet again. The meeting was in a serious mood. For the first time since T. had strolled into the car-park on the first day of the holidays his position was in danger. It only needed a single use of his real name and the gang would be at his heels.

"What did you do it for?" Blackie asked. He was just, he had no jealousy, he was anxious to retain T. in the gang if he could. It was the word "beautiful" that worried him—that belonged to a class world that you could still see parodied at the Wormsley Common Empire by a man wearing a top hat and a monocle, with a haw-haw accent. He was tempted to say, "My dear Trevor, old chap," and unleash his hell hounds. "If you'd broken in," he said sadly—that indeed would have been an exploit worthy of the gang.

"This was better," T. said. "I found out things." He continued to stare at his feet, not meeting anybody's eye, as though he were absorbed in some dream he was unwilling—or ashamed—to share.

"What things?"

"Old Misery's going to be away all tomorrow and Bank Holiday."

Blackie said with relief, "You mean we could break in?"

"And pinch things?" somebody asked.

Blackie said, "Nobody's going to pinch things. Breaking in—that's good enough, isn't it? We don't want any court stuff."

"I don't want to pinch anything," T. said. "I've got a better idea."

"What is it?"

T. raised eyes, as grey and disturbed as the drab August day. "We'll pull it down," he said. "We'll destroy it."

Blackie gave a single hoot of laughter and then, like Mike, fell quiet, daunted by the serious implacable gaze. "What'd the police be doing all the time?" he said.

"They'd never know. We'd do it from inside. I've found a way in." He said with a sort of intensity, "We'd be like worms, don't you see, in an apple. When we came out again there'd be nothing there, no stair-case, no panels, nothing but just walls, and then we'd make the walls fall down—somehow."

"We'd go to jug," Blackie said.

"Who's to prove? And anyway we wouldn't have pinched anything." He added without the smallest flicker of glee, "There wouldn't be anything to pinch after we'd finished."

"I've never heard of going to prison for breaking things," Summers said.

"There wouldn't be time," Blackie said. "I've seen housebreakers at work."

"There are twelve of us," T. said. "We'd organize."

"None of us know how—"

"I know," T. said. He looked across at Blackie, "Have you got a better plan?"

"Today," Mike said tactlessly, "we're pinching free rides—"

"Free rides," T. said. "You can stand down, Blackie, if you'd rather. . . ."

"The gang's got to vote."

"Put it up then."

Blackie said uneasily, "It's proposed that tomorrow and Monday we destroy Old Misery's house."

"Here, here," said a fat boy called Joe.

"Who's in favor?"

T. said, "It's carried."

"How do we start?" Summers asked.

"He'll tell you," Blackie said. It was the end of his leadership. He went away to the back of the car-park and began to kick a stone, dribbling it this way and that. There was only one old Morris in the park, for few cars were left there except lorries: without an attendant there was no safety. He took a flying kick at the car and scraped a little paint off the rear mudguard. Beyond, paying no more attention to him than to a stranger, the gang had gathered round T.; Blackie was dimly aware of the fickleness of favor. He thought of going home, of never returning, of letting them all discover the hollowness of T.'s leadership, but suppose after all what T. proposed was possible—nothing like it had ever been done before. The fame of the Wormsley Common car-park gang would surely reach around London. There would be headlines in the papers. Even the grown-up gangs who ran the betting at the all-in wrestling and the barrow-boys would hear with respect of how Old Misery's house had been destroyed. Driven by the pure, simple, and altruistic ambition of fame for the gang, Blackie came back to where T. stood in the shadow of Misery's wall.

T. was giving his orders with decision: it was as though this plan had been with him all his life, pondered through the seasons, now in his fifteenth year crystallized with the pain of puberty. "You," he said to Mike, "bring some big nails, the biggest you can find, and a hammer. Anyone else who can better bring a hammer and a screwdriver. We'll need plenty of them. Chisels too. We can't have too many chisels. Can anybody bring a saw?"

"I can," Mike said.

"Not a child's saw," T. said. "A real saw."

Blackie realized he had raised his hand like any ordinary member of the gang.

"Right, you bring one, Blackie. But now there's a difficulty. We want a hacksaw."

"What's a hacksaw?" someone asked.

"You can get 'em at Woolworth's," Summers said.

The fat boy called Joe said gloomily, "I knew it would end in a collection."

"I'll get one myself," T. said. "I don't want your money. But I can't buy a sledge hammer."

Blackie said, "They are working on number fifteen. I know where they'll leave their stuff for Bank Holiday."

"Then that's all," T. said. "We meet here at nine sharp."

"I've got to go to church," Mike said.

"Come over the wall and whistle. We'll let you in."

— 2 —

On Sunday morning all were punctual except Blackie, even Mike. Mike had had a stroke of luck. His mother felt ill, his father was tired after Saturday night, and he was told to go to church alone with many warnings of what would happen if he strayed. Blackie had had difficulty in smuggling out the saw, and then in finding the sledge hammer at the back of number 15. He approached the house from a lane at the rear of the garden, for fear of the policeman's beat along the main road. The tired evergreens kept off a stormy sun: another wet Bank Holiday was being prepared over the Atlantic, beginning in swirls of dust under the trees. Blackie climbed the wall into Misery's garden.

There was no sign of anybody anywhere. The loo stood like a tomb in a neglected graveyard. The curtains were drawn. The house slept. Blackie lumbered nearer with the saw and the sledge hammer. Perhaps after all nobody had turned up: the plan had been a wild invention: they had woken wiser. But when he came close to the back door he could hear a confusion of sound, hardly louder than a hive in swarm: a clickety-clack, a bang bang bang, a scraping, a creaking, a sudden painful crack. He thought, It's true, and whistled.

They opened the back door to him and he came in. He had at once the impression of organization, very different from the old happy-go-lucky ways under his leadership. For a while he wandered up and down stairs looking for T. Nobody addressed him: he had a sense of great urgency, and already he could begin to see the plan. The interior of the house was being carefully demolished without touching the outer walls. Summers with hammer and chisel was ripping out the skirting-boards in the ground floor dining room: he had already smashed the panels of the door. In the same room Joe was heaving up the parquet blocks, exposing the soft wood floor-boards over the cellar. Coils of wire came out of the damaged skirting and Mike sat happily on the floor, clipping the wires.

On the curved stairs two of the gang were working hard with an inadequate child's saw on the banisters—when they saw Blackie's big saw they signaled for it wordlessly. When he next saw them a quarter of the banisters had been dropped into the hall. He found T. at last in the bathroom—he sat moodily in the least cared-for room in the house, listening to the sounds coming up from below.

"You've really done it," Blackie said with awe. "What's going to happen?"

"We've only just begun," T. said. He looked at the sledge hammer and gave his instructions. "You stay here and break the bath and the wash-basin. Don't bother about the pipes. They come later."

Mike appeared at the door. "I've finished the wire, T.," he said.

"Good. You've just got to go wandering round now. The kitchen's in the basement. Smash all the china and glass and bottles you can lay hold of. Don't turn on the taps—we don't want a flood—yet. Then go into all the rooms and turn out drawers. If they are locked get one of the others to break them open. Tear up any papers you find and smash all the ornaments. Better take a carving knife with you from the kitchen. The bedroom's opposite here. Open the pillows and tear up the sheets. That's enough for the moment. And you, Blackie, when you've finished in here crack the plaster in the passage up with your sledge hammer."

"What are you going to do?" Blackie asked.

"I'm looking for something special," T. said.

It was nearly lunch time before Blackie had finished and went in search of T. Chaos had advanced. The kitchen was a shambles of broken glass and china. The dining room was stripped of parquet, the skirting was up, the door had been taken off its hinges, and the destroyers had moved up a floor. Streaks of light came in through the closed shutters where they worked with the seriousness of creators—and destruction after all is a form of creation. A kind of imagination had seen this house as it had now become.

Mike said, "I've got to go home for dinner."

"Who else?" T. asked, but all the others on one excuse or another had brought provisions with them.

They squatted in the ruins of the room and swapped unwanted sandwiches. Half an hour for lunch and they were at work again. By the time Mike returned, they were on the top floor, and by six the superficial damage was completed. The doors were all off, all the skirtings raised, the furniture pillaged and ripped and smashed—no one could have slept in the house except on a bed of broken plaster. T. gave his orders—eight o'clock next morning—and to escape notice they climbed singly over the garden wall, into the car-park. Only Blackie and T. were left; the light had nearly gone, and when they touched a switch, nothing worked—Mike had done his job thoroughly.

"Did you find anything special?" Blackie asked.

T. nodded. "Come over here," he said, "and look." Out of both pockets he drew bundles of pound notes. "Old Misery's savings," he said. "Mike ripped out the mattress, but he missed them."

"What are you going to do? Share them?"

"We aren't thieves," T. said. "Nobody's going to steal anything from this house. I kept these for you and me—a celebration." He knelt down on the floor and counted them out—there were seventy in all. "We'll burn them," he said, "one by one," and taking it in turns they held a note upwards and lit the top corner, so that the flame burnt slowly towards their fingers. The grey ash floated above them and fell on their heads like age. "I'd like to see Old Misery's face when we are through," T. said.

"You hate him a lot?" Blackie asked.

"Of course I don't hate him," T. said. "There'd be no fun if I hated him." The last burning note illuminated his brooding face. "All this hate and love," he said, "it's soft, it's hooey. There's only things, Blackie," and he looked round the room crowded with the unfamiliar shadows of half things, broken things, former things. "I'll race you home, Blackie," he said.

— *3* —

Next morning the serious destruction started. Two were missing—Mike and another boy whose parents were off to Southend and Brighton in spite of the slow warm drops that had begun to fall and the rumble of thunder in the estuary like the first guns of the old blitz. "We've got to hurry," T. said.

Summers was restive. "Haven't we done enough?" he said. "I've been given a bob for slot machines. This is like work."

"We've hardly started," T. said. "Why, there's all the floors left, and the stairs. We haven't taken out a single window. You voted like the others. We are going to *destroy* this house. There won't be anything left when we've finished."

They began again on the first floor picking up the top floor-boards next the outer wall, leaving the joists exposed. Then they sawed through the joists and retreated into the hall, as what was left of the floor heeled and sank. They had learnt with practice, and the second floor collapsed more easily. By the evening an odd exhilaration seized them as they looked down the great hollow of the house. They ran risks and made mistakes: when they thought of the windows it was too late to reach them. "Cor," Joe said, and dropped a penny down into the dry rubble-filled well. It cracked and span among the broken glass.

"Why did we start this?" Summers asked with astonishment; T. was already on the ground, digging at the rubble, clearing a space along the outer wall. "Turn on the taps," he said. "It's too dark for anyone to see now, and in the morning it won't matter." The water overtook them on the stairs and fell through the floorless rooms.

It was then they heard Mike's whistle at the back. "Something's wrong," Blackie said. They could hear his urgent breathing as they unlocked the door.

"The bogies?" Summers asked.

"Old Misery," Mike said. "He's on his way." He put his head between his knees and retched. "Ran all the way," he said with pride.

"But why?" T. said. "He told me. . . ." He protested with the fury of the child he had never been, "It isn't fair."

"He was down at Southend," Mike said, "and he was on the train coming back. Said it was too cold and wet." He paused and gazed at the water. "My, you've had a storm here. Is the roof leaking?"

"How long will he be?"

"Five minutes. I gave Ma the slip and ran."

"We better clear," Summers said, "we've done enough, anyway."

"Oh, no, we haven't. Anybody could do this"—"this" was the shattered hollowed house with nothing left but the walls. Yet walls could be preserved. Façades were valuable. They could build inside again more beautifully than before. This could again be a home. He said angrily, "We've got to finish. Don't move. Let me think."

"There's no time," a boy said.

"There's got to be a way," T. said. "We couldn't have got thus far. . . ."

"We've done a lot," Blackie said.

"No. No, we haven't. Somebody watch the front."

"We can't do any more."

"He may come in at the back."

"Watch the back too." T. began to plead. "Just give me a minute and I'll fix it. I swear I'll fix it." But his authority had gone with his ambiguity. He was only one of the gang. "Please," he said.

"Please," Summers mimicked him, and then suddenly struck home with the fatal name. "Run along home, Trevor."

T. stood with his back to the rubble like a boxer knocked groggy against the ropes. He had no words as his dreams shook and slid. Then Blackie acted before the gang had time to laugh, pushing Summers backward. "I'll watch the front, T.," he said, and cautiously he opened the shutters of the hall. The grey wet common stretched ahead, and the lamps gleamed in the puddles. "Someone's coming, T. No, it's not him. What's your plan, T.?"

"Tell Mike to go out to the loo and hide close beside it. When he hears me whistle he's got to count ten and start to shout."

"Shout what?"

"Oh, 'Help,' anything."

"You hear, Mike," Blackie said. He was the leader again. He took a quick look between the shutters. "He's coming, T."

"Quick, Mike. The loo. Stay here, Blackie, all of you till I yell."

"Where are you going, T.?"

"Don't worry. I'll see to this. I said I would, didn't I?"

Old Misery came limping off the common. He had mud on his shoes and he stopped to scrape them on the pavement's edge. He didn't want to soil his house, which stood jagged and dark between the bomb sites, saved so narrowly, as he believed, from destruction. Even the fan-light had been left unbroken by the bomb's blast. Somewhere somebody whistled. Old Misery looked sharply round. He didn't trust whistles. A child was shouting: it seemed to come from his own garden. Then a boy ran into the road from the car-park. "Mr. Thomas," he called, "Mr. Thomas."

"What is it?"

"I'm terribly sorry, Mr. Thomas. One of us got taken short, and we thought you wouldn't mind, and now he can't get out."

"What do you mean, boy?"

"He's got stuck in your loo."

"He'd no business— Haven't I seen you before?"

"You showed me your house."

"So I did. So I did. That doesn't give you the right to—"

"Do hurry, Mr. Thomas. He'll suffocate."

"Nonsense. He can't suffocate. Wait till I put my bag in."

"I'll carry your bag."

"Oh, no, you don't. I carry my own."

"This way, Mr. Thomas."

"I can't get in the garden that way. I've got to go through the house."

"But you *can* get in the garden this way, Mr. Thomas. We often do."

"You often do?" He followed the boy with a scandalized fascination. "When? What right. . . ."

"Do you see . . . ? The wall's low."

"I'm not going to climb walls into my own garden. It's absurd."

"This is how we do it. One foot here, one foot there, and over." The boy's face peered down, an arm shot out, and Mr. Thomas found his bag taken and deposited on the other side of the wall.

"Give me back my bag," Mr. Thomas said. From the loo a boy yelled and yelled. "I'll call the police."

"Your bag's all right, Mr. Thomas. Look. One foot there. On your

right. Now just above. To your left." Mr. Thomas climbed over his own
garden wall. "Here's your bag, Mr. Thomas."

"I'll have the wall built up," Mr. Thomas said, "I'll not have you boys
coming over here, using my loo." He stumbled on the path, but the boy
caught his elbow and supported him. "Thank you, thank you, my boy,"
he murmured automatically. Somebody shouted again through the dark.
"I'm coming, I'm coming," Mr. Thomas called. He said to the boy beside
him, "I'm not unreasonable. Been a boy myself. As long as things are
done regular. I don't mind you playing round the place Saturday mornings. Sometimes I like company. Only it's got to be regular. One of you
asks leave and I say Yes. Sometimes I'll say No. Won't feel like it. And
you come in at the front door and out at the back. No garden walls."

"Do get him out, Mr. Thomas."

"He won't come to any harm in my loo," Mr. Thomas said, stumbling
slowly down the garden. "Oh, my rheumatics," he said. "Always get 'em
on Bank Holiday. I've got to go careful. There's loose stones here. Give
me your hand. Do you know what my horoscope said yesterday? 'Abstain
from any dealings in first half of week. Danger of serious crash.' That
might be on this path," Mr. Thomas said. "They speak in parables and
double meanings." He paused at the door of the loo. "What's the matter
in there?" he called. There was no reply.

"Perhaps he's fainted," the boy said.

"Not in my loo. Here, you, come out," Mr. Thomas said, and giving a
great jerk at the door he nearly fell on his back when it swung easily
open. A hand first supported him and then pushed him hard. His head
hit the opposite wall and he sat heavily down. His bag hit his feet. A
hand whipped the key out of the lock and the door slammed. "Let me
out," he called, and heard the key turn in the lock. "A serious crash," he
thought, and felt dithery and confused and old.

A voice spoke to him softly through the star-shaped hole in the door.
"Don't worry, Mr. Thomas," it said, "we won't hurt you, not if you stay
quiet."

Mr. Thomas put his head between his hands and pondered. He had
noticed that there was only one lorry in the car-park, and he felt certain
that the driver would not come for it before the morning. Nobody could
hear him from the road in front, and the lane at the back was seldom
used. Anyone who passed there would be hurrying home and would not
pause for what they would certainly take to be drunken cries. And if he
did call "Help," who, on a lonely Bank Holiday evening, would have
the courage to investigate? Mr. Thomas sat on the loo and pondered
with the wisdom of age.

After a while it seemed to him that there were sounds in the silence—
they were faint and came from the direction of his house. He stood up
and peered through the ventilation-hole—between the cracks in one of

the shutters he saw a light, not the light of a lamp, but the wavering light that a candle might give. Then he thought he heard the sound of hammering and scraping and chipping. He thought of burglars—perhaps they had employed the boy as a scout, but why should burglars engage in what sounded more and more like a stealthy form of carpentry? Mr. Thomas let out an experimental yell, but nobody answered. The noise could not even have reached his enemies.

— 4 —

Mike had gone home to bed, but the rest stayed. The question of leadership no longer concerned the gang. With nails, chisels, screwdrivers, anything that was sharp and penetrating they moved around the inner walls worrying at the mortar between the bricks. They started too high, and it was Blackie who hit on the damp course and realized the work could be halved if they weakened the joints immediately above. It was a long, tiring, unamusing job, but at last it was finished. The gutted house stood there balanced on a few inches of mortar between the damp course and the bricks.

There remained the most dangerous task of all, out in the open at the edge of the bomb-site. Summers was sent to watch the road for passers-by, and Mr. Thomas, sitting on the loo, heard clearly now the sound of sawing. It no longer came from his house, and that a little reassured him. He felt less concerned. Perhaps the other noises too had no significance.

A voice spoke to him through the hole. "Mr. Thomas."

"Let me out," Mr. Thomas said sternly.

"Here's a blanket," the voice said, and a long grey sausage was worked through the hole and fell in swathes over Mr. Thomas's head.

"There's nothing personal," the voice said. "We want you to be comfortable tonight."

"Tonight," Mr. Thomas repeated incredulously.

"Catch," the voice said. "Penny buns—we've buttered them, and sausage-rolls. We don't want you to starve, Mr. Thomas."

Mr. Thomas pleaded desperately. "A joke's a joke, boy. Let me out and I won't say a thing. I've got rheumatics. I got to sleep comfortable."

"You wouldn't be comfortable, not in your house, you wouldn't. Not now."

"What do you mean, boy?" But the footsteps receded. There was only the silence of night: no sound of sawing. Mr. Thomas tried one more yell, but he was daunted and rebuked by the silence—a long way off an owl hooted and made away again on its muffled flight through the soundless world.

At seven next morning the driver came to fetch his lorry. He climbed into the seat and tried to start the engine. He was vaguely aware of a voice shouting, but it didn't concern him. At last the engine responded and he backed the lorry until it touched the great wooden shore that supported Mr. Thomas's house. That way he could drive right out and down the street without reversing. The lorry moved forward, was momentarily checked as though something were pulling it from behind, and then went on to the sound of a long rumbling crash. The driver was astonished to see bricks bouncing ahead of him, while stones hit the roof of his cab. He put on his brakes. When he climbed out the whole landscape had suddenly altered. There was no house beside the car-park, only a hill of rubble. He went round and examined the back of his car for damage, and found a rope tied there that was still twisted at the other end round part of a wooden strut.

The driver again became aware of somebody shouting. It came from the wooden erection which was the nearest thing to a house in that desolation of broken brick. The driver climbed the smashed wall and unlocked the door. Mr. Thomas came out of the loo. He was wearing a grey blanket to which flakes of pastry adhered. He gave a sobbing cry. "My house," he said. "Where's my house?"

"Search me," the driver said. His eye lit on the remains of a bath and what had once been a dresser and he began to laugh. There wasn't anything left anywhere.

"How dare you laugh," Mr. Thomas said. "It was my house. My house."

"I'm sorry," the driver said, making heroic efforts, but when he remembered the sudden check to his lorry, the crash of bricks falling, he became convulsed again. One moment the house had stood there with such dignity between the bomb-sites like a man in a top hat, and then, bang, crash, there wasn't anything left—not anything. He said, "I'm sorry. I can't help it, Mr. Thomas. There's nothing personal, but you got to admit it's funny."

Flannery O'Connor (1925–   )

A GOOD MAN IS HARD TO FIND

The Misfit supposes that he is enacting a lurid morality play, but Miss O'Connor's prose is as bright and bleak as the world of comic books and Coca-Cola from which the rest of her characters draw the system of distractions they use instead of a religion. It is The Misfit who senses some lack in this normal world. He has as much to tell the grandmother as she has to tell him, but they are not listening to one another.

Though there is no identifiable narrator, the story has a point of view implied in the texture of its language. Try to find a passage where this point of view can be isolated. Are you meant to share it?

THE grandmother didn't want to go to Florida. She wanted to visit some of her connections in east Tennessee and she was seizing at every chance to change Bailey's mind. Bailey was the son she lived with, her only boy. He was sitting on the edge of his chair at the table, bent over the orange sports section of the *Journal.* "Now look here, Bailey," she said, "see here, read this," and she stood with one hand on her thin hip and the other rattling the newspaper at his bald head. "Here this fellow that calls himself The Misfit is aloose from the Federal Pen and headed toward Florida and you read here what it says he did to these people. Just you read it. I wouldn't take my children in any direction with a criminal like that aloose in it. I couldn't answer to my conscience if I did."

Bailey didn't look up from his reading so she wheeled around then and faced the children's mother; a young woman in slacks, whose face was as broad and innocent as a cabbage and was tied around with a green head-kerchief that had two points on the top like rabbit's ears. She was sitting on the sofa, feeding the baby his apricots out of a jar. "The children have been to Florida before," the old lady said. "You all ought to take them somewhere else for a change so they would see different parts of the world and be broad. They never have been to east Tennessee."

The children's mother didn't seem to hear her, but the eight-year-old boy, John Wesley, a stocky child with glasses, said, "If you don't want to go to Florida, why dontcha stay at home?" He and the little girl, June Star, were reading the funny papers on the floor.

"She wouldn't stay at home to be queen for a day," June Star said without raising her yellow head.

"Yes, and what would you do if this fellow, The Misfit, caught you?" the grandmother asked.

"I'd smack his face," John Wesley said.

"She wouldn't stay at home for a million bucks," June Star said. "Afraid she'd miss something. She has to go everywhere we go."

"All right, Miss," the grandmother said. "Just remember that the next time you want me to curl your hair."

June Star said her hair was naturally curly.

The next morning the grandmother was the first one in the car, ready to go. She had her big black valise that looked like the head of a hippopotamus in one corner, and underneath it she was hiding a basket with Pitty Sing, the cat, in it. She didn't intend for the cat to be left alone in the house for three days because he would miss her too much and she was afraid he might brush against one of the gas burners and accidentally asphyxiate himself. Her son, Bailey, didn't like to arrive at a motel with a cat.

She sat in the middle of the back seat with John Wesley and June Star on either side of her. Bailey and the children's mother and the baby sat in the front and they left Atlanta at eight forty-five with the mileage on the car at 55890. The grandmother wrote this down because she thought it would be interesting to say how many miles they had been when they got back. It took them twenty minutes to reach the outskirts of the city.

The old lady settled herself comfortably, removing her white cotton gloves and putting them up with her purse on the shelf in front of the back window. The children's mother still had on slacks and still had her head tied up in a green kerchief, but the grandmother had on a navy blue straw sailor hat with a bunch of white violets on the brim and a navy blue dress with a small white dot in the print. Her collar and cuffs were white organdy trimmed with lace and at her neckline she had pinned a purple spray of cloth violets containing a sachet. In case of an accident, anyone seeing her dead on the highway would know at once that she was a lady.

She said she thought it was going to be a good day for driving, neither too hot nor too cold, and she cautioned Bailey that the speed limit was fifty-five miles an hour and that the patrolmen hid themselves behind billboards and small clumps of trees and sped out after you before you had a chance to slow down. She pointed out interesting details of the scenery: Stone Mountain; the blue granite that in some places came up to both sides of the highway; the brilliant red clay banks slightly streaked with purple; and the various crops that made rows of green lace-work on the ground. The trees were full of silver-white sunlights and the meanest of them sparkled. The children were reading comic magazines and their mother had gone back to sleep.

"Let's go through Georgia fast so we won't have to look at it much," John Wesley said.

"If I were a little boy," said the grandmother, "I wouldn't talk about my native state that way. Tennessee has the mountains and Georgia has the hills."

"Tennessee is just a hillbilly dumping ground," John Wesley said, "and Georgia is a lousy state too."

"You said it," June Star said.

"In my time," said the grandmother, folding her thin veined fingers, "children were more respectful of their native states and their parents and everything else. People did right then. Oh look at the cute little pickaninny!" she said and pointed to a Negro child standing in the door of a shack. "Wouldn't that make a picture, now?" she asked and they all turned and looked at the little Negro out of the back window. He waved.

"He didn't have any britches on," June Star said.

"He probably didn't have any," the grandmother explained. "Little niggers in the country don't have things like we do. If I could paint, I'd paint that picture," she said.

The children exchanged comic books.

The grandmother offered to hold the baby and the children's mother passed him over the front seat to her. She set him on her knee and bounced him and told him about the things they were passing. She rolled her eyes and screwed up her mouth and stuck her leathery thin face into his smooth bland one. Occasionally he gave her a faraway smile. They passed a large cotton field with five or six graves fenced in the middle of it, like a small island. "Look at the graveyard!" the grandmother said, pointing it out. "That was the old family burying ground. That belonged to the plantation."

"Where's the plantation?" John Wesley asked.

"Gone With the Wind," said the grandmother. "Ha. Ha."

When the children finished all the comic books they had brought, they opened the lunch and ate it. The grandmother ate a peanut butter sandwich and an olive and would not let the children throw the box and the paper napkins out the window. When there was nothing else to do they played a game by choosing a cloud and making the other two guess what shape it suggested. John Wesley took one the shape of a cow and June Star guessed a cow and John Wesley said, no, an automobile, and June Star said he didn't play fair, and they began to slap each other over the grandmother.

The grandmother said she would tell them a story if they would keep quiet. When she told a story, she rolled her eyes and waved her head and was very dramatic. She said once when she was a maiden lady she had been courted by a Mr. Edgar Atkins Teagarden from Jasper, Georgia. She said he was a very good-looking man and a gentleman and that he brought her a watermelon every Saturday afternoon with his initials cut in it, E.A.T. Well, one Saturday, she said, Mr. Teagarden brought the watermelon and there was nobody at home and he left it on the front porch and returned in his buggy to Jasper, but she never got the watermelon, she said, because a nigger boy ate it when he saw the initials, E. A. T.! This story tickled John Wesley's funny bone and he giggled and giggled but June Star didn't think it was any good. She said she wouldn't marry a man that just brought her a watermelon on Saturday. The grandmother said she would have done well to marry Mr. Teagarden because he was a gentleman and had bought Coca-Cola stock when it first came out and that he had died only a few years ago, a very wealthy man.

They stopped at The Tower for barbecued sandwiches. The Tower was a part-stucco and part-wood filling station and dance hall set in a clearing outside of Timothy. A fat man named Red Sammy Butts ran it and there were signs stuck here and there on the building and for miles up and down the highway saying, TRY RED SAMMY'S FAMOUS BARBECUE. NONE LIKE FAMOUS RED SAMMY'S! RED SAM! THE FAT BOY WITH THE HAPPY LAUGH. A VETERAN! RED SAMMY'S YOUR MAN!

Red Sammy was lying on the bare ground outside The Tower with his head under a truck while a gray monkey about a foot high, chained to a small chinaberry tree, chattered nearby. The monkey sprang back into the tree and got on the highest limb as soon as he saw the children jump out of the car and run toward him.

Inside, The Tower was a long dark room with a counter at one end and tables at the other and dancing space in the middle. They all sat down at a broad table next to the nickelodeon and Red Sam's wife, a tall burnt-brown woman with hair and eyes lighter than her skin, came and took their order. The children's mother put a dime in the machine and played "The Tennessee Waltz," and the grandmother said that tune always made her want to dance. She asked Bailey if he would like to dance but he only glared at her. He didn't have a naturally sunny disposition like she did and trips made him nervous. The grandmother's brown eyes were very bright. She swayed her head from side to side and pretended she was dancing in her chair. June Star said play something she could tap to so the children's mother put in another dime and played a fast number and June Star stepped out onto the dance floor and did her tap routine.

"Ain't she cute?" Red Sam's wife said, leaning over the counter. "Would you like to come be my little girl?"

"No, I certainly wouldn't," June Star said. "I wouldn't live in a broken-down place like this for a million bucks!" and she ran back to the table.

"Ain't she cute?" the woman repeated, stretching her mouth politely.

"Aren't you ashamed?" hissed the grandmother.

Red Sam came in and told his wife to quit lounging on the counter and hurry up with these people's order. His khaki trousers reached just to his hip bones and his stomach hung over them like a sack of meal swaying under his shirt. He came over and sat down at a table nearby and let out a combination sigh and yodel. "You can't win," he said. "You can't win," and he wiped his sweating red face off with a gray handkerchief. "These days you don't know who to trust," he said. "Ain't that the truth?"

"People are certainly not nice like they used to be," said the grandmother.

"Two fellers come in here last week," Red Sammy said, "driving a Chrysler. It was a old beat-up car but it was a good one and these boys looked all right to me. Said they worked at the mill and you know I let them fellers charge the gas they bought? Now why did I do that?"

"Because you're a good man!" the grandmother said at once.

"Yes'm, I suppose so," Red Sam said as if he were struck with this answer.

His wife brought the orders, carrying the five plates all at once without a tray, two in each hand and one balanced on her arm. "It isn't a soul in this green world of God's that you can trust," she said. "And I don't count nobody out of that, not nobody," she repeated, looking at Red Sammy.

"Did you read about that criminal, The Misfit, that's escaped?" asked the grandmother.

"I wouldn't be a bit surprised if he didn't attact this place right here," said the woman. "If he hears about it being here, I wouldn't be none surprised to see him. If he hears it's two cent in the cash register, I wouldn't be a tall surprised if he. . . ."

"That'll do," Red Sam said. "Go bring these people their Co'Colas," and the woman went off to get the rest of the order.

"A good man is hard to find," Red Sammy said. "Everything is getting terrible. I remember the day you could go off and leave your screen door unlatched. Not no more."

He and the grandmother discussed better times. The old lady said that in her opinion Europe was entirely to blame for the way things were now. She said the way Europe acted you would think we were made of money and Red Sam said it was no use talking about it, she was exactly right. The children ran outside into the white sunlight and looked at the monkey in the lacy chinaberry tree. He was busy catching fleas on himself and biting each one carefully between his teeth as if it were a delicacy.

They drove off again into the hot afternoon. The grandmother took cat naps and woke up every few minutes with her own snoring. Outside of Toombsboro she woke up and recalled an old plantation that she had visited in this neighborhood once when she was a young lady. She said the house had six white columns across the front and that there was an avenue of oaks leading up to it and two little wooden trellis arbors on either side in front where you sat down with your suitor after a stroll in the garden. She recalled exactly which road to turn off to get to it. She knew that Bailey would not be willing to lose any time looking at an old house, but the more she talked about it, the more she wanted to see it once again and find out if the little twin arbors were still standing. "There was a secret panel in this house," she said craftily, not telling the truth but wishing that she were, "and the story went that all the family silver was hidden it it when Sherman came through but it was never found. . . ."

"Hey!" John Wesley said. "Let's go see it! We'll find it! We'll poke all the woodwork and find it! Who lives there? Where do you turn off at? Hey Pop, can't we turn off there?"

"We never have seen a house with a secret panel!" June Star shrieked. "Let's go to the house with the secret panel! Hey, Pop, can't we go see the house with the secret panel!"

"It's not far from here, I know," the grandmother said. "It wouldn't take over twenty minutes."

Bailey was looking straight ahead. His jaw was as rigid as a horseshoe. "No," he said.

The children began to yell and scream that they wanted to see the house with the secret panel. John Wesley kicked the back of the front seat and June Star hung over her mother's shoulder and whined desperately into her ear that they never had any fun even on their vacation, that they could never do what THEY wanted to do. The baby began to scream and John Wesley kicked the back of the seat so hard that his father could feel the blows in his kidney.

"All right!" he shouted and drew the car to a stop at the side of the road. "Will you all shut up? Will you all just shut up for one second? If you don't shut up, we won't go anywhere."

"It would be very educational for them," the grandmother murmured.

"All right," Bailey said, "but get this. This is the only time we're going to stop for anything like this. This is the one and only time."

"The dirt road that you have to turn down is about a mile back," the grandmother directed. "I marked it when we passed."

"A dirt road," Bailey groaned.

After they had turned around and were headed toward the dirt road, the grandmother recalled other points about the house, the beautiful glass over the front doorway and the candle lamp in the hall. John Wesley said that the secret panel was probably in the fireplace.

"You can't go inside this house," Bailey said. "You don't know who lives there."

"While you all talk to the people in front, I'll run around behind and get in a window," John Wesley suggested.

"We'll all stay in the car," his mother said.

They turned onto the dirt road and the car raced roughly along in a swirl of pink dust. The grandmother recalled the times when there were no paved roads and thirty miles was a day's journey. The dirt road was hilly and there were sudden washes in it and sharp curves on dangerous embankments. All at once they would be on a hill, looking down over the blue tops of trees for miles around, then the next minute, they would be in a red depression with the dust-coated trees looking down on them.

"This place had better turn up in a minute," Bailey said, "or I'm going to turn around."

The road looked as if no one had traveled on it in months.

"It's not much farther," the grandmother said and just as she said it, a horrible thought came to her. The thought was so embarrassing that she turned red in the face and her eyes dilated and her feet jumped up, upsetting her valise in the corner. The instant the valise moved, the newspaper top she had over the basket under it rose with a snarl and Pitty Sing, the cat, sprang onto Bailey's shoulder.

The children were thrown to the floor and their mother, clutching the baby, was thrown out the door onto the ground; the old lady was thrown into the front seat. The car turned over once and landed right-side-up in a gulch on the side of the road. Bailey remained in the driver's seat with the cat—gray-striped with a broad white face and an orange nose—clinging to his neck like a caterpillar.

As soon as the children saw they could move their arms and legs, they scrambled out of the car, shouting, "We've had an ACCIDENT!" The grandmother was curled up under the dashboard, hoping she was injured so that Bailey's wrath would not come down on her all at once. The horrible thought she had had before the accident was that the house she had remembered so vividly was not in Georgia but in Tennessee.

Bailey removed the cat from his neck with both hands and flung it out the window against the side of a pine tree. Then he got out of the car and started looking for the children's mother. She was sitting against the side of the red gutted ditch, holding the screaming baby, but she only had a cut down her face and a broken shoulder. "We've had an ACCIDENT!" the children screamed in a frenzy of delight.

"But nobody's killed," June Star said with disappointment as the grandmother limped out of the car, her hat still pinned to her head but the broken front brim standing up at a jaunty angle and the violet spray hanging off the side. They all sat down in the ditch, except the children, to recover from the shock. They were all shaking.

"Maybe a car will come along," said the children's mother hoarsely.

"I believe I have injured an organ," said the grandmother, pressing her side, but no one answered her. Bailey's teeth were clattering. He had on a yellow sport shirt with bright blue parrots designed in it and his face was as yellow as the shirt. The grandmother decided that she would not mention that the house was in Tennessee.

The road was about ten feet above and they could see only the tops of the trees on the other side of it. Behind the ditch they were sitting in there were more woods, tall and dark and deep. In a few minutes they saw a car some distance away on top of a hill, coming slowly as if the occupants were watching them. The grandmother stood up and waved both arms dramatically to attract their attention. The car continued to come on slowly, disappeared around a bend and appeared again, moving even slower, on top of the hill they had gone over. It was a big black battered hearselike automobile. There were three men it it.

It came to a stop just over them and for some minutes, the driver looked down with a steady expressionless gaze to where they were sitting, and didn't speak. Then he turned his head and muttered something to the other two and they got out. One was a fat boy in black trousers and a red sweat shirt with a silver stallion embossed on the front of it. He moved around on the right side of them and stood staring, his mouth partly open in a kind of loose grin. The other had on khaki pants and a blue striped coat and a gray hat pulled down very low, hiding most of his face. He came around slowly on the left side. Neither spoke.

The driver got out of the car and stood by the side of it, looking down at them. He was an older man than the other two. His hair was just beginning to gray and he wore silver-rimmed spectacles that gave him a scholarly look. He had a long creased face and didn't have on any shirt or undershirt. He had on blue jeans that were too tight for him and was holding a black hat and a gun. The two boys also had guns.

"We've had an ACCIDENT!" the children screamed.

The grandmother had the peculiar feeling that the bespectacled man was someone she knew. His face was as familiar to her as if she had known him all her life but she could not recall who he was. He moved away from the car and began to come down the embankment, placing his feet carefully so that he wouldn't slip. He had on tan and white shoes and no socks, and his ankles were red and thin. "Good afternoon," he said. "I see you all had you a little spill."

"We turned over twice!" said the grandmother.

"Oncet," he corrected. "We seen it happen. Try their car and see will it run, Hiram," he said quietly to the boy with the gray hat.

"What you got that gun for?" John Wesley asked. "Whatcha gonna do with that gun?"

"Lady," the man said to the children's mother, "would you mind calling them children to sit down by you? Children make me nervous. I want all you all to sit down right together there where you're at."

"What are you telling us what to do for?" June Star asked.

Behind them the line of woods gaped like a dark open mouth. "Come here," said their mother.

"Look here now," Bailey began suddenly, "we're in a predicament! We're in. . . ."

The grandmother shrieked. She scrambled to her feet and stood staring.

"You're The Misfit!" she said. "I recognized you at once!"

"Yes'm," the man said, smiling slightly as if he were pleased in spite of himself to be known, "but it would have been better for all of you, lady, if you hadn't of reckernized me."

Bailey turned his head sharply and said something to his mother that shocked even the children. The old lady began to cry and The Misfit reddened.

"Lady," he said, "don't you get upset. Sometimes a man says things he don't mean. I don't reckon he meant to talk to you thataway."

"You wouldn't shoot a lady, would you?" the grandmother said and removed a clean handkerchief from her cuff and began to slap at her eyes with it.

The Misfit pointed the toe of his shoe into the ground and made a little hole and then covered it up again. "I would hate to have to," he said.

"Listen," the grandmother almost screamed, "I know you're a good man. You don't look a bit like you have common blood. I know you must come from nice people!"

"Yes mam," he said, "finest people in the world." When he smiled he showed a row of strong white teeth. "God never made a finer woman than my mother and my daddy's heart was pure gold," he said. The boy with the red sweat shirt had come around behind them and was standing with his gun at his hip. The Misfit squatted down on the ground. "Watch them children, Bobby Lee," he said. "You know they make me nervous." He looked at the six of them huddled together in front of him and he seemed to be embarrassed as if he couldn't think of anything to say. "Ain't a cloud in the sky," he remarked, looking up at it. "Don't see no sun but don't see no cloud neither."

"Yes, it's beautiful day," said the grandmother. "Listen," she said, "you shouldn't call yourself The Misfit because I know you're a good man at heart. I can just look at you and tell."

"Hush!" Bailey yelled. "Hush! Everybody shut up and let me handle this!" He was squatting in the position of a runner about to sprint forward but he didn't move.

"I pre-chate that, lady," The Misfit said and drew a little circle in the ground with the butt of his gun.

"It'll take a half a hour to fix this here car," Hiram called, looking over the raised hood of it.

"Well, first you and Bobby Lee get him and that little boy to step over yonder with you," The Misfit said, pointing to Bailey and John Wesley. "The boys want to ast you something," he said to Bailey. "Would you mind stepping back in them woods there with them?"

"Listen," Bailey began, "we're in a terrible predicament! Nobody realizes what this is," and his voice cracked. His eyes were as blue and intense as the parrots in his shirt and he remained perfectly still.

The grandmother reached up to adjust her hat brim as if she were going to the woods with him but it came off in her hand. She stood staring at it and after a second she let it fall on the ground. Hiram pulled Bailey up by the arm as if he were assisting an old man. John Wesley caught hold of his father's hand and Bobby Lee followed. They went off toward the woods and just as they reached the dark edge, Bailey turned and supporting himself against a gray naked pine trunk, he shouted, "I'll be back in a minute, Mamma, wait on me!"

"Come back this instant!" his mother shrilled but they all disappeared into the woods.

"Bailey Boy!" the grandmother called in a tragic voice but she found she was looking at The Misfit squatting on the ground in front of her. "I just know you're a good man," she said desperately. "You're not a bit common!"

"Nome, I ain't a good man," The Misfit said after a second as if he had considered her statement carefully, "but I ain't the worst in the world neither. My daddy said I was different breed of dog from my brothers and sisters. 'You know,' Daddy said, 'it's some that can live their whole life out without asking about it and it's others has to know why it is, and this boy is one of the latters. He's going to be into everything!'" He put on his black hat and looked up suddenly and then away deep into the woods as if he were embarrassed again. "I'm sorry I don't have on a shirt before you ladies," he said, hunching his shoulders slightly. "We buried our clothes that we had on when we escaped and we're just making do until we can get better. We borrowed these from some folks we met," he explained.

"That's perfectly all right," the grandmother said. "Maybe Bailey has an extra shirt in his suitcase."

"I'll look and see terrectly," The Misfit said.

"Where are they taking him?" the children's mother screamed.

"Daddy was a card himself," The Misfit said. "You couldn't put anything over on him. He never got in trouble with the Authorities though. Just had the knack of handling them."

"You could be honest too if you'd only try," said the grandmother. "Think how wonderful it would be to settle down and live a comfortable life and not have to think about somebody chasing you all the time."

The Misfit kept scratching in the ground with the butt of his gun as if he were thinking about it. "Yes'm, somebody is always after you," he murmured.

The grandmother noticed how thin his shoulder blades were just behind his hat because she was standing up looking down on him. "Do you ever pray?" she asked.

He shook his head. All she saw was the black hat wiggle between his shoulder blades. "Nome," he said.

There was a pistol shot from the woods, followed closely by another. Then silence. The old lady's head jerked around. She could hear the wind move through the tree tops like a long satisfied insuck of breath. "Bailey Boy!" she called.

"I was a gospel singer for a while," The Misfit said. "I been most everything. Been in the arm service, both land and sea, at home and abroad, been twict married, been an undertaker, been with the railroads, plowed Mother Earth, been in a tornado, seen a man burnt alive oncet," and he looked up at the children's mother and the little girl who were sitting close together, their faces white and their eyes glassy; "I even seen a woman flogged," he said.

"Pray, pray," the grandmother began, "pray, pray. . . ."

"I never was a bad boy that I remember of," The Misfit said in an almost dreamy voice, "but somewheres along the line I done something wrong and got sent to the penitentiary. I was buried alive," and he looked up and held her attention to him by a steady stare.

"That's when you should have started to pray," she said. "What did you do to get sent to the penitentiary that first time?"

"Turn to the right, it was a wall," The Misfit said, looking up again at the cloudless sky. "Turn to the left, it was a wall. Look up it was a ceiling, look down it was a floor. I forget what I done, lady. I set there and set there, trying to remember what it was I done and I ain't recalled it to this day. Oncet in a while, I would think it was coming to me, but it never come."

"Maybe they put you in by mistake," the old lady said vaguely.

"Nome," he said. "It wasn't no mistake. They had the papers on me."

"You must have stolen something," she said.

The Misfit sneered slightly. "Nobody had nothing I wanted," he said. "It was a head-doctor at the penitentiary said what I had done was kill my daddy but I known that for a lie. My daddy died in nineteen ought nineteen of the epidemic flu and I never had a thing to do with it. He was buried in the Mount Hopewell Baptist churchyard and you can go there and see for yourself."

"If you would pray," the old lady said, "Jesus would help you."

"That's right," The Misfit said.

"Well then, why don't you pray?" she asked trembling with delight suddenly.

"I don't want no hep," he said. "I'm doing all right by myself."

Bobby Lee and Hiram came ambling back from the woods. Bobby Lee was dragging a yellow shirt with bright blue parrots in it.

"Throw me that shirt, Bobby Lee," The Misfit said. The shirt came flying at him and landed on his shoulder and he put it on. The grandmother couldn't name what the shirt reminded her of. "No, lady," The Misfit said while he was buttoning it up, "I found out the crime don't matter. You can do one thing or you can do another, kill a man or take a tire off his car, because sooner or later you're going to forget what it was you done and just be punished for it."

The children's mother had begun to make heaving noises as if she couldn't get her breath. "Lady," he asked, "would you and that little girl like to step off yonder with Bobby Lee and Hiram and join your husband?"

"Yes, thank you," the mother said faintly. Her left arm dangled helplessly and she was holding the baby, who had gone to sleep, in the other. "Hep that lady up, Hiram," The Misfit said as she struggled to climb out of the ditch, "and Bobby Lee, you hold onto that little girl's hand."

"I don't want to hold hands with him," June Star said. "He reminds me of a pig."

The fat boy blushed and laughed and caught her by the arm and pulled her off into the woods after Hiram and her mother.

Alone with The Misfit, the grandmother found that she had lost her voice. There was not a cloud in the sky nor any sun. There was nothing around her but woods. She wanted to tell him that he must pray. She opened and closed her mouth several times before anything came out. Finally she found herself saying, "Jesus. Jesus," meaning, Jesus will help you, but the way she was saying it, it sounded as if she might be cursing.

"Yes'm," The Misfit said as if he agreed. "Jesus thown everything off balance. It was the same case with Him as with me except He hadn't committed any crime and they could prove I had committed one because they had the papers on me. Of course," he said, "they never shown me my papers. That's why I sign myself now. I said long ago, you get you a signature and sign everything you do and keep a copy of it. Then you'll know what you done and you can hold up the crime to the punishment and see do they match and in the end you'll have something to prove you ain't been treated right. I call myself The Misfit," he said, "because I can't make what all I done wrong fit what all I gone through in punishment."

There was a piercing scream from the woods, followed closely by a pistol report. "Does it seem right to you, lady, that one is punished a heap and another ain't punished at all?"

"Jesus!" the old lady cried. "You've got good blood! I know you wouldn't shoot a lady! I know you come from nice people! Pray! Jesus, you ought not to shoot a lady. I'll give you all the money I've got!"

"Lady," The Misfit said, looking beyond her far into the woods, "there never was a body that give the undertaker a tip."

There were two more pistol reports and the grandmother raised her head like a parched old turkey hen crying for water and called, "Bailey Boy, Bailey Boy!" as if her heart would break.

"Jesus was the only One that ever raised the dead," The Misfit continued, "and He shouldn't have done it. He thown everything off balance. If He did what He said, then it's nothing for you to do but thow away everything and follow Him, and if He didn't then it's nothing for you to do but enjoy the few minutes you got left the best way you can—by killing somebody or burning down his house or doing some other meanness to him. No pleasure but meanness," he said and his voice had become almost a snarl.

"Maybe He didn't raise the dead," the old lady mumbled, not knowing what she was saying and feeling so dizzy that she sank down in the ditch with her legs twisted under her.

"I wasn't there so I can't say He didn't," The Misfit said. "I wisht I had of been there," he said, hitting the ground with his fist. "It ain't right I wasn't there because if I had of been there I would of known. Listen lady," he said in a high voice, "if I had of been there I would of known and I wouldn't be like I am now." His voice seemed about to crack and the grandmother's head cleared for an instant. She saw the man's face twisted close to her own as if he were going to cry and she murmured, "Why, you're one of my babies. You're one of my own children!" She reached out and touched him on the shoulder. The Misfit sprang back as if a snake had bitten him and shot her three times through the chest. Then he put his gun down on the ground and took off his glasses and began to clean them.

Hiram and Bobby Lee returned from the woods and stood over the ditch, looking down at the grandmother who half sat and half lay in a puddle of blood with her legs crossed under her like a child's and her face smiling up at the cloudless sky.

Without his glasses, The Misfit's eyes were red-rimmed and pale and defenseless-looking. "Take her off and thow her where you thown the others," he said, picking up the cat that was rubbing itself against his leg.

"She was a talker, wasn't she?" Bobby Lee said, sliding down the ditch with a yodel.

"She would of been a good woman," The Misfit said, "if it had been somebody there to shoot her every minute of her life."

"Some fun!" Bobby Lee said.

"Shut up, Bobby Lee," The Misfit said. "It's no real pleasure in life."

Henry James (1843–1916)

THE PUPIL

The Pupil, though he has little aging to do, does age as the story progresses. Does he too come to think of his tutor as one to be used? Father, son, and daughters are types, mother is a lively caricature, pupil and teacher are human beings in the foreground; and having established these planes of moral reality, James can surround Morgan, as he ages, with the menace of moving back to one of the simpler planes. In the latter pages of the story he is already playing at living in a simpler kind of fiction than James is writing.

— *1* —

THE poor young man hesitated and procrastinated: it cost him such an effort to broach the subject of terms, to speak of money to a person who spoke only of feelings and, as it were, of the aristocracy. Yet he was unwilling to take leave, treating his engagement as settled, without some more conventional glance in that direction than he could find an opening for in the manner of the large affable lady who sat there drawing a pair of soiled *gants de Suède* through a fat jewelled hand and, at once pressing and gliding, repeated over and over everything but the thing he would have liked to hear. He would have liked to hear the figure of his salary; but just as he was nervously about to sound that note the little boy came back—the little boy Mrs. Moreen had sent out of the room to fetch her fan. He came back without the fan, only with the casual observation that he couldn't find it. As he dropped this cynical confession he looked straight and hard at the candidate for the honor of taking his education in hand. This personage reflected somewhat grimly that the first thing he should have to teach his little charge would be to appear to address himself to his mother when he spoke to her—especially not to make her such an improper answer as that.

When Mrs. Moreen bethought herself of this pretext for getting rid of their companion Pemberton supposed it was precisely to approach the

From *The Better Sort*. Reprinted by permission of Paul R. Reynolds & Son.

delicate subject of his remuneration. But it had been only to say some things about her son that it was better a boy of eleven shouldn't catch. They were extravagantly to his advantage save when she lowered her voice to sigh, tapping her left side familiarly, "And all overclouded by *this,* you know; all at the mercy of a weakness—!" Pemberton gathered that the weakness was in the region of the heart. He had known the poor child was not robust: this was the basis on which he had been invited to treat, through an English lady, an Oxford acquaintance, then at Nice, who happened to know both his needs and those of the amiable American family looking out for something really superior in the way of a resident tutor.

The young man's impression of his prospective pupil, who had come into the room as if to see for himself the moment Pemberton was admitted, was not quite the soft solicitation the visitor had taken for granted. Morgan Moreen was somehow sickly without being "delicate," and that he looked intelligent—it is true Pemberton wouldn't have enjoyed his being stupid—only added to the suggestion that, as with his big mouth and big ears he really couldn't be called pretty, he might too utterly fail to please. Pemberton was modest, was even timid; and the chance that his small scholar would prove cleverer than himself had quite figured, to his anxiety, among the dangers of an untried experiment. He reflected, however, that these were risks one had to run when one accepted a position, as it was called, in a private family; when as yet one's university honors had, pecuniarily speaking, remained barren. At any rate when Mrs. Moreen got up as to intimate that, since it was understood he would enter upon his duties within the week she would let him off now, he succeeded, in spite of the presence of the child, in squeezing out a phrase about the rate of payment. It was not the fault of the conscious smile which seemed a reference to the lady's expensive identity, it was not the fault of this demonstration, which had, in a sort, both vagueness and point, if the allusion didn't sound rather vulgar. This was exactly because she became still more gracious to reply: "Oh I can assure you that all that will be quite regular."

Pemberton only wondered, while he took up his hat, what "all that" was to amount to—people had such different ideas. Mrs. Moreen's words, however, seemed to commit the family to a pledge definite enough to elicit from the child a strange little comment in the shape of the mocking foreign ejaculation "Oh la-la!"

Pemberton, in some confusion, glanced at him as he walked slowly to the window with his back turned, his hands in his pockets and the air in his elderly shoulders of a boy who didn't play. The young man wondered if he should be able to teach him to play, though his mother had said it would never do and that this was why school was impossible.

Mrs. Moreen exhibited no discomfiture; she only continued blandly: "Mr. Moreen will be delighted to meet your wishes. As I told you, he has been called to London for a week. As soon as he comes back you shall have it out with him."

This was so frank and friendly that the young man could only reply, laughing as his hostess laughed: "Oh I don't imagine we shall have much of a battle."

"They'll give you anything you like," the boy remarked unexpectedly, returning from the window. "We don't mind what anything costs—we live awfully well."

"My darling, you're too quaint!" his mother exclaimed, putting out to caress him a practiced but ineffectual hand. He slipped out of it, but looked with intelligent innocent eyes at Pemberton, who had already had time to notice that from one moment to the other his small satiric face seemed to change its time of life. At this moment it was infantine, yet it appeared also to be under the influence of curious intuitions and knowledges. Pemberton rather disliked precocity and was disappointed to find gleams of it in a disciple not yet in his teens. Nevertheless he divined on the spot that Morgan wouldn't prove a bore. He would prove on the contrary a source of agitation. This idea held the young man, in spite of a certain repulsion.

"You pompous little person! We're not extravagant!" Mrs. Moreen gaily protested, making another unsuccessful attempt to draw the boy to her side. "You must know what to expect," she went on to Pemberton.

"The less you expect the better!" her companion interposed. "But we *are* people of fashion."

"Only so far as *you* make us so!" Mrs. Moreen tenderly mocked. "Well then, on Friday—don't tell me you're superstitious—and mind you don't fail us. Then you'll see us all. I'm so sorry the girls are out. I guess you'll like the girls. And, you know, I've another son, quite different from this one."

"He tries to imitate me," Morgan said to their friend.

"He tries? Why he's twenty years old!" cried Mrs. Moreen.

"You're very witty," Pemberton remarked to the child—a proposition his mother echoed with enthusiasm, declaring Morgan's sallies to be the delight of the house.

The boy paid no heed to this; he only enquired abruptly of the visitor, who was surprised afterwards that he hadn't struck him as offensively forward: "Do you *want* very much to come?"

"Can you doubt it after such a description of what I shall hear?" Pemberton replied. Yet he didn't want to come at all; he was coming because he had to go somewhere, thanks to the collapse of his fortune at the end of a year abroad spent on the system of putting his scant

patrimony into a single full wave of experience. He had had his full
wave but couldn't pay the score at his inn. Moreover he had caught in
the boy's eyes the glimpse of a far-off appeal.

"Well, I'll do the best I can for you," said Morgan; with which he
turned away again. He passed out of one of the long windows; Pemberton saw him go and lean on the parapet of the terrace. He remained
there while the young man took leave of his mother, who, on Pemberton's looking as if he expected a farewell from him, interposed with:
"Leave him, leave him; he's so strange!" Pemberton supposed her to fear
something he might say. "He's a genius—you'll love him," she added.
"He's much the most interesting person in the family." And before he
could invent some civility to oppose to this she wound up with: "But
we're all good, you know!"

"He's a genius—you'll love him!" were words that recurred to our
aspirant before the Friday, suggesting among many things that geniuses
were not invariably loveable. However, it was all the better if there was
an element that would make tutorship absorbing: he had perhaps taken
too much for granted it would only disgust him. As he left the villa
after his interview he looked up at the balcony and saw the child leaning over it. "We shall have great larks!" he called up.

Morgan hung fire a moment and then gaily returned: "By the time
you come back I shall have thought of something witty!"

This made Pemberton say to himself "After all, he's rather nice."

— 2 —

On the Friday he saw them all, as Mrs. Moreen had promised, for
her husband had come back and the girls and the other son were at
home. Mr. Moreen had a white moustache, a confiding manner and, in
his buttonhole, the ribbon of a foreign order—bestowed, as Pemberton
eventually learned, for services. For what services he never clearly ascer-
tained: this was a point—one of a larger number—that Mr. Moreen's
manner never confided. What it emphatically did confide was that he
was even more a man of the world than you might first make out. Ulick,
the firstborn, was in visible training for the same profession—under the
disadvantage as yet, however, of a buttonhole but feebly floral and a
moustache with no pretensions to type. The girls had hair and figures
and manners and small fat feet, but had never been out alone. As for
Mrs. Moreen, Pemberton saw on a nearer view that her elegance was
intermittent and her parts didn't always match. Her husband, as she had
promised, met with enthusiasm Pemberton's ideas in regard to a salary.
The young man had endeavored to keep these stammerings modest, and
Mr. Moreen made it no secret that *he* found them wanting in "style."

He further mentioned that he aspired to be intimate with his children, to be their best friend, and that he was always looking out for them. That was what he went off for, to London and other places—to look out; and this vigilance was the theory of life, as well as the real occupation, of the whole family. They all looked out, for they were very frank on the subject of its being necessary. They desired it to be understood that they were earnest people, and also that their fortune, though quite adequate for earnest people, required the most careful administration. Mr. Moreen, as the parent bird, sought sustenance for the nest. Ulick invoked support mainly at the club, where Pemberton guessed that it was usually served on green cloth. The girls used to do up their hair and their frocks themselves, and our young man felt appealed to to be glad, in regard to Morgan's education, that, though it must naturally be of the best, it didn't cost too much. After a little he *was* glad, forgetting at times his own needs in the interest inspired by the child's character and culture and the pleasure of making easy terms for him.

During the first weeks of their acquaintance Morgan had been as puzzling as a page in an unknown language—altogether different from the obvious little Anglo-Saxons who had misrepresented childhood to Pemberton. Indeed the whole mystic volume in which the boy had been amateurishly bound demanded some practice in translation. Today, after a considerable interval, there is something phantasmagoric, like a prismatic reflexion or a serial novel, in Pemberton's memory of the queerness of the Moreens. If it were not for a few tangible tokens—a lock of Morgan's hair cut by his own hand, and the half-dozen letters received from him when they were disjoined—the whole episode and the figures peopling it would seem too inconsequent for anything but dreamland. Their supreme quaintness was their success—as it appeared to him for a while at the time; since he had never seen a family so brilliantly equipped for failure. Wasn't it success to have kept him so hatefully long? Wasn't it success to have drawn him in that first morning at *déjeuner,* the Friday he came—it was enough to *make* one superstitious— so that he utterly committed himself, and this not by calculation or on a signal, but from a happy instinct which made them, like a band of gypsies, work so neatly together? They amused him as much as if they had really been a band of gypsies. He was still young and had not seen much of the world—his English years had been properly arid; therefore the reversed conventions of the Moreens—for they had *their* desperate properties—struck him as topsy-turvy. He had encountered nothing like them at Oxford; still less had any such note been struck to his younger American ear during the four years at Yale in which he had richly supposed himself to be reacting against a Puritan strain. The reaction of the Moreens, at any rate, went ever so much further. He had thought himself very sharp that first day in hitting them all off in his mind with the "cosmopolite" label. Later it seemed feeble and colorless—confessedly helplessly provisional.

He yet when he first applied it felt a glow of joy—for an instructor he was still empirical—rise from the apprehension that living with them would really be to see life. Their sociable strangeness was an imitation of that—their chatter of tongues, their gaiety and good humour, their infinite dawdling (they were always getting themselves up, but it took for ever, and Pemberton had once found Mr. Moreen shaving in the drawing room), their French, their Italian and, cropping up in the foreign fluencies, their cold tough slices of American. They lived on maccaroni and coffee—they had these articles prepared in perfection—but they knew recipes for a hundred other dishes. They overflowed with music and song, were always humming and catching each other up, and had a sort of professional acquaintance with Continental cities. They talked of "good places" as if they had been pickpockets or strolling players. They had at Nice a villa, a carriage, a piano and a banjo, and they went to official parties. They were a perfect calendar of the "days" of their friends; which Pemberton knew them, when they were indisposed, to get out of bed to go to, and which made the week larger than life when Mrs. Moreen talked of them with Paula and Amy. Their initiations gave their new inmate at first an almost dazzling sense of culture. Mrs. Moreen had translated something at some former period—an author whom it made Pemberton feel *borné* never to have heard of. They could imitate Venetian and sing Neapolitan, and when they wanted to say something very particular communicated with each other in an ingenious dialect of their own, an elastic spoken cipher which Pemberton at first took for some *patois* of one of their countries, but which he "caught on to" as he would not have grasped provincial development of Spanish or German.

"It's the family language—Ultramoreen," Morgan explained to him drolly enough; but the boy rarely condescended to use it himself, though he dealt in colloquial Latin as if he had been a little prelate.

Among all the "days" with which Mrs. Moreen's memory was taxed she managed to squeeze in one of her own, which her friends sometimes forgot. But the house drew a frequented air from the number of fine people who were freely named there and from several mysterious men with foreign titles and English clothes whom Morgan called the Princes and who, on sofas with the girls, talked French very loud—though sometimes with some oddity of accent—as if to show they were saying nothing improper. Pemberton wondered how the Princes could ever propose in that tone and so publicly: he took for granted cynically that this was what was desired of them. Then he recognized that even for the chance of such an advantage Mrs. Moreen would never allow Paula and Amy to receive alone. These young ladies were not at all timid, but it was just the safeguards that made them so candidly free. It was a houseful of Bohemians who wanted tremendously to be Philistines.

In one respect, however, certainly, they achieved no rigor—they were wonderfully amiable and ecstatic about Morgan. It was a genuine tenderness, an artless admiration, equally strong in each. They even praised his beauty, which was small, and were as afraid of him as if they felt him of finer clay. They spoke of him as a little angel and a prodigy— they touched on his want of health with long, vague faces. Pemberton feared at first an extravagance that might make him hate the boy, but before this happened he had become extravagant himself. Later, when he had grown rather to hate the others, it was a bribe to patience for him that they were at any rate nice about Morgan, going on tiptoe if they fancied he was showing symptoms, and even giving up somebody's "day" to procure him a pleasure. Mixed with this too was the oddest wish to make him independent, as if they had felt themselves not good enough for him. They passed him over to the new members of their circle very much as if wishing to force some charity of adoption on so free an agent and get rid of their own charge. They were delighted when they saw Morgan take so to his kind playfellow, and could think of no higher praise for the young man. It was strange how they contrived to reconcile the appearance, and indeed the essential fact, of adoring the child with their eagerness to wash their hands of him. Did they want to get rid of him before he should find them out? Pemberton was finding them out month by month. The boy's fond family, however this might be, turned their back with exaggerated delicacy, as if to avoid the reproach of interfering. Seeing in time how little he had in common with them—it was by *them* he first observed it; they proclaimed it with complete humility— his companion was moved to speculate on the mysteries of transmission, the far jumps of heredity. Where his detachment from most of the things they represented had come from was more than an observer could say— it certainly had burrowed under two or three generations.

As for Pemberton's own estimate of his pupil, it was a good while before he got the point of view, so little had he been prepared for it by the smug young barbarians to whom the tradition of tutorship, as hitherto revealed to him, had been adjusted. Morgan was scrappy and surprising, deficient in many properties supposed common to the *genus* and abounding in others that were the portion only of the supernaturally clever. One day his friend made a great stride: it cleared up the question to perceive that Morgan *was* supernaturally clever and that, though the formula was temporarily meagre, this would be the only assumption on which one could successfully deal with him. He had the general quality of a child for whom life had not been simplified by school, a kind of homebred sensibility which might have been bad for himself but was charming for others, and a whole range of refinement and perception—

little musical vibrations as taking as picked-up airs—begotten by wandering about Europe at the tail of his migratory tribe. This might not have
been an education to recommend in advance, but its results with so
special a subject were as appreciable as the marks on a piece of fine
porcelain. There was at the same time in him a small strain of stoicism,
doubtless the fruit of having had to begin early to bear pain, which
counted for pluck and made it of less consequence that he might have
been thought at school rather a polyglot little beast. Pemberton indeed
quickly found himself rejoicing that school was out of the question: in
any million of boys it was probably good for all but one, and Morgan was
that millionth. It would have made him comparative and superior—it
might have made him really require kicking. Pemberton would try to be
school himself—a bigger seminary than five hundred grazing donkeys,
so that, winning no prizes, the boy would remain unconscious and irresponsible and amusing—amusing, because, though life was already intense in his childish nature, freshness still made there a strong draught
for jokes. It turned out that even in the still air of Morgan's various dis-
abilities jokes flourished greatly. He was a pale lean acute undeveloped
little cosmopolite, who liked intellectual gymnastics and who also, as
regards the behavior of mankind, had noticed more things than you
might suppose, but who nevertheless had his proper playroom of super-
stitions, where he smashed a dozen toys a day.

— 3 —

At Nice once, toward evening, as the pair rested in the open air after
a walk, and looked over the sea at the pink western lights, he said suddenly to his comrade: "Do you like it, you know—being with us all in
this intimate way?"

"My dear fellow, why should I stay if I didn't?"

"How do I know you'll stay? I'm almost sure you won't, very long."

"I hope you don't mean to dismiss me," said Pemberton.

Morgan debated, looking at the sunset. "I think if I did right I ought
to."

"Well, I know I'm supposed to instruct you in virtue; but in that case
don't do right."

"You're very young—fortunately," Morgan went on, turning to him
again.

"Oh yes, compared with you!"

"Therefore it won't matter so much if you do lose a lot of time."

"That's the way to look at it," said Pemberton accommodatingly.

They were silent a minute; after which the boy asked: "Do you like
my father and my mother very much?"

"Dear me, yes. Charming people."

Morgan received this with another silence; then unexpectedly, familiarly, but at the same time affectionately, he remarked: "You're a jolly old humbug!"

For a particular reason the words made our young man change color. The boy noticed in an instant that he had turned red, whereupon he turned red himself and pupil and master exchanged a longish glance in which there was a consciousness of many more things than are usually touched upon, even tacitly, in such a relation. It produced for Pemberton an embarrassment; it raised in a shadowy form a question—this was the first glimpse of it—destined to play a singular and, as he imagined, owing to the altogether peculiar conditions, an unprecedented part in his intercourse with his little companion. Later, when he found himself talking with the youngster in a way in which few youngsters could ever have been talked with, he thought of that clumsy moment on the bench at Nice as the dawn of an understanding that had broadened. What had added to the clumsiness then was that he thought it his duty to declare to Morgan that he might abuse him, Pemberton, as much as he liked, but must never abuse his parents. To this Morgan had the easy retort that he hadn't dreamed of abusing them; which appeared to be true: it put Pemberton in the wrong.

"Then why am I a humbug for saying I think them charming?" the young man asked, conscious of a certain rashness.

"Well—they're not your parents."

"They love you better than anything in the world—never forget that," said Pemberton.

"Is that why you like them so much?"

"They're very kind to me," Pemberton replied evasively.

"You *are* a humbug!" laughed Morgan, passing an arm into his tutor's. He leaned against him looking off at the sea again and swinging his long thin legs.

"Don't kick my shins," said Pemberton while he reflected "Hang it, I can't complain of them to the child!"

"There's another reason too," Morgan went on, keeping his legs still.

"Another reason for what?"

"Besides their not being your parents."

"I don't understand you," said Pemberton.

"Well, you will before long. All right!"

He did understand fully before long, but he made a fight even with himself before he confessed it. He thought it the oddest thing to have a struggle with the child about. He wondered he didn't hate the hope of the Moreens for bringing the struggle on. But by the time it began any such sentiment for that scion was closed to him. Morgan was a special case, and to know him was to accept him on his own odd terms. Pember-

ton had spent his aversion to special cases before arriving at knowledge.
When at last he did arrive his quandary was great. Against every interest
he had attached himself. They would have to meet things together. Before they went home that evening at Nice the boy had said, clinging to
his arm:

"Well, at any rate you'll hang on to the last."

"To the last?"

"Till you're fairly beaten."

"*You* ought to be fairly beaten!" cried the young man, drawing him
closer.

— 4 —

A year after he had come to live with them Mr. and Mrs. Moreen
suddenly gave up the villa at Nice. Pemberton had got used to suddenness, having seen it practiced on a considerable scale during two jerky
little tours—one in Switzerland the first summer, and the other late in the
winter, when they all ran down to Florence and then, at the end of ten
days, liking it much less than they had intended, straggled back in mysterious depression. They had returned to Nice "for ever," as they said;
but this didn't prevent their squeezing, one rainy muggy May night, into
a second-class railway carriage—you could never tell by which class they
would travel—where Pemberton helped them to stow away a wonderful
collection of bundles and bags. The explanation of this maneuver was
that they had determined to spend the summer "in some bracing place";
but in Paris they dropped into a small furnished apartment—a fourth
floor in a third-rate avenue, where there was a smell on the staircase and
the *portier* was hateful—and passed the next four months in blank in-
digence.

The better part of this baffled sojourn was for the preceptor and his
pupil, who, visiting the Invalides and Notre Dame, the Conciergerie
and all the museums, took a hundred remunerative rambles. They
learned to know their Paris, which was useful for they came back another
year for a longer stay, the general character of which in Pemberton's
memory today mixes pitiably and confusedly with that of the first. He
sees Morgan's shabby knickerbockers—the everlasting pair that didn't
match his blouse and that as he grew longer could only grow faded. He
remembers the particular holes in his three or four pair of colored stockings.

Morgan was dear to his mother, but he never was better dressed than
was absolutely necessary—partly, no doubt, by his own fault, for he was
as indifferent to his appearance as a German philosopher. "My dear fellow, you *are* coming to pieces," Pemberton would say to him in skeptical

remonstrance; to which the child would reply, looking at him serenely up and down: "My dear fellow, so are you! I don't want to cast you in the shade." Pemberton could have no rejoinder for this—the assertion so closely represented the fact. If, however, the deficiencies of his own wardrobe were a chapter by themselves, he didn't like his little charge to look too poor. Later he used to say "Well, if we're poor, why, after all, shouldn't we look it?" and he consoled himself with thinking there was something rather elderly and gentlemanly in Morgan's disrepair—it differed from the untidiness of the urchin who plays and spoils his things. He could trace perfectly the degrees by which, in proportion as her little son confined himself to his tutor for society, Mrs. Moreen shrewdly forbore to renew his garments. She did nothing that didn't show, neglected him because he escaped notice, and then, as he illustrated this clever policy, discouraged at home his public appearances. Her position was logical enough—those members of her family who did show had to be showy.

During this period and several others Pemberton was quite aware of how he and his comrade might strike people; wandering languidly through the Jardin des Plantes as if they had nowhere to go, sitting on the winter days in the galleries of the Louvre, so splendidly ironical to the homeless, as if for the advantage of the *calorifère*. They joked about it sometimes: it was the sort of joke that was perfectly within the boy's compass. They figured themselves as part of the vast vague hand-to-mouth multitude of the enormous city and pretended they were proud of their position in it—it showed them "such a lot of life" and made them conscious of a democratic brotherhood. If Pemberton couldn't feel a sympathy in destitution with his small companion—for after all Morgan's fond parents would never have let him really suffer—the boy would at least feel it with him, so it came to the same thing. He used sometimes to wonder what people would think they were—to fancy they were looked askance at, as if it might be a suspected case of kidnapping. Morgan wouldn't be taken for a young patrician with a preceptor—he wasn't smart enough; though he might pass for his companion's sickly little brother. Now and then he had a five-franc piece, and except once, when they bought a couple of lovely neckties, one of which he made Pemberton accept, they laid it out scientifically in old books. This was sure to be a great day, always spent on the quays, in a rummage of the dusty boxes that garnish the parapets. Such occasions helped them to live, for their books ran low very soon after the beginning of their acquaintance. Pemberton had a good many in England, but he was obliged to write to a friend and ask him kindly to get some fellow to give him something for them.

If they had to relinquish that summer the advantage of the bracing climate, the young man couldn't but suspect this failure of the cup when at their very lips to have been the effect of a rude jostle of his own. This had represented his first blow-out, as he called it, with his patrons; his first successful attempt—though there was little other success about it—to bring them to a consideration of his impossible position. As the ostensible eve of a costly journey the moment had struck him as favorable to an earnest protest, the presentation of an ultimatum. Ridiculous as it sounded, he had never yet been able to compass an uninterrupted private interview with the elder pair or with either of them singly. They were always flanked by their elder children, and poor Pemberton usually had his own little charge at his side. He was conscious of its being a house in which the surface of one's delicacy got rather smudged; nevertheless he had preserved the bloom of his scruple against announcing to Mr. and Mrs. Moreen with publicity that he shouldn't be able to go on longer without a little money. He was still simple enough to suppose Ulick and Paula and Amy might not know that since his arrival he had only had a hundred and forty francs; and he was magnanimous enough to wish not to compromise their parents in their eyes. Mr. Moreen now listened to him, as he listened to every one and to every thing, like a man of the world, and seemed to appeal to him—though not of course too grossly—to try and be a little more of one himself. Pemberton recognized in fact the importance of the character—from the advantage it gave Mr. Moreen. He was not even confused or embarrassed, whereas the young man in his service was more so than there was any reason for. Neither was he surprised—at least any more than a gentleman had to be who freely confessed himself a little shocked—though not perhaps strictly at Pemberton.

"We must go into this, mustn't we, dear?" he said to his wife. He assured his young friend that the matter should have his very best attention; and he melted into space as elusively as if, at the door, he were taking an inevitable but deprecatory precedence. When, the next moment, Pemberton found himself alone with Mrs. Moreen it was to hear her say "I see, I see"—stroking the roundness of her chin and looking as if she were only hesitating between a dozen easy remedies. If they didn't make their push Mr. Moreen could at least disappear for several days. During his absence his wife took up the subject again spontaneously, but her contribution to it was merely that she had thought all the while they were getting on so beautifully. Pemberton's reply to this revelation was that unless they immediately put down something on account he would leave them on the spot and forever. He knew she would wonder how he would get away, and for a moment expected her to inquire. She didn't, for which he was almost grateful to her, so little was he in a position to tell.

"You won't, you *know* you won't—you're too interested," she said. "You *are* interested, you know you are, you dear kind man!" She laughed with almost condemnatory archness, as if it were a reproach—though she wouldn't insist; and flirted a soiled pocket handkerchief at him.

Pemberton's mind was fully made up to take his step the following week. This would give him time to get an answer to a letter he had dispatched to England. If he did in the event nothing of the sort—that is, if he stayed another year and then went away only for three months—it was not merely because before the answer to his letter came (most unsatisfactory when it did arrive) Mr. Moreen generously counted out to him, and again with the sacrifice to "form" of a marked man of the world, three hundred francs in elegant ringing gold. He was irritated to find that Mrs. Moreen was right, that he couldn't at the pinch bear to leave the child. This stood out clearer for the very reason that, the night of his desperate appeal to his patrons, he had seen fully for the first time where he was. Wasn't it another proof of the success with which those patrons practiced their arts that they had managed to avert for so long the illuminating flash? It descended on our friend with a breadth of effect which perhaps would have struck a spectator as comical, after he had returned to his little servile room, which looked into a close court where a bare dirty opposite wall took, with the sound of shrill clatter, the reflection of lighted back windows. He had simply given himself away to a band of adventurers. The idea, the word itself, wore a romantic horror for him—he had always lived on such safe lines. Later it assumed a more interesting, almost a soothing, sense: it pointed a moral, and Pemberton could enjoy a moral. The Moreens were adventurers not merely because they didn't pay their debts, because they lived on society, but because their whole view of life, dim and confused and instinctive, like that of clever color-blind animals, was speculative and rapacious and mean. Oh they were "respectable," and that only made them more *immondes!* The young man's analysis, while he brooded, put it at last very simply—they were adventurers because they were toadies and snobs. That was the completest account of them—it was the law of their being. Even when this truth became vivid to their ingenious inmate he remained unconscious of how much his mind had been prepared for it by the extraordinary little boy who had now become such a complication in his life. Much less could he then calculate on the information he was still to owe the extraordinary little boy.

— 5 —

But it was during the ensuing time that the real problem came up— the problem of how far it was excusable to discuss the turpitude of parents with a child of twelve, of thirteen, of fourteen. Absolutely inexcusable and quite impossible it of course at first appeared; and indeed the question didn't press for some time after Pemberton had received his three hundred francs. They produced a temporary lull, a relief from the sharpest pressure. The young man frugally amended his wardrobe and even had a few francs in his pocket. He thought the Moreens looked at him as if he were almost too smart, as if they ought to take care not to spoil him. If Mr. Moreen hadn't been such a man of the world he would perhaps have spoken of the freedom of such neckties on the part of a subordinate. But Mr. Moreen was always enough a man of the world to let things pass—he had certainly shown that. It was singular how Pemberton guessed that Morgan, though saying nothing about it, knew something had happened. But three hundred francs, especially when one owed money, couldn't last for ever; and when the treasure was gone—the boy knew when it had failed—Morgan did break ground. The party had returned to Nice at the beginning of the winter, but not to the charming villa. They went to an hotel, where they stayed three months, and then moved to another establishment, explaining that they had left the first because, after waiting and waiting, they couldn't get the rooms they wanted. These apartments, the rooms they wanted, were generally very splendid; but fortunately they never *could* get them— fortunately, I mean, for Pemberton, who reflected always that if they had got them there would have been a still scanter educational fund. What Morgan said at last was said suddenly, irrelevantly, when the moment came, in the middle of a lesson, and consisted of the apparently unfeeling words: "You ought to *filer*, you know—you really ought."

Pemberton stared. He had learnt enough French slang from Morgan to know that to *filer* meant to cut sticks. "Ah my dear fellow, don't turn me off!"

Morgan pulled a Greek lexicon toward him—he used a Greek-German —to look out a word, instead of asking it of Pemberton. "You can't go on like this, you know."

"Like what, my boy?"

"You know they don't pay you up," said Morgan, blushing and turning his leaves.

"Don't pay me?" Pemberton stared again and feigned amazement. "What on earth put that into your head?"

"It has been there a long time," the boy replied, rummaging his book.

Pemberton was silent, then he went on: "I say, what are you hunting for? They pay me beautifully."

"I'm hunting for the Greek for awful whopper," Morgan dropped.

"Find that rather for gross impertinence and disabuse your mind. What do I want of money?"

"Oh that's another question!"

Pemberton wavered—he was drawn in different ways. The severely correct thing would have been to tell the boy that such a matter was none of his business and bid him go on with his lines. But they were really too intimate for that; it was not the way he was in the habit of treating him; there had been no reason it should be. On the other hand Morgan had quite lighted on the truth—he really shouldn't be able to keep it up much longer; therefore why not let him know one's real motive for forsaking him? At the same time it wasn't decent to abuse to one's pupil the family of one's pupil; it was better to misrepresent than to do that. So in reply to his comrade's last exclamation he just declared, to dismiss the subject, that he had received several payments.

"I say—I say!" the boy ejaculated, laughing.

"That's all right," Pemberton insisted. "Give me your written rendering."

Morgan pushed a copybook across the table, and he began to read the page, but with something running in his head that made it no sense. Looking up after a minute or two he found the child's eyes fixed on him and felt in them something strange. Then Morgan said: "I'm not afraid of the stern reality."

"I haven't yet seen the thing you *are* afraid of—I'll do you that justice!"

This came out with a jump—it was perfectly true—and evidently gave Morgan pleasure. "I've thought of it a long time," he presently resumed.

"Well, don't think of it any more."

The boy appeared to comply, and they had a comfortable and even an amusing hour. They had a theory that they were very thorough, and yet they seemed always to be in the amusing part of lessons, the intervals between the dull dark tunnels, where there were waysides and jolly views. Yet the morning was brought to a violent end by Morgan's suddenly leaning his arms on the table, burying his head in them and bursting into tears: at which Pemberton was the more startled that, as it then came over him, it was the first time he had ever seen the boy cry and that the impression was consequently quite awful.

The next day, after much thought, he took a decision and, believing it to be just, immediately acted on it. He cornered Mr. and Mrs. Moreen again and let them know that if on the spot they didn't pay him all they owed him he wouldn't only leave their house but would tell Morgan exactly what had brought him to it.

"Oh you *haven't* told him?" cried Mrs. Moreen with a pacifying hand on her well-dressed bosom.

"Without warning you? For what do you take me?" the young man returned.

Mr. and Mrs. Moreen looked at each other; he could see that they appreciated, as tending to their security, his superstition of delicacy, and yet that there was a certain alarm in their relief. "My dear fellow," Mr.

Moreen demanded, "what use *can* you have, leading the quiet life we all do, for such a lot of money?"—a question to which Pemberton made no answer, occupied as he was in noting that what passed in the mind of his patrons was something like: "Oh then, if we've felt that the child, dear little angel, has judged us and how he regards us, and we haven't been betrayed, he must have guessed—and in short it's *general!*" an inference that rather stirred up Mr. and Mrs. Moreen, as Pemberton had desired it should. At the same time, if he had supposed his threat would do something towards bringing them round, he was disappointed to find them taking for granted—how vulgar their perception *had* been!—that he had already given them away. There was a mystic uneasiness in their parental breasts, and that had been the inferior sense of it. None the less, however, his threat did touch them; for if they had escaped it was only to meet a new danger. Mr. Moreen appealed to him, on every precedent, as a man of the world; but his wife had recourse, for the first time since his domestication with them, to a fine *hauteur,* reminding him that a devoted mother, with her child, had arts that protected her against gross misrepresentation.

"I should misrepresent you grossly if I accused you of common honesty!" our friend replied; but as he closed the door behind him sharply, thinking he had not done himself much good, while Mr. Moreen lighted another cigarette, he heard his hostess shout after him more touchingly:

"Oh you do, you *do,* put the knife to one's throat!"

The next morning, very early, she came to his room. He recognized her knock, but had no hope she brought him money; as to which he was wrong, for she had fifty francs in her hand. She squeezed forward in her dressing gown, and he received her in his own, between his bathtub and his bed. He had been tolerably schooled by this time to the "foreign ways" of his hosts. Mrs. Moreen was ardent, and when she was ardent she didn't care what she did; so she now sat down on his bed, his clothes being on the chairs, and, in her preoccupation, forgot, as she glanced round, to be ashamed of giving him such a horrid room. What Mrs. Moreen's ardor now bore upon was the design of persuading him that in the first place she was very good-natured to bring him fifty francs, and that in the second, if he would only see it, he was really too absurd to expect to be *paid*. Wasn't he paid enough without perpetual money—wasn't he paid by the comfortable luxurious home he enjoyed with them all, without a care, an anxiety, a solitary want? Wasn't he sure of his position, and wasn't that everything to a young man like him, quite unknown, with singularly little to show, the ground of whose exorbitant pretensions it had never been easy to discover? Wasn't he paid above all by the sweet relation he had established with Morgan—quite ideal as from master to pupil—and by the simple privilege of knowing and living with so amazingly gifted a child; than whom really (and she meant

literally what she said) there was no better company in Europe? Mrs.
Moreen herself took to appealing to him as a man of the world; she said
"*Voyons, mon cher,*" and "My dear man, look here now"; and urged him
to be reasonable, putting it before him that it was truly a chance for him.
She spoke as if, according as he *should* be reasonable, he would prove
himself worthy to be her son's tutor and of the extraordinary confidence
they had placed in him.

After all, Pemberton reflected, it was only a difference of theory and
the theory didn't matter much. They had hitherto gone on that of re-
munerated, as now they would go on that of gratuitous, service; but why
should they have so many words about it? Mrs. Moreen at all events
continued to be convincing; sitting there with her fifty francs she talked
and reiterated as women reiterate, and bored and irritated him, while he
leaned against the wall with his hands in the pockets of his wrapper,
drawing it together round his legs and looking over the head of his
visitor at the grey negations of his window. She wound up with saying:
"You see I bring you a definite proposal."

"A definite proposal?"

"To make our relations regular, as it were—to put them on a comfortable footing."

"I see—it's a system," said Pemberton. "A kind of organized blackmail."

Mrs. Moreen bounded up, which was exactly what he wanted. "What
do you mean by that?"

"You practice on one's fears—one's fears about the child if one should
go away."

"And pray what would happen to him in that event?" she demanded
with majesty.

"Why, he'd be alone with *you.*"

"And pray with whom *should* a child be but with those whom he
loves most?"

"If you think that, why don't you dismiss me?"

"Do you pretend he loves you more than he loves *us?*" cried Mrs.
Moreen.

"I think he ought to. I make sacrifices for him. Though I've heard of
those *you* make I don't see them."

Mrs. Moreen stared a moment; then with emotion she grasped her
inmate's hand. "*Will* you make it—the sacrifice?"

He burst out laughing. "I'll see. I'll do what I can. I'll stay a little
longer. Your calculation's just—I *do* hate intensely to give him up; I'm
fond of him and he thoroughly interests me, in spite of the inconven-
ience I suffer. You know my situation perfectly. I haven't a penny in the
world and, occupied as you see me with Morgan, am unable to earn
money."

Mrs. Moreen tapped her undressed arm with her folded bank note. "Can't you write articles? Can't you translate as I do?"

"I don't know about translating; it's wretchedly paid."

"I'm glad to earn what I can," said Mrs. Moreen with prodigious virtue.

"You ought to tell me who you do it for." Pemberton paused a moment, and she said nothing; so he added: "I've tried to turn off some little sketches, but the magazines won't have them—they're declined with thanks."

"You see then you're not such a phoenix," his visitor pointedly smiled—"to pretend to abilities you're sacrificing for our sake."

"I haven't time to do things properly," he ruefully went on. Then as it came over him that he was almost abjectly good-natured to give these explanations he added: "If I stay on longer it must be on one condition—that Morgan shall know distinctly on what footing I am."

Mrs. Moreen demurred. "Surely you don't want to show off to a child?"

"To show you off, do you mean?"

Again she cast about, but this time it was to produce a still finer flower. "And you talk of blackmail!"

"You can easily prevent it," said Pemberton.

"And you talk of practicing on fears!" she bravely pushed on.

"Yes, there's no doubt I'm a great scoundrel."

His patroness met his eyes—it was clear she was in straits. Then she thrust out her money at him. "Mr. Moreen desired me to give you this on account."

"I'm much obliged to Mr. Moreen, but we have no account."

"You won't take it?"

"That leaves me more free," said Pemberton.

"To poison my darling's mind?" groaned Mrs. Moreen.

"Oh your darling's mind—!" the young man laughed.

She fixed him a moment, and he thought she was going to break out tormentedly, pleadingly: "For God's sake, tell me what is in it!" But she checked this impulse—another was stronger. She pocketed the money—the crudity of the alternative was comical—and swept out of the room with the desperate concession: "You may tell him any horror you like!"

— 6 —

A couple of days after this, during which he had failed to profit by so free a permission, he had been for a quarter of an hour walking with his charge in silence when the boy became sociable again with the remark: "I'll tell you how I know it; I know it through Zénobie."

"Zénobie? Who in the world is *she?*"

"A nurse I used to have—ever so many years ago. A charming woman. I liked her awfully, and she liked me."

"There's no accounting for tastes. What is it you know through her?"

"Why what their idea is. She went away because they didn't fork out. She did like me awfully, and she stayed two years. She told me all about it—that at last she could never get her wages. As soon as they saw how much she liked me they stopped giving her anything. They thought she'd stay for nothing—just *because,* don't you know?" And Morgan had a queer little conscious lucid look. "She did stay ever so long—as long as she could. She was only a poor girl. She used to send money to her mother. At last she couldn't afford it any longer, and went away in a fearful rage one night—I mean of course in a rage against *them.* She cried over me tremendously, she hugged me nearly to death. She told me all about it," the boy repeated. "She told me it was their idea. So I guessed, ever so long ago, that they have had the same idea with you."

"Zénobie was very sharp," said Pemberton. "And she made you so."

"Oh that wasn't Zénobie; that was nature. And experience!" Morgan laughed.

"Well, Zénobie was a part of your experience."

"Certainly I was a part of hers, poor dear!" the boy wisely sighed. "And I'm part of yours."

"A very important part. But I don't see how you know I've been treated like Zénobie."

"Do you take me for the biggest dunce you've known?" Morgan asked, "Haven't I been conscious of what we've been through together?"

"What we've been through?"

"Our privations—our dark days."

"Oh, our days have been bright enough."

Morgan went on in silence for a moment. Then he said: "My dear chap, you're a hero!"

"Well, you're another!" Pemberton retorted.

"No I'm not, but I ain't a baby. I won't stand it any longer. You must get some occupation that pays. I'm ashamed, I'm ashamed!" quavered the boy with a ring of passion, like some high silver note from a small cathedral chorister, that deeply touched his friend.

"We ought to go off and live somewhere together," the younger man said.

"I'll go like a shot if you'll take me."

"I'd get some work that would keep us both afloat," Pemberton continued.

"So would I. Why shouldn't *I* work? I ain't such a beastly little muff as *that* comes to."

"The difficulty is that your parents wouldn't hear of it. They'd never part with you; they worship the ground you tread on. Don't you see the proof of it?" Pemberton developed. "They don't dislike me; they wish me no harm; they're very amiable people; but they're perfectly ready to expose me to any awkwardness in life for your sake."

The silence in which Morgan received his fond sophistry struck Pemberton somehow as expressive. After a moment the child repeated: "You *are* a hero!" Then he added: "They leave me with you altogether. You've all the responsibility. They put me off on you from morning till night. Why then should they object to my taking up with you completely? I'd help you."

"They're not particularly keen about my being helped, and they delight in thinking of you as *theirs*. They're tremendously proud of you."

"I'm not proud of *them*. But you know that," Morgan returned.

"Except for the little matter we speak of they're charming people," said Pemberton, not taking up the point made for his intelligence, but wondering greatly at the boy's own, and especially at this fresh reminder of something he had been conscious of from the first—the strangest thing in his friend's large little composition, a temper, a sensibility, even a private ideal, which made him as privately disown the stuff his people were made of. Morgan had in secret a small loftiness which made him acute about betrayed meanness; as well as a critical sense for the manners immediately surrounding him that was quite without precedent in a juvenile nature, especially when one noted that it had not made this nature "old-fashioned," as the word is of children—quaint or wizened or offensive. It was as if he had been a little gentleman and had paid the penalty by discovering that he was the only such person in his family. This comparison didn't make him vain, but it could make him melancholy and a trifle austere. While Pemberton guessed at these dim young things, shadows of shadows, he was partly drawn on and partly checked, as for a scruple, by the charm of attempting to sound the little cool shallows that were so quickly growing deeper. When he tried to figure to himself the morning twilight of childhood, so as to deal with it safely, he saw it was never fixed, never arrested, that ignorance, at the instant he touched it, was already flushing faintly into knowledge, that there was nothing that at a given moment you could say an intelligent child didn't know. It seemed to him that he himself knew too much to imagine Morgan's simplicity and too little to disembroil his tangle.

The boy paid no heed to his last remark; he only went on: "I'd have spoken to them about their idea, as I call it, long ago, if I hadn't been sure what they'd say."

"And what would they say?"

"Just what they said about what poor Zénobie told me—that it was a horrid dreadful story, that they had paid her every penny they owed her."

"Well, perhaps they had," said Pemberton.

"Perhaps they've paid you!"

"Let us pretend they have, and *n'en parlons plus.*"

"They accused her of lying and cheating"—Morgan stuck to historic truth. "That's why I don't want to speak to them."

"Lest they should accuse me too?" To this Morgan made no answer, and his companion, looking down at him—the boy turned away his eyes, which had filled—saw that he couldn't have trusted himself to utter. "You're right. Don't worry them," Pemberton pursued. "Except for that, they *are* charming people."

"Except for *their* lying and *their* cheating?"

"I say—I say!" cried Pemberton, imitating a little tone of the lad's which was itself an imitation.

"We must be frank, at the last; we *must* come to an understanding," said Morgan with the importance of the small boy who lets himself think he is arranging great affairs—almost playing at shipwreck or at Indians. "I know all about everything."

"I dare say your father has his reasons," Pemberton replied, but too vaguely, as he was aware.

"For lying and cheating?"

"For saving and managing and turning his means to the best account. He has plenty to do with his money. You're an expensive family."

"Yes, I'm very expensive," Morgan concurred in a manner that made his preceptor burst out laughing.

"He's saving for *you,*" said Pemberton. "They think of you in everything they do."

"He might, while he's about it, save a little—" The boy paused, and his friend waited to hear what. Then Morgan brought out oddly: "A little reputation."

"Oh there's plenty of that. That's all right!"

"Enough of it for the people they know, no doubt. The people they know are awful."

"Do you mean the princes? We mustn't abuse the princes."

"Why not? They haven't married Paula—they haven't married Amy. They only clean out Ulick."

"You *do* know everything!" Pemberton declared.

"No I don't after all. I don't know what they live on, or how they live, or *why* they live! What have they got and how did they get it? Are they rich, are they poor, or have they a *modeste aisance?* Why are they always chiveying me about—living one year like ambassadors and the next like paupers? Who are they, anyway, and what are they? I've thought of all that—I've thought of a lot of things. They're so beastly worldly. That's what I hate most—oh, I've *seen* it! All they care about is to make an appearance and to pass for something or other. What the dickens do they want to pass for? What *do* they, Mr. Pemberton?"

"You pause for a reply," said Pemberton, treating the question as a joke, yet wondering too and greatly struck with his mate's intense if imperfect vision. "I haven't the least idea."

"And what good does it do? Haven't I seen the way people treat them —the 'nice' people, the ones they want to know? They'll take anything from them—they'll lie down and be trampled on. The nice ones hate that—they just sicken them. You're the only really nice person we know."

"Are you sure? They don't lie down for me!"

"Well, you shan't lie down for them. You've got to go—that's what you've got to do," said Morgan.

"And what will become of you?"

"Oh I'm growing up. I shall get off before long. I'll see you later."

"You had better let me finish you," Pemberton urged, lending himself to the child's strange superiority.

Morgan stopped in their walk, looking up at him. He had to look up much less than a couple of years before—he had grown, in his loose lean-ness, so long and high. "Finish me?" he echoed.

"There are such a lot of jolly things we can do together yet. I want to turn you out—I want you to do me credit."

Morgan continued to look at him. "To give you credit—do you mean?"

"My dear fellow, you're too clever to live."

"That's just what I'm afraid you think. No, no; it isn't fair—I can't endure it. We'll separate next week. The sooner it's over the sooner to sleep."

"If I hear of anything—any other chance—I promise to go," Pemberton said.

Morgan consented to consider this. "But you'll be honest," he demanded; "you won't pretend you haven't heard?"

"I'm much more likely to pretend I have."

"But what can you hear of, this way, stuck in a hole with us? You ought to be on the spot, to go to England—you ought to go to America."

"One would think you were *my* tutor!" said Pemberton.

Morgan walked on and after a little had begun again: "Well, now that you know I know and that we look at the facts and keep nothing back—it's much more comfortable, isn't it?"

"My dear boy, it's so amusing, so interesting, that it will surely be quite impossible for me to forego such hours as these."

This made Morgan stop once more. "You *do* keep something back. Oh you're not straight—I am!"

"How am I not straight?"

"Oh you've got your idea!"

"My idea?"

"Why that I probably shan't make old—make older—bones, and that you can stick it out till I'm removed."

"You *are* too clever to live!" Pemberton repeated.

"I call it a mean idea," Morgan pursued. "But I shall punish you by the way I hang on."

"Look out or I'll poison you!" Pemberton laughed.

"I'm stronger and better every year. Haven't you noticed that there hasn't been a doctor near me since you came?"

"*I'm* your doctor," said the young man, taking his arm and drawing him tenderly on again.

Morgan proceeded and after a few steps gave a sigh of mingled weariness and relief. "Ah now that we look at the facts it's all right!"

— 7 —

They looked at the facts a good deal after this; and one of the first consequences of their doing so was that Pemberton stuck it out, in his friend's parlance, for the purpose. Morgan made the facts so vivid and so droll, and at the same time so bald and so ugly, that there was fascination in talking them over with him, just as there would have been heartlessness in leaving him alone with them. Now that the pair had such perceptions in common it was useless for them to pretend they didn't judge such people; but the very judgment and the exchange of perceptions created another tie. Morgan had never been so interesting as now that he himself was made plainer by the sidelight of these confidences. What came out in it most was the small fine passion of his pride. He had plenty of that, Pemberton felt—so much that one might perhaps wisely wish for it some early bruises. He would have liked his people to have a spirit and had waked up to the sense of their perpetually eating humble pie. His mother would consume any amount, and his father would consume even more than his mother. He had a theory that Ulick had wriggled out of an "affair" at Nice: there had once been a flurry at home, a regular panic, after which they all went to bed and took medicine, not to be accounted for on any other supposition. Morgan had a romantic imagination, fed by poetry and history, and he would have liked those who "bore his name"—as he used to say to Pemberton with the humor that made his queer delicacies manly—to carry themselves with an air. But their one idea was to get in with people who didn't want them and to take snubs as if they were honorable scars. Why people didn't want them more he didn't know—that was people's own affair; after all, they weren't superficially repulsive, they were a hundred times cleverer than most of the dreary grandees, the "poor swells" they rushed about Europe to catch up with. "After all, they *are* amusing—they are!" he used to pronounce with the wisdom of the ages. To which Pemberton always replied: "Amusing—the great Moreen troupe? Why they're altogether delightful; and if it weren't for the hitch that you and I (feeble performers!) make in the *ensemble* they'd carry everything before them."

What the boy couldn't get over was the fact that this particular blight seemed, in a tradition of self-respect, so undeserved and so arbitrary. No doubt people had a right to take the line they liked; but why should *his* people have liked the line of pushing and toadying and lying and cheating? What had their forefathers—all decent folk, so far as he knew—done to them, or what had *he* done to them? Who had poisoned their blood with the fifth-rate social ideal, the fixed idea of making smart acquaintances and getting into the *monde chic,* especially when it was foredoomed to failure and exposure? They showed so what they were after; that was what made the people they wanted not want *them.* And never a wince for dignity, never a throb of shame at looking each other in the face, never any independence or resentment or disgust. If his father or his brother would only knock someone down once or twice a year! Clever as they were, they never guessed the impression they made. They were good-natured, yes—as good-natured as Jews at the doors of clothing shops! But was that the model one wanted one's family to follow? Morgan had dim memories of an old grandfather, the maternal, in New York, whom he had been taken across the ocean at the age of five to see: a gentleman with a high neckcloth and a good deal of pronunciation, who wore a dress coat in the morning, which made one wonder what he wore in the evening, and had, or was supposed to have, "property," and something to do with the Bible Society. It couldn't have been but that *he* was a good type. Pemberton himself remembered Mrs. Clancy, a widowed sister of Mr. Moreen's, who was as irritating as a moral tale and had paid a fortnight's visit to the family at Nice shortly after he came to live with them. She was "pure and refined," as Amy said over the banjo, and had the air of not knowing what they meant when they talked, and of keeping something rather important back. Pemberton judged that what she kept back was an approval of many of their ways; therefore it was to be supposed that she too was of a good type, and that Mr. and Mrs. Moreen and Ulick and Paula and Amy might easily have been of a better one if they would.

But that they wouldn't was more and more perceptible from day to day. They continued to "chivey," as Morgan called it, and in due time became aware of a variety of reasons for proceeding to Venice. They mentioned a great many of them—they were always strikingly frank and had the brightest friendly chatter, at the late foreign breakfast in especial, before the ladies had made up their faces, when they leaned their arms on the table, had something to follow the demitasse, and, in the heat of familiar discussion as to what they "really ought" to do, fell inevitably into the languages in which they could *tutoyer*. Even Pemberton liked them then; he could endure even Ulick when he heard him give his little flat voice for the "sweet sea-city." That was what made him have a sneaking kindness for them—that they were so out of the workaday world and kept him so out of it. The summer had waned when, with cries of ecstasy, they all passed out on the balcony that overhung the Grand Canal. The sunsets then were splendid and the Dorringtons had arrived. The Dorringtons were the only reason they hadn't talked of at breakfast; but the reasons they didn't talk of at breakfast always came out in the end. The Dorringtons on the other hand came out very little; or else when they did they stayed—as was natural— for hours, during which periods Mrs. Moreen and the girls sometimes called at their hotel (to see if they had returned) as many as three times running. The gondola was for the ladies, as in Venice too there were "days," which Mrs. Moreen knew in their order an hour after she arrived. She immediately took one herself, to which the Dorringtons never came, though on a certain occasion when Pemberton and his pupil were together at Saint Mark's—where, taking the best walks they had ever had and haunting a hundred churches, they spent a great deal of time—they saw the old lord turn up with Mr. Moreen and Ulick, who showed him the dim basilica as if it belonged to them. Pemberton noted how much less, among its curiosities, Lord Dorrington carried himself as a man of the world; wondering too whether, for such services, his companions took a fee from him. The autumn at any rate waned, the Dorringtons departed, and Lord Verschoyle, the eldest son, had proposed neither for Amy nor for Paula.

One sad November day, while the wind roared round the old palace and the rain lashed the lagoon, Pemberton, for exercise and even somewhat for warmth—the Moreens were horribly frugal about fires; it was a cause of suffering to their inmate—walked up and down the big bare *sala* with his pupil. The scagliola floor was cold, the high battered casements shook in the storm, and the stately decay of the place was unrelieved by a particle of furniture. Pemberton's spirits were low, and it came over him that the fortune of the Moreens was now even lower. A blast of desolation, a portent of disgrace and disaster, seemed to draw through the comfortless hall. Mr. Moreen and Ulick were in the Piazza, looking out for something, strolling drearily, in mackintoshes, under the arcades; but still, in spite of mackintoshes, unmistakeable men of the world. Paula and Amy were in bed—it might have been thought they were staying there to keep warm. Pemberton looked askance at the boy at his side, to see to what extent he was conscious of these dark omens. But Morgan, luckily for him, was now mainly conscious of growing taller and stronger and indeed of being in his fifteenth year. This fact was intensely interesting to him and the basis of a private theory—which, however, he had imparted to his tutor—that in a little while he should stand on his own feet. He considered that the situation would change— that in short he should be "finished," grown up, producible in the world of affairs and ready to prove himself of sterling ability. Sharply as he was capable at times of analyzing, as he called it, his life, there were happy hours when he remained, as he also called it—and as the name, really, of their right ideal—"jolly" superficial; the proof of which was his fundamental assumption that he should presently go to Oxford, to Pemberton's college, and aided and abetted by Pemberton, do the most wonderful things. It depressed the young man to see how little in such a project he took account of ways and means: in other connections he mostly kept to the measure. Pemberton tried to imagine the Moreens at Oxford and fortunately failed; yet unless they were to adopt it as a residence there would be no *modus vivendi* for Morgan. How could he live without an allowance, and where was the allowance to come from? He, Pemberton, might live on Morgan; but how could Morgan live on *him*? What was to become of him anyhow? Somehow the fact that he was a big boy now, with better prospects of health, made the question of his future more difficult. So long as he was markedly frail, the great consideration he inspired seemed enough of an answer to it. But at the bottom of Pemberton's heart was the recognition of his probably being strong enough to live and not yet strong enough to struggle or to thrive. Morgan himself at any rate was in the first flush of the rosiest consciousness of adolescence, so that the beating of the tempest seemed to him after all but the voice of life and the challenge of fate. He had on his shabby little overcoat, with the collar up, but was enjoying his walk.

It was interrupted at last by the appearance of his mother at the end of the *sala*. She beckoned him to come to her, and while Pemberton saw him, complaisant, pass down the long vista and over the damp false marble, he wondered what was in the air. Mrs. Moreen said a word to the boy and made him go into the room she had quitted. Then, having closed the door after him, she directed her steps swiftly to Pemberton. There *was* something in the air, but his wildest flight of fancy wouldn't have suggested what it proved to be. She signified that she had made a pretext to get Morgan out of the way, and then she inquired— without hesitation—if the young man could favor her with the loan of three louis. While, before bursting into a laugh, he stared at her with surprise, she declared that she was awfully pressed for the money; she was desperate for it—it would save her life.

"Dear lady, *c'est trop fort!*" Pemberton laughed in the manner and with the borrowed grace of idiom that marked the best colloquial, the best anecdotic, moments of his friends themselves. "Where in the world do you suppose I should get three louis, *du train dont vous allez?*"

"I thought you worked—wrote things. Don't they pay you?"

"Not a penny."

"Are you such a fool as to work for nothing?"

"You ought surely to know that."

Mrs. Moreen stared, then she colored a little. Pemberton saw she had quite forgotten the terms—if "terms" they could be called—that he had ended by accepting from herself; they had burdened her memory as little as her conscience. "Oh yes, I see what you mean—you've been very nice about that; but why drag it in so often?" She had been perfectly urbane with him ever since the rough scene of explanation in his room the morning he made her accept *his* "terms"—the necessity of his making his case known to Morgan. She had felt no resentment after seeing there was no danger Morgan would take the matter up with her. Indeed, attributing this immunity to the good taste of his influence with the boy, she had once said to Pemberton "My dear fellow, it's an immense comfort you're a gentleman." She repeated this in substance now. "Of course you're a gentleman—that's a bother the less!" Pemberton reminded her that he had not "dragged in" anything that wasn't already in as much as his foot was in his shoe; and she also repeated her prayer that, somewhere and somehow, he would find her sixty francs. He took the liberty of hinting that if he could find them it wouldn't be to lend them to *her*—as to which he consciously did himself injustice, knowing that if he had them he would certainly put them at her disposal. He accused himself, at bottom and not unveraciously, of a fantastic, a demoralized sympathy with her. If misery made strange bedfellows, it also made strange sympathies. It was moreover a part of the abasement of living with such people that one had to make vulgar retorts, quite out of one's own tradition of good manners. "Morgan, Morgan, to what pass have I come for you?" he groaned while Mrs. Moreen floated voluminously down the *sala* again to liberate the boy, wailing as she went that everything was too odious.

Before their young friend was liberated there came a thump at the door communicating with the staircase, followed by the apparition of a dripping youth who poked in his head. Pemberton recognized him as the bearer of a telegram and recognized the telegram as addressed to himself. Morgan came back as, after glancing at the signature—that of a relative in London—he was reading the words: "Found jolly job for you, engagement to coach opulent youth on own terms. Come at once." The answer happily was paid and the messenger waited. Morgan, who had drawn near, waited too and looked hard at Pemberton; and Pemberton, after a moment, having met his look, handed him the telegram. It was really by wise looks—they knew each other so well now—that, while the telegraph-boy, in his waterproof cape, made a great puddle on the floor, the thing was settled between them. Pemberton wrote the answer with a pencil against the frescoed wall, and the messenger departed. When he had gone the young man explained himself.

"I'll make a tremendous charge; I'll earn a lot of money in a short time, and we'll live on it."

"Well, I hope the opulent youth will be a dismal dunce—he probably will," Morgan parenthesized—"and keep you a long time a-hammering of it in."

"Of course the longer he keeps me the more we shall have for our old age."

"But suppose *they* don't pay you!" Morgan awfully suggested.

"Oh there are not two such—!" But Pemberton pulled up; he had been on the point of using too invidious a term. Instead of this he said "Two such fatalities."

Morgan flushed—the tears came to his eyes. *"Dites toujours* two such rascally crews!" Then in a different tone he added: "Happy opulent youth!"

"Not if he's a dismal dunce."

"Oh, they're happier then. But you can't have everything, can you?" the boy smiled.

Pemberton held him fast, hands on his shoulders—he had never loved him so. "What will become of *you,* what will you do?" He thought of Mrs. Moreen, desperate for sixty francs.

"I shall become an *homme fait.*" And then as if he recognized all the bearings of Pemberton's allusions: "I shall get on with them better when you're not here."

"Ah don't say that—it sounds as if I set you against them!"

"You do—the sight of you. It's all right; you know what I mean. I shall be beautiful. I'll take their affairs in hand; I'll marry my sisters."

"You'll marry yourself!" joked Pemberton; as high, rather tense pleasantry would evidently be the right, or the safest, tone for their separation.

It was, however, not purely in this strain that Morgan suddenly asked: "But I say—how will you get to your jolly job? You'll have to telegraph to the opulent youth for money to come on."

Pemberton bethought himself. "They won't like that, will they?"

"Oh look out for them!"

Then Pemberton brought out his remedy. "I'll go to the American Consul; I'll borrow some money of him—just for the few days, on the strength of the telegram."

Morgan was hilarious. "Show him the telegram—then collar the money and stay!"

Pemberton entered into the joke sufficiently to reply that for Morgan he was really capable of that; but the boy, growing more serious, and to prove he hadn't meant what he said, not only hurried him off to the Consulate—since he was to start that evening, as he had wired to his friend—but made sure of their affair by going with him. They splashed through the tortuous perforations and over the humpbacked bridges, and they passed through the Piazza, where they saw Mr. Moreen and Ulick go into a jeweler's shop. The Consul proved accommodating—Pemberton said it wasn't the letter, but Morgan's grand air—and on their way back they went into Saint Mark's for a hushed ten minutes. Later they took up and kept up the fun of it to the very end; and it seemed to Pemberton a part of that fun that Mrs. Moreen, who was very angry when he had announced her his intention, should charge him, grotesquely and vulgarly and in reference to the loan she had vainly endeavored to effect, with bolting lest they should "get something out" of him. On the other hand, he had to do Mr. Moreen and Ulick the justice to recognize that when on coming in *they* heard the cruel news they took it like perfect men of the world.

— 8 —

When he got at work with the opulent youth, who was to be taken in hand for Balliol, he found himself unable to say if this aspirant had really such poor parts or if the appearance were only begotten of his own long association with an intensely living little mind. From Morgan he heard half a dozen times: the boy wrote charming young letters, a patchwork of tongues, with indulgent postscripts in the family Volapuk and, in little squares and rounds and crannies of the text, the drollest illustrations—letters that he was divided between the impulse to show his present charge as a vain, a wasted incentive, and the sense of something in them that publicity would profane. The opulent youth went up in due course and failed to pass; but it seemed to add to the presumption that brilliancy was not expected of him all at once that his parents, condoning the lapse, which they good-naturedly treated as little as possible as if it were Pemberton's, should have sounded the rally again, begged the young coach to renew the siege.

The young coach was now in a position to lend Mrs. Moreen three louis, and he sent her a post-office order even for a larger amount. In return for his favor he received a frantic scribbled line from her: "Implore you to come back instantly—Morgan dreadfully ill." They were on the rebound, once more in Paris—often as Pemberton had seen them depressed he had never seen them crushed—and communication was therefore rapid. He wrote to the boy to ascertain the state of his health, but awaited the answer in vain. He accordingly, after three days, took an abrupt leave of the opulent youth and, crossing the Channel, alighted at the small hotel, in the quarter of the Champs Élysées, of which Mrs. Moreen had given him the address. A deep if dumb dissatisfaction with this lady and her companions bore him company: they couldn't be vulgarly honest, but they could live at hotels, in velvety *entresols,* amid a smell of burnt pastilles, surrounded by the most expensive city in Europe. When he had left them in Venice it was with an irrepressible suspicion that something was going to happen; but the only thing that could have taken place was again their masterly retreat. "How is he? where is he?" he asked of Mrs. Moreen; but before she could speak these questions were answered by the pressure round his neck of a pair of arms, in shrunken sleeves, which still were perfectly capable of an effusive young foreign squeeze.

"Dreadfully ill—I don't see it!" the young man cried. And then to Morgan: "Why on earth didn't you relieve me? Why didn't you answer my letter?"

Mrs. Moreen declared that when she wrote he was very bad, and Pemberton learned at the same time from the boy that he had answered every letter he had received. This led to the clear inference that Pemberton's note had been kept from him so that the game to be practiced should not be interfered with. Mrs. Moreen was prepared to see the fact exposed, as Pemberton saw the moment he faced her that she was prepared for a good many other things. She was prepared above all to maintain that she had acted from a sense of duty, that she was enchanted she had got him over, whatever they might say, and that it was useless of him to pretend he didn't know in all his bones that his place at such a time was with Morgan. He had taken the boy away from them and now had no right to abandon him. He had created for himself the gravest responsibilities and must at least abide by what he had done.

"Taken him away from you?" Pemberton exclaimed indignantly.

"Do it—do it for pity's sake; that's just what I want. I can't stand *this* —and such scenes. They're awful frauds—poor dears!" These words broke from Morgan, who had intermitted his embrace, in a key which made Pemberton turn quickly to him and see that he had suddenly seated himself, was breathing in great pain and was very pale.

"*Now* do you say he's not in a state, my precious pet?" shouted his mother, dropping on her knees before him with clasped hands, but touching him no more than if he had been a gilded idol. "It will pass— it's only for an instant; but don't say such dreadful things!"

"I'm all right—all right," Morgan panted to Pemberton, whom he sat looking up at with a strange smile, his hands resting on either side on the sofa.

"Now do you pretend I've been dishonest, that I've deceived?" Mrs. Moreen flashed at Pemberton as she got up.

"It isn't *he* says it, it's I!" the boy returned, apparently easier but sinking back against the wall; while his restored friend, who had sat down beside him, took his hand and bent over him.

"Darling child, one does what one can; there are so many things to consider," urged Mrs. Moreen. "It's his *place*—his only place. You see *you* think it is now."

"Take me away—take me away," Morgan went on, smiling to Pemberton with his white face.

"Where shall I take you, and how—oh *how*, my boy?" the young man stammered, thinking of the rude way in which his friends in London held that, for his convenience, with no assurance of prompt return, he had thrown them over; of the just resentment with which they would already have called in a successor, and of the scant help to finding fresh employment that resided for him in the grossness of his having failed to pass his pupil.

"Oh we'll settle that. You used to talk about it," said Morgan. "If we can only go all the rest's a detail."

"Talk about it as much as you like, but don't think you can attempt it. Mr. Moreen would never consent—it would be so *very* hand-to-mouth," Pemberton's hostess beautifully explained to him. Then to Morgan she made it clearer: "It would destroy our peace, it would break our hearts. Now that he's back it will be all the same again. You'll have your life, your work, and your freedom, and we'll all be happy as we used to be. You'll bloom and grow perfectly well, and we won't have any more silly experiments, will we? They're too absurd. It's Mr. Pemberton's place—every one in his place. You in yours, your papa in his, me in mine—*n'est-ce pas, chéri?* We'll all forget how foolish we've been and have lovely times."

She continued to talk and to surge vaguely about the little draped stuffy salon while Pemberton sat with the boy, whose color gradually came back; and she mixed up her reasons, hinting that there were going to be changes, that the other children might scatter (who knew?—Paula had her ideas) and that then it might be fancied how much the poor old parent-birds would want the little nestling. Morgan looked at Pemberton, who wouldn't let him move; and Pemberton knew exactly how he felt at hearing himself called a little nestling. He admitted that he had had one or two bad days, but he protested afresh against the wrong of his mother's having made them the ground of an appeal to poor Pemberton. Poor Pemberton could laugh now, apart from the comicality of Mrs. Moreen's mustering so much philosophy for her defense—she seemed to shake it out of her agitated petticoats, which knocked over the light gilt chairs—so little did their young companion, *marked,* unmistakably marked at the best, strike him as qualified to repudiate any advantage.

He himself was in for it at any rate. He should have Morgan on his hands again indefinitely; though indeed he saw the lad had a private theory to produce which would be intended to smooth this down. He was obliged to him for it in advance; but the suggested amendment didn't keep his heart rather from sinking, any more than it prevented him from accepting the prospect on the spot, with some confidence, moreover, that he should do even better if he could have a little supper. Mrs. Moreen threw out more hints about the changes that were to be looked for, but she was such a mixture of smiles and shudders—she confessed she was very nervous—that he couldn't tell if she were in high feather or only in hysterics. If the family was really at last going to pieces, why shouldn't she recognize the necessity of pitching Morgan into some sort of lifeboat? This presumption was fostered by the fact that they were established in luxurious quarters in the capital of pleasure; that was exactly where they naturally *would* be established in view of going to pieces. Moreover, didn't she mention that Mr. Moreen and the others were enjoying themselves at the opera with Mr. Granger, and wasn't *that* also precisely where one would look for them on the eve of a smash? Pemberton gathered that Mr. Granger was a rich vacant American—a big bill with a flourishy heading and no items; so that one of Paula's "ideas" was probably that this time she hadn't missed fire— by which straight shot indeed she would have shattered the general cohesion. And if the cohesion was to crumble what would become of poor Pemberton? He felt quite enough bound up with them to figure to his alarm as a dislodged block in the edifice.

It was Morgan who eventually asked if no supper had been ordered for him; sitting with him below, later, at the dim delayed meal, in the presence of a great deal of corded green plush, a plate of ornamental biscuit and an aloofness marked on the part of the waiter. Mrs. Moreen had explained that they had been obliged to secure a room for the visitor out of the house; and Morgan's consolation—he offered it while Pemberton reflected on the nastiness of lukewarm sauces—proved to be, largely, that this circumstance would facilitate their escape. He talked of their escape—recurring to it often afterwards—as if they were making up a "boy's book" together. But he likewise expressed his sense that there was something in the air, that the Moreens couldn't keep it up much longer. In point of fact, as Pemberton was to see, they kept it up for five or six months. All the while, however, Morgan's contention was designed to cheer him. Mr. Moreen and Ulick, whom he had met the day after his return, accepted that return like perfect men of the world. If Paula and Amy treated it even with less formality an allowance was to be made for them, inasmuch as Mr. Granger hadn't come to the opera after all. He had only placed his box at their service, with a bouquet for each of the party; there was even one apiece, embittering the thought of his profusion, for Mr. Moreen and Ulick. "They're all like that," was Morgan's comment; "at the very last, just when we think we've landed them they're back in the deep sea!"

Morgan's comments in these days were more and more free; they even included a large recognition of the extraordinary tenderness with which he had been treated while Pemberton was away. Oh yes, they couldn't do enough to be nice to him, to show him they had him on their mind and make up for his loss. That was just what made the whole thing so sad and caused him to rejoice after all in Pemberton's return—he had to keep thinking of their affection less, had less sense of obligation. Pemberton laughed out at this last reason, and Morgan blushed and said "Well, dash it, you know what I mean." Pemberton knew perfectly what he meant; but there were a good many things that—dash it too!—it didn't make any clearer. This episode of his second sojourn in Paris stretched itself out wearily, with their resumed readings and wanderings and maunderings, their potterings on the quays, their hauntings of the museums, their occasional lingerings in the Palais Royal when the first sharp weather came on and there was a comfort in warm emanations, before Chevet's wonderful succulent window. Morgan wanted to hear all about the opulent youth—he took an immense interest in him. Some of the details of his opulence—Pemberton could spare him none of them—evidently fed the boy's appreciation of all his friend had given up to come back to him; but, in addition to the greater reciprocity established by that heroism, he had always his little brooding theory, in which there was a frivolous gaiety too, that their long probation was drawing to a close. Morgan's conviction that the Moreens couldn't go on much longer kept pace with the unexpended impetus with which, from month to month, they did go on. Three weeks after Pemberton had rejoined them they went on to another level, a dingier one than the first; but Morgan rejoiced that his tutor had at least still not sacrificed the advantage of a room outside. He clung to the romantic utility of this when the day, or rather the night, should arrive for their escape.

For the first time, in this complicated connection, our friend felt his collar gall him. It was, as he had said to Mrs. Moreen in Venice, *trop fort*—everything was *trop fort*. He could neither really throw off his blighting burden nor find in it the benefit of a pacified conscience or of a rewarded affection. He had spent all the money accruing to him in England, and he saw his youth going and that he was getting nothing back for it. It was all very well of Morgan to count it for reparation that he should now settle on him permanently—there was an irritating flaw in such a view. He saw what the boy had in his mind; the conception that as his friend had had the generosity to come back he must show his gratitude by giving him his life. But the poor friend didn't desire the gift—what could he do with Morgan's dreadful little life? Of course at the same time that Pemberton was irritated he remembered the reason, which was very honorable to Morgan and which dwelt simply in his making one so forget that he was no more than a patched urchin. If one dealt with him on a different basis one's misadventures were one's own fault. So Pemberton waited in a queer confusion of yearning and alarm for the catastrophe which was held to hang over the house of Moreen, of which he certainly at moments felt the symptoms brush his cheek and as to which he wondered much in what form it would find its liveliest effect.

Perhaps it would take the form of sudden dispersal—a frightened *sauve qui peut*, a scuttling into selfish corners. Certainly they were less elastic than of yore; they were evidently looking for something they didn't find. The Dorringtons hadn't reappeared, the princes had scattered; wasn't that the beginning of the end? Mrs. Moreen had lost her reckoning of the famous "days"; her social calendar was blurred—it had turned its face to the wall. Pemberton suspected that the great, the cruel discomfiture had been the unspeakable behavior of Mr. Granger, who seemed not to know what he wanted, or, what was much worse, what *they* wanted. He kept sending flowers, as if to bestrew the path of his retreat, which was never the path of a return. Flowers were all very well, but—Pemberton could complete the proposition. It was now positively conspicuous that in the long run the Moreens were a social failure; so that the young man was almost grateful the run had not been short. Mr. Moreen indeed was still occasionally able to get away on business and, what was more surprising, was likewise able to get back. Ulick had no club, but you couldn't have discovered it from his appearance, which was as much as ever that of a person looking at life from the window of such an institution; therefore Pemberton was doubly surprised at an answer he once heard him make his mother in the desperate tone of a man familiar with the worst privations. Her question Pemberton had not quite caught; it appeared to be an appeal for a suggestion as to whom they might get to take Amy. "Let the Devil take her!" Ulick snapped; so that Pemberton could see that they had not only lost their amiability but had ceased to believe in themselves. He could also see that if Mrs. Moreen was trying to get people to take her children she might be regarded as closing the hatches for the storm. But Morgan would be the last she would part with.

One winter afternoon—it was a Sunday—he and the boy walked far together in the Bois de Boulogne. The evening was so splendid, the cold lemon-colored sunset so clear, the stream of carriages and pedestrians so amusing, and the fascination of Paris so great, that they stayed out later than usual and became aware that they should have to hurry home to arrive in time for dinner. They hurried accordingly, arm-in-arm, good-humored and hungry, agreeing that there was nothing like Paris after all and that after everything too that had come and gone they were not yet sated with innocent pleasures. When they reached the hotel they found that, though scandalously late, they were in time for all the dinner they were likely to sit down to. Confusion reigned in the apartments of the Moreens—very shabby ones this time, but the best in the house—and before the interrupted service of the table, with objects displaced almost as if there had been a scuffle and a great wine stain from an overturned bottle, Pemberton couldn't blink the fact that there had been a scene of the last proprietary firmness. The storm had come—they were all seeking refuge. The hatches were down, Paula and Amy were invisible—they had never tried the most casual art upon Pemberton, but he felt they had enough of an eye to him not to wish to meet him as young ladies whose frocks had been confiscated—and Ulick appeared to have jumped overboard. The host and his staff, in a word, had ceased to "go on" at the pace of their guests, and the air of embarrassed detention, thanks to a pile of gaping trunks in the passage, was strangely commingled with the air of indignant withdrawal.

When Morgan took all this in—and he took it in very quickly—he colored to the roots of his hair. He had walked from his infancy among difficulties and dangers, but he had never seen a public exposure. Pemberton noticed in a second glance at him that the tears had rushed into his eyes and that they were tears of a new and untasted bitterness. He wondered an instant, for the boy's sake, whether he might successfully pretend not to understand. Not successfully, he felt, as Mr. and Mrs. Moreen, dinnerless by their extinguished hearth, rose before him in their little dishonored salon, casting about with glassy eyes for the nearest port in such a storm. They were not prostrate, but were horribly white, and Mrs. Moreen had evidently been crying. Pemberton quickly learned, however, that her grief was not for the loss of her dinner, much as she usually enjoyed it, but the fruit of a blow that struck even deeper, as she made all haste to explain. He would see for himself, so far as that went, how the great change had come, the dreadful bolt had fallen, and how they would now all have to turn themselves about. Therefore, cruel as it was to them to part with their darling, she must look to him to carry a little further the influence he had so fortunately acquired with the boy—to induce his young charge to follow him into some modest retreat. They depended on him—that was the fact—to take their delightful child temporarily under his protection: it would leave Mr. Moreen and herself so much more free to give the proper attention (too little, alas! had been given) to the readjustment of their affairs.

"We trust you—we feel we *can*," said Mrs. Moreen, slowly rubbing her plump white hands and looking with compunction hard at Morgan, whose chin, not to take liberties, her husband stroked with a tentative paternal forefinger.

"Oh yes—we feel that we *can*. We trust Mr. Pemberton fully, Morgan," Mr. Moreen pursued.

Pemberton wondered again if he might pretend not to understand;

but everything good gave way to the intensity of Morgan's understanding. "Do you mean he may take me to live with him forever and ever?" cried the boy. "May take me away, away, anywhere he likes?"

"For ever and ever? *Comme vous-y-allez?*" Mr. Moreen laughed indulgently. "For as long as Mr. Pemberton may be so good."

"We've struggled, we've suffered," his wife went on; "but you've made him so your own that we've already been through the worst of the sacrifice."

Morgan had turned away from his father—he stood looking at Pemberton with a light in his face. His sense of shame for their common humiliated state had dropped; the case had another side—the thing was to clutch at *that*. He had a moment of boyish joy, scarcely mitigated by the reflection that with this unexpected consecration of his hope—too sudden and too violent; the turn taken was away from a *good* boy's book —the "escape" was left on their hands. The boyish joy was there an instant, and Pemberton was almost scared at the rush of gratitude and affection that broke through his first abasement. When he stammered "My dear fellow, what do you say to *that?*" how could one not say something enthusiastic? But there was more need for courage at something else that immediately followed and that made the lad sit down quickly on the nearest chair. He had turned quite livid and had raised his hand to his left side. They were all three looking at him, but Mrs. Moreen suddenly bounded forward. "Ah, his darling little heart!" she broke out; and this time, on her knees before him and without respect for the idol, she caught him ardently in her arms. "You walked him too far, you hurried him too fast!" she hurled over her shoulder at Pemberton. Her son made no protest, and the next instant, still holding him, she sprang up with her face convulsed and with the terrified cry "Help, help! he's going, he's gone!" Pemberton saw with equal horror, by Morgan's own stricken face, that he was beyond their wildest recall. He pulled him half out of his mother's hands, and for a moment, while they held him together, they looked all their dismay into each other's eyes. "He couldn't stand it with his weak organ," said Pemberton—"the shock, the whole scene, the violent emotion."

"But I thought he *wanted* to go to you!" wailed Mrs. Moreen.

"I *told* you he didn't, my dear," her husband made answer. Mr. Moreen was trembling all over and was in his way as deeply affected as his wife. But after the very first he took his bereavement as a man of the world.

Wyndham Lewis (1882–1957)

TIME THE TIGER

Lewis practiced repeatedly a single narrative rhythm: the leisurely accretion of charged detail, terminating in an explosion. "Time the Tiger," despite its use of partisan passions, is not a partisan story. The slow-motion climax examines impartially the fervors released on both sides without understating their harvest of loneliness and misery.

— 1 —

It was, as usual in London about that time of the year, endeavoring to snow. There had been a hard frost for days, in fact it was so cold that in any other country it would have snowed long ago. The sky was a constipated mass, yellowed by the fog, suspended over a city awaiting the deluge. It was eight-thirty in the morning. The streets of Rotting Hill were like Pompeii with Vesuvius in catastrophic eruption, a dull glare, saffronish in color, providing an unearthly uniformity. The self-centered precipitancy of the bowed pedestrians resembled a procession of fugitives.

Mark Robins was standing at his bathroom window. His eye followed with displeasure the absurdly ominous figures moving under mass-pressure to be there at nine o'clock, passing on through the hollow twilit streets towards the swarming undergrounds. It was the urgency that jarred, their will-to-live as a machine.

He could see into the lighted baker's shop. The lady known in his private mind as "bum-face" arranged yesterday's and of course the day before yesterday's pastry in the window. Whenever he saw the old pastries ranged in the window he thought of that air of uprightness and invincible integrity owned by the little master-baker. Why were his loaves the least white, the greyest, of any in Rotting Hill? He held very strong opinions on the subject of the socialist administration: perhaps cause and effect. His bread became as hard as a brick within forty-eight hours. It became like that in the stomach too if you failed to expel it promptly. This baker's views on the socialist government were as forcible as a pickpocket's are regarding the police force, only the baker's had the added force of moral indignation.

Then, as Mark idly watched, "Fringe" (in his private mind she was known as that) erect and white in her chemist's uniform, came out of Willough's. She moved like clockwork, as steady as the swan on the surface of the lake. Whenever she turned she turned abruptly at right angles with the precision of a Royal Marine. She had been a she-soldier. Mark approved of "Fringe," and regretfully noted how she stopped, pivoted to face at right angles, and entered the baker's shop (as she did every morning) and selected an aging pastry. However, she worked in a chemist's and no doubt kept her bowels open.

In several windows of the lofty Victorian houses—all Private Hotels— where the diligent refugees of Rotting Hill were already at work on their biographies of Goethe or of Meyerbeer, there was electric light. The silversmith and diamond merchant was (typical of his class! thought Mark) the latest riser of the tradesmen of Rotting Hill. The last snores of the night blew out of his nostrils upon the little fluttery moustache as his head lay on the pillow beside that of Mrs. Silversmith. Both the Silversmiths and Mark had a low opinion of the other's morale: their flats so situated that nothing that went on in one was exactly a closed book for the other—especially in view of the prohibitive cost of material for curtains and the veils that in happier times shroud our domestic interiors.

Mark withdrew from the window. He sighed. He did not know why he sighed. But a large white "Ascot heater" stood in a corner of the bathroom which no longer produced hot water. Three months earlier the mechanic of the gas service had called for the routine clean-up. Since then it had been out of action. Mark boiled some water in the kitchen and washed: then he filled the kettle again, and again put it on to boil. After that he went to his guest's room, knocked at the door, and put his head inside.

"Charles! Stop dreaming and get up. I have put some water on to boil for you."

"Thank you, Mark. Whooah!" Charles yawned.

"You slept well?"

"Perfectly."

"Good."

"Whooah."

As he went to his room Mark was smiling. "Whooah!" was so like Charles. Seeing Charles in bed "whooahing" had caused him for some reason to think of Ida Dyat, Charles's sister. He thought of her, as he always did, in repose. Action was not her element: so, though on horse-

back her hair was dramatic as a maenad's, he preferred to think of the
stationary cloud of dull gold as she lay back in an armchair reading a
book. The indolent red lips he would see for preference at their most
indolent, when she had been too lazy to smile and had smiled with her
eyes instead—which was less trouble. Her beauty was preraphaelite at
its best, brooding or dreaming in some equivalent of the mirror of the
Lady of Shalott.

It was a certain inactivity in Ida's composition which attracted him
most, and it was that, too, that accounted for his romantic attachment
remaining in a state of abortive repression, contained within the forms
of youthful camaraderie: Mark being one of those men who needed,
if not to be hunted by the female, at least to be reminded that women
are sexual phenomena. But always a warm wind from the past rushed
into his mind when he had, as now, these images of her. Then the image
suddenly dissolved, his smile faded. For Ida must be a hag of forty-five,
he thought. Thinking of Ida as greying and pathetic was so immensely
distasteful that he began moving quickly and noisily about. Old Charles
stopped young though, he thought. "Whooah." Mark smiled again.

But he soon forgot Charles's sea-lion cry, for he became grimly absorbed in dressing. His bedroom was a far more efficient refrigerator
than the "Ascot heater" was a heater. However, the Briton regards chilli-
ness as next to godliness. Mark would have been quite as displeased had
the refrigerator failed as he had been at the defection of the "heater."

Taking a fresh shirt out of the drawer he identified it—as the one
with the smallest buttonholes of any. This abnormality was revealed by
all new shirts to some degree. With the shirt in question the buttons
refused to go in. Each buttonhole had to be forcibly entered, the one at
the top entailing as much sometimes as five minutes' strenuous thumbing.
Unquestionably this afforded him that grim satisfaction the Briton experiences when senseless obstacles are placed in his way or life bristles
with purposeful mischance, all food for his "grit." But in this case there
was another factor: namely the credit and good name of a socialist Brit-
ain. Probably it would prove a better advertisement if British manufacturers turned out serviceable shirts—easy to button up and with such
conveniences as are prized by self-indulgent foreigners. It was like our
taxation. Few foreigners understood *that*. Taxes such as *we* can stand
up to would cause a revolution anywhere else. Only *we* have the guts to
"take it." Besides, the obvious explanation of the smallness of these buttonholes aroused Mark's party-zeal: the motive was *profit*. It saved labor
and time in the factory to make them small. It was a relief to one's feelings to reflect that the days were numbered of "free enterprise" shirt
manufacture.

Even the best shirts tended to shrink and the buttonholes lost width
in the wash quite as much as the sleeves lost length, if only a little. But

the button naturally was unaffected. Any slight dilation of the button-holes attendant upon the constant passage, in and out, of the button, was less than its shrinkage in the wash. It *had* of course occurred to Mark to purchase a few dozen shirt buttons, smaller than those on the shirt. But although there were many sorts of buttons in the shops, shirt buttons (oddly enough) were practically unobtainable.

As he pulled on a sock one of his fingernails caught in the wool. With an almost new pair of nail scissors he attempted to cut off the chipped nail. But the scissors were already loose and of a metal formerly un-known to cutlery. The nail was bent by them, it was not severed. He fell back on his nail file. After a little he gave that up, and stuck a band-aid over the nail.

The quality of all goods supplied by the sundriesmen had inevitably deteriorated. Then he knew about the small piratic factories that turned out the defective steel goods, inundating England with gimcrack mer-chandise, and felt grateful that their days were numbered in a col-lectivist society.

Mark was superstitious. To start the day in slippers appeared to him almost an ill omen. The shoes on which his choice fell, on this occasion, were his recently acquired £5 brown pair. Of these he was still rather proud—an emotion the shoes were not fitted to inspire. And Charles had assured him that there was no pair of shoes to be had worth putting on your feet under seven pounds ten.

With these shoes he invariably attempted, completely without suc-cess, to tie a bow. The shoelaces were too short. In England today the statutory length for shoelaces is fourteen inches. It is illegal to supply laces longer than that. Mark was not aware that he had to thank the Government for this idiotic difficulty, and put it down to some dishonest manufacturer selling short weight on the plea of a nonexistent "short-age." As usual, for all his stout fingerwork, he got nothing but a solitary loop, one for the left foot, one for the right.

He rose to his feet, the petty frustrations involved in the act of dress-ing done with. A tweed jacket hung from a peg. No peasant weaver could ever have been responsible for the vulgarity of the color. Mark, who had paid twenty pounds for it, eyed it dubiously. It was about the maximum price for a ready-made tweed. All first-quality tweeds, of course, must be reserved for export. But *why* (the question had once forced its way into Mark's mind) need what was left for the home market be so ugly and vulgar?

Another question: Why should all ready-made jackets, cardigans, jumpers, be made for small and frail men? Mark was tall and muscular, so *that* question it would have been inhuman to ignore. But it was easily answered, too. Far less material was required for a small man or a child than for someone of Mark's size. Consequently the manufacturers preferred to think that Englishmen, with a few exceptions, are stunted and emaciated.

Mark took the jacket off the hanger and a phoney smell of ersatz peat assailed his nostrils. It was with no possessive glow he put on this practically new garment, and as he left the bedroom he registered depression. He could not guess why *sans amour et sans haine* his heart was so full of a low-grade pain.

There was no sound of Charles, so he went into the kitchen to prepare the breakfast. He took the "Strachey loaf," as Charles cheaply called it, out of the bread tin. Officially it was one day old, but when he applied the bread-saw it was like sawing brick. He sawed off four slices and grilled them two at a time. The kettle had been refilled and was acquiring a little heat. He threw the remainder of his butter ration into the repast, added a few pinches of alleged Darjeeling to the pseudo-Ceylon in the teapot: placed on the tray the two dishes of cereal, a teaspoonful of sugar for each. Sugar was always a bad shortage with him. He took down a jar marked "Strawberry Jam," recognized by housewives as mainly pectin and/or carrot pulp, given appropriate local color of course and flavor to match. There was neither nourishment nor pleasure to be had from it. Charles appeared, yawning and smiling.

"Why, no Mrs. Bristers?" he inquired.

"Oh, *she* does not come when I have 'flu."

"Why?"

"Because—I *believe* this is the reason—Mrs. Bristers thinks I am putting it on. Swinging the lead."

"When you quit malingering she comes back."

"Yes. Of course, she malingers herself meanwhile. She calls off her malinger as soon as I announce my recovery."

"Anything I can do," Charles said, "in Mrs. Bristers' absence?"

He was given the kettle to carry.

"How do you feel this morning?" The guest put the question.

Mark hesitated a moment. "Depressed!" he confided. "Unaccountably depressed."

— 2 —

They both moved into the living room, the lightly laden Charles in the van.

"What a poisonous day," Charles shouted, and the room was in fact so dark that when a match was struck to light the gas fire it was like a miniature firework display.

"A bit of fog," Mark conceded with didactic firmness.

Where the weather was concerned Mark was always on the defensive, because people were apt to blame the Government for the weather. Then, he had a feeling that very bad weather (of which there was an awful lot) *was,* in fact, compromising in a brave new day.

They sat down facing one another and Mark poured out the tea.

"Ah, that is a capital idea." Charles picked up a piece of toast and examined it. "The dreadful bread arrives disguised as good old-fashioned toast."

"Let's see, you like sugar?" Mark looked up, a cube poised above the cup.

"If you think it won't spoil the tea!"

Mark laughed. Even a bureaucrat laughs sometimes on such occasions, as a clergyman would consider it politic to laugh at not *too* coarse an anecdote. Besides, he was fond of tea. "It is certainly not good tea," he said in a firm voice. "I have tried to coax some decent tea out of my grocer. But I really believe he had none."

"Have you tipped him?"

"Good gracious, no!" Mark protested.

Charles shook his head, dogmatically flourishing a piece of toast. "I am afraid you cannot expect to get anything if you don't oil their palms."

Mark's was a damp smile.

"Do you," he inquired, "go around oiling everyone's palm? I know that is done. But it does not strike me as very nice. You may get the lion's share that way, but it is the behavior of a less noble animal. I will not say a *rat.*"

"A pig, you think, eh!" Charles laughed, drinking with relish. "Best to drink this stuff while it is so *hot* you can't taste it."

Since Mark had worked at the Ministry of Education and since Charles had become a farmer of a rather lurid black-market type, they had started arguing differently. In their discussions in the old days nothing more concrete or subjective, as a rule, was touched on than the present Catholic revival or the currency of the Incas. Also when, in easygoing debate, Charles' opinion prevailed, Mark did not mind in the least. Today, however, he would defend his position, at times, almost acrimoniously, particularly where the issue was political. This was very unMarklike.

Mark Robins and Charles Dyat had known one another as schoolboys, been at Marlborough, then at Oxford together. Neither had formed any close friendship except this one of theirs. But its rationale was not likemindedness. Charles was what is labelled "a leader type." Mark had little taste for responsibility. These two facts alone may have provided the essential ingredients for a friendship.

Theirs was not quite the comic marriage-of-opposites, instances of which are so common. Leaving aside physical contrast—Charles who was fair, being only of middling height, and Mark being a tall black-haired man—Charles looked at life from a certain social eminence (an imaginary one), whereas Mark was uninterested in social distinctions. Where intellectual distinctions are concerned he was rather romantic, from which circumstance Charles had benefited. Charles he considered very brilliant, unquestionably destined for great things. Again, were one to investigate and collate, their roots would reveal a common soil exploited to different ends. Both came from the prosperous professional middle class: but Charles's father had been a successful and a pretentious country lawyer, who ran at one time a butler and footman, his large house, Tadicombe Priory, standing in half a dozen acres of pseudopark, a small satellite farm completing the picture; Mark's father, on the other hand, was a Manchester doctor with a big practice, with neither time nor inclination to emulate his most snooty patients.

So the conversation had taken the acrimonious turn it nowadays was always liable to do. Mark ate his handful of cereal, inadequately sweetened with the teaspoonful of sugar (although the Jamaicans were starving because nobody wanted their sugar cane). Charles noisily tested the friability of a blackened and gritty crust, smeared with ersatz jam. Then Charles sat back, and after a minute or two took up again the question of tipping.

"Of course I go around oiling palms," he began aggressively. "Your masters don't need to—they have their farms like Stalin's commissars and their privileges. But you and I have to exude *pourboires* or our health would suffer. You can't live on one ration book without tipping. Tipping is the black market of the poor."

Mark no longer hesitated to recognize the political gulf which yawned and gaped between them. Charles smiled his tough gay smile, belonging to his cavalier complex, as he glanced into the yawning chasm. The white hairs in his brushed-off-the-mouth moustache were not numerous enough to make it "gray," the gold-gray of the temples he kept clipped. In the yellow gloom he sat up, eyes dancing, a gallant little daguerreotype darkened by the fog of time. Mark returned his gaze, with a bit of a waver, across the grim period-piece of sham-tea, sham-jam, "processed" butter, gray bread scorched into toast. He admired, as he had always done, the lawless eye, the witty mouth.

Charles was too monotonously destructive, however: he had an *individualist itch to pick holes*, in Mark's phrase. Where Mark would be apt to respect the most pernicious by-law, Charles would be quite certain to break it. Was he not (in imagination) of the class that made the laws? As part of his synthetic "aristocratic" outfit he despised all laws and the law-abiding. But the great social changes since 1945 of necessity complicated the role of the synthetic "aristocrat." Charles was towered over by a hostile Zeitgeist. Mark saw quite well this menacing shadow looming over his friend as he argued: for the natural lawgiver had become a potential outlaw.

"In our young days, Mark," Charles said softly, "it was *you,* you know, who were the little Tory, I the little radical. Do you remember?"

Mark agreed that he had been a dreadful reactionary and that Charles had been most frightfully advanced. "A perfect devil, in fact!" he laughed a little derisively.

Charles pushed his cup towards the teapot. "May I have some more of that bloody tea? Yes, you were quite shocked at my red tie."

"*I was!*"

Flushed and animated, Charles had laid aside his imperious technique—he had chosen to soothe and to charm. For the second time that morning Charles forcibly recalled his sister—the submerged sexual asset in this friendship was brought into play. Mark softened at once in response: and it was with eyes still moist that he looked up and cooperated in recalling the pleasurable absurdities of undergraduate youth. "You did really alarm me at one time," he confessed. "We nearly parted company forever on the subject of Trotsky, for whom you had a most irrational admiration. Do you, I wonder, retain any vestige of that obsession?"

"He would be better than this lot!" Charles answered. He emptied his cup. "For what we have received by gracious permission of the Ministry of Food may the Lord make us truly thankful."

"Amen," said Mark. Charles lighted a cigarette, then rather abruptly he announced:

"No, I am no Tory. I am just a defeatist."

Frown lines returned to Mark's forehead, he bent a questioning eye upon the peccant Charles.

"You should not be that," he said.

"Why not?" Charles asked, with amiable truculence. "We are not going to win the Peace on monkey-nuts and black bread, whether as socialists or Churchillites. I suppose I am, after all, *not* defeatist. I don't want England to degenerate into a slum, presided over by a sanctimonious official class. If I despaired as you do and sold out to Beelzebub, then I should complain no more of course—I should say *yes* to bad tea, to bad bread, to the purchase tax, to the income tax, to no petrol, to three-and-sixpence for cigarettes, and to a doctrine of servile submission."

"If you think it is the way to win the Peace, Charles—to use your ridiculous expression—to find fault . . . ?"

But Charles broke in impatiently.

"Of course one must find fault, Mark. You work for them, that is another matter. But why on earth should *I* swallow their rotten tea, and smoke their extortionately priced cigarettes (two shillings and tuppence of the three-and-sixpence goes to the Government) and say it is heaven? Besides, mankind cannot dispense with fault finding, or call it by its proper name, criticism. If an inventor were enraptured with every model he produced, even his first rough draft, if he dispensed with the principle of trial and error—if he tested but *never discarded*—he would not get very far."

"Nor would he if he listened to every ignorant suggestion."

"The trouble is that all the experts are outside, not inside, the Government and its committees."

"Quite untrue, but go on."

"These people are not *trying,* however, that is my main complaint. They have in mind something quite different from a prosperous society. They have in mind an object society. When you and I yearn for good tea and for white bread, that is 'reactionary'."

"Which is utter nonsense, Charles. There *is* a world food crisis. I am sorry, but there is."

"Do you really believe that? Are you incapable of using your reason, have they deprived you of that, my poor Mark?"

"No. It is not I who am irrational. . . ."

Charles gathered himself for an assault upon the citadel of Unreason, and Mark, smiling nervously, manned the walls.

"I am as sure as that I am sitting in this chair—it seems to me self-evident, that the most irksome of the restrictions and shortages are not economic but ideologic, political. A government which wanted to create an atmosphere differing from that of a poorhouse, which is what we experience, could do so without risk of any kind to its economic stability. Why is there no rationing in Switzerland, a country which imports proportionately just as much food as we do? Why are things more 'normal' in France, Italy, Belgium, Holland? The answer is that our rulers do not wish for a return to normality. They desire to maintain abnormality and 'crisis.' Even in Western Germany there is much more food than here."

They had both pushed their chairs back a little from the table, the glow from their cigarettes sometimes lit up their faces in the yellow gloom, which the electric light did not banish.

"It it really necessary for me to point out why England appears worse off than neighboring countries?" Mark asked testily. "It is easy enough to explain, and it is very much to her credit that she does so appear."

"Oh, yeees?"

"Yes. In other west European countries Marshall Aid has reached the top crust only, the idea being that it would somehow, some of it, trickle down to the bottom. A return to normal *luxury* was in that way rapidly achieved. You mentioned Western Germany. The most dreadful contrasts exist there—of a new *Schiebertum* in stark contrast with an indescribable poverty. They have just fixed prices so high that only the rich can buy the best food—and then they abandon rationing! So could we easily if we were so inhumane as to adopt that method! In England rationing stopped the well-off from getting all the food. It is a façade of immoral luxury in Paris that makes the French seem 'better off' than the English to the tourist. Underneath the gilded crust those countries are *worse* off. You ought to know better than to believe. . . ."

"So ought you, so ought you!" Charles yelled delightedly, waving his hands. "Don't you believe all that stuff about a thin gilded top crust, with famine underneath. In Paris restaurants frequented by taxi drivers you feed better than at the Savoy. *Anywhere* in France one can eat far better, far more, and far cheaper, than here in England. *And* there is no filthy purchase tax either. You forgot to mention that!"

"Really, old chap . . . !"

"Be patient. We English are in the presence of a Great Design. The big idea is to push this people down to a living plane strictly that of the average manual worker. That is the first phase. When they have us tied up with controls so that we cannot move hand or foot and have drugged us with dogmas, the idea is to push the entire mass down lower yet, to a carefully regulated peonage, paid possibly with scrip, all shops state-owned. Nothing must stick up above the primitive level decreed except the Party. Even such tiny protuberances as us, Mark, with our hankering after good tea (of the old middle-class days) are an offense. The 'crisis' atmosphere is of the same kind as the wartime blackout. All are now agreed that the blackout was grossly overdone in England if not totally pointless. It was 'atmosphere.' This tasteless tea is *atmosphere*. So is that ghastly bread!"

Mark had been listening more attentively at last, but his expression became much more severe. He examined his friend—the eloquent moustachioed mouth, the eager ideologic eye, the inflection of the "county": he watched as if engaged in making a diagnosis, with a patient who revealed symptoms more and more disquieting. As Charles stopped his host suddenly stood up.

"Charles, you are hopeless," Mark told him quietly—in a tone in which a doctor would wind up, "and I fear it is *malignant*."

"Incurable. I am chronically sick of the present Government."

"Where on earth did you collect all those batty beliefs? A Great Design! Socialists are sparing you, Charles, the exquisite inconveniences of a bloody revolution."

"Fiddlesticks. Like Kerensky they are paving the way for communism." Mark shook his head.

"You get your politics from the *Daily Express*." He stretched. "I am going to get my mail."

"Postman doesn't bring it up any more—pops it in a box downstairs—

have to fetch it yourself—serve you right!" Charles chanted, lying back, his face to the ceiling and puffing derisive smoke through his moustache.

Mark stopped at the door. "Egotist! Why should that poor devil climb fifty flights of flat-stairs every morning and get varicose veins and fallen arches!"

"He did before!" Charles called after him. "And—he's varicosed already. His feet are as flat as a pancake!"

Mark roared back from the stair-head. "You will be a postman yourself in your next incarnation."

"Not going to have any more lives," howled Charles. "This life is quite enough for me!"

When Mark got back, muttering "excuse me" he tore open a buff envelope, glanced at the contents, and hastened to the telephone. He dialed a number and waited. With an irritable sigh he hung up and redialed. After a minute or so he rehung and dialed a single number.

Charles laughed. "Telephone not working this morning? The exchange will see what they can do! Dial O."

"Will you try and get me Whitehall 6688? . . . Yes, I have dialed twice. There was absolutely no sound. . . . Thank you." (A long pause.) "Number engaged? But there are twenty lines at least. . . . Thank you." (A long pause.) "What? . . . The number is Whitehall 6688 not Whitechapel 8866. . . . No, it is *not* 8866. . . . All right."

During this pause Charles chattered. "It keeps a lot of people out of mischief playing telephones. An American woman wrote to my paper the other day that it took longer to get through to Brighton than to Buffalo, New York."

Mark was speaking at the telephone. "Yes. I am having a blood test at twelve o'clock. . . . No, they think it is all right. . . . I will. I will mail it tonight."

Mark looked at his watch, quickly dialed again. Then he exploded.

"Are you Temple Bar 5032 or *not!* . . . Oh, 8976. I see. Sorry." He rehung and dialed again. A short pause. "What is your number? . . . Not 8976 *again!* . . . Oh damn. Sorry."

Mark rehung and dialed a single number.

"The symbolical number Zero!" observed Charles as he went to the door. "You are showing the Dunkirk spirit, stout fellow. You haven't left your post at the telephone. You have to vacate all numbers except Zero. So you go and live with good old Zero. Why not always dial O? Why have any truck with anything but Zero?"

Ten minutes later Mark was setting off, a brown paper parcel held against the stomach. Charles joined him.

"Going to be bled?" said he.

"If you care to call it that."

"Just what you need as a matter of fact, bleeding."

"You think so, Charles?"

"What we all have to put up with, *you* deny the existence of. *You* bottle up the curses to which I give vent! *You* suppress more than I spit out. One of these fine days at that rotten old telephone you will explode, the bad blood you bottle up will tear you apart—*bang!*"

Mark laughed. "You have got it all wrong! The telephone staff are. . . ."

"Wonderful—I know, I know, all ought to have a Victoria Cross and a Nobel Prize. And so ought you—so ought you! Come along and be bled —quick."

Outside the flat-door before pulling it shut, Mark stood still and fixed an Ancient-Mariner-like eye upon Charles.

"Let me tell you something, Charlie!"

"Yes?"

"All the intelligent people I know—*intelligent,* Charles, intelligent— are socialists. They have discovered suddenly that they are socialists."

"You mean all the smart alecks."

"Oh no. For it is *stupid,* Charles, to be a little black-marketeer. Not very intelligent, Charles!" And Mark poked Charles with a stiff fore-finger.

"And, Mark, my lad!" Charles poked an expressive forefinger into Mark's midriff. "The winning side, eh! Cowardly cowardly custard!"

Mark growled with sporting glee and his eyes sparkled as he flattened the tip of his square-headed forefinger upon Charles' chest. "Not so, Robin Hood! Not so, Dick Turpin! You will end with a price on your head!"

"Ha! And *your* head"—and Charles flattened his forefinger upon Mark's cheekbone—"won't fetch a farthing if it ever comes up in a witches' auction. *This yes-man's skull one farding!* No bids."

"I suppose, Charlot, you pat yourself on the back," and Mark flat-tened his forefingertip on Charles's arm. "You outwit the police, yes? Rich Americans get their black-market eggs, illegal rashers, and what not, thanks to good little Charlie! Fine intelligent work, what!"

"And you, my smart man," Charles poked him pointedly with his finger, "you have one egg a week and crow as though the millennium were here!"

And they went shouting down the stairs, jabbing each other mirth-fully with their forefingers.

— *3* —

During the remainder of that day the two friends might be found in various parts of the town, up to 11 P.M. when they returned to Rotting

Hill. Their cab took them up Wimpole Street on the way to the Heppel
Laboratories. As they ascended one of the two celebrated streets of
costly medicinemen, Charles reacted characteristically to his surroundings. "The art of medicine," he said, "will decay in this country. The
National Health Act writes *finis* to fine work in surgery and dentistry,
and doctors will sink to the status of druggists—with more responsibility
and less pay." To which Mark replied, "Charles—rubbish! When medicine ceases to be a profitable racket as it is at present it will be far better placed to make real advances. They may even discover a cure for
the common cold."

The man with the dirty white clinical coat who let them in said: "I
suppose it's for a blood-draw?" "I imagine so," said Charles. "My friend
is badly in need of a *letting*." The man himself looked like a blood donor
in the last stages of pernicious anemia, but he was a hectically talkative
Cockney.

When Mark's turn came to go in to be "drawn" he expected to find
himself in a laboratory, spectacularly antiseptic, white jars and tubes
containing human blood, labeled and ready for diagnosis, lined up on
glass shelves. The tools for "the draw" would be much in evidence. But
this was a socialist dream. What actually happened was so much the
reverse that Mark supposed a preliminary interview was considered
necessary.

A dingy sitting room of the Trollope period was where he found himself. No vacuum cleaner ever came near the dusty shelves and decrepit
leather armchairs. The doctor would have been all the better for a little
mechanical suction too. But he was unmistakably a doctor: he invited
Mark, with great urbanity and kindness, to take off his jacket and to be
seated near him beside an untidy desk: and when they were both smil-
ingly seated close together by the desk he invited Mark to roll up a
sleeve. This was it, then!

The doctor, still smiling, examined Mark's left and right arms, well
stocked with muscles and fat. "I think we will take it from the finger,"
he announced with quiet affability—he could not have spoken more
softly or smiled with better breeding. "Your hands are very cold," the
doctor remarked sympathetically. And indeed, the room was so cold that
Mark's hands were like ice rather than flesh. The doctor was evidently
used to this complication. He led his case to a washbasin. There the
hands were practically boiled, and they both went back to the chairs
again. The doctor smiled with exquisite courtesy and kindness. "Warmer
now!" he said. "Yes. The *hands* are," said Mark. The doctor apologeti-
cally took his right hand and gently stroked the middle finger with a
piece of wet cotton wool. Then rather unexpectedly he jabbed an instrument deep into the ball of the fingertip.

The doctor drew out the instrument and proceeded to squeeze the hole he had made quite viciously. He murmured a complaint about the paucity of blood, then jabbed his instrument in again. "Sorry!" he murmured (he was a very perfect gentleman) and started squeezing again and collecting the red trickle.

"My blood," said Mark, "refuses to visit so exposed an outpost of my body. It lurks in the well-covered trunk until I get into a warmer room. Then it may come out."

The doctor smiled gently and indulgently as he fixed on the band-aid and said, "I am so sorry the room is not warmer. When we throw out this government, Mr. Robins . . . !" Mark looked at him severely as he put his jacket on and very coldly observed: "It is not the government that is to blame, sir, as you know quite well! Good day." As they were being shown out by the hysterical anemic Cockney with the dirty white coat, Mark inquired, "Is this a National Health Service place?" to which the answer came with a laugh "No, sir . . . not by a long shot. We *do* have National Health Service patients, sir, when the other laboratories are flooded out as I might say with them. Let me see, yes, sir, there was one of them this morning, sir." Charles burst into a laugh which caused the doorman to jump almost out of his dirty white coat.

"I," said Mark sternly, "am that National Health Service patient. I shall immediately report the filthy condition of this place, and the lamentable disregard of sepsis. Why do you not send that coat to the wash? Good morning!"

Charles remained on the doorstep holding his sides, which a gargantuan laugh threatened to split. He stamped about gasping for breath.

"You are growing into an idiot!" said Mark.

"But I would not have missed that for anything. 'Why don't you send it to the wash?' Ha, ha! Sublime! The Welfare State in action. An informer!" And he pointed at his friend a trembling finger. "Snooper!"

"Shut up." Mark walked smartly away.

But Mark had not lost Charles. As he entered the marble halls of the Richelieu near Piccadilly, Charles was at his side—or he was at Charles'. This most famous establishment has always specialized in poor food. But the grill room lunch was a carefully calculated insult to the British palate, delivered by a staff of deaf but noisy Italians, who flung the plates down on the table, and rushed away, deaf to the protests which at once arose. The "soupe brésilienne" was dirty yellow water, the "foie braisée mode de Mayence" was literally a piece of blackened shoe leather, the "pommes soufflées Richelieu" had never "blown" and tasted of last month's fats, and the "baba au rhum" had no rum and was not a baba. The coffee tasted so rancid and bitter that one sip was more than enough.

"If you put a five shilling ceiling on what may be charged for a meal. . . ." said Charles in answer to Mark's muttered apology, lighting a cigarette. "A man has to live."

"He does not have to live at the expense of the community. *This* is bad behavior!"

"Report 'em!" Charles winked at him.

Mark eyed the wine list with distaste. "What will you have, Charles?" They had a double "Fine Maison" and Mark spoke of Ida. "I was thinking the other day," he said, "we haven't met since . . . when *was it?* Being out of England most of the war years in the East damages one's time-sense, deflates the perspectives or something."

"It was 1936 I believe, down at Tadpole's."

"So it was, so it was!"

"As a matter of fact," Charles told him, "she is coming down to stay with me and is coming to London tomorrow."

"Is she really—you didn't tell me, Charles. . . ."

A mixed expression came into Mark's face, which he struggled to conceal. It was the outcome of inharmonious emotions. In his effort to shut off the true expression he acquired one of sheepish benevolence. "How is old Ida now?" he asked, frowning in sympathetic puzzlement, as if he had asked a pretty difficult question. "I have often meant to get you to tell me how she spends her time. You don't see much of her, do you, but *I* haven't seen her for over ten years. I was awfully sorry to have missed her last year. That was your fault! Has she altered . . . I mean become a blue-stocking or anything?"

Charles smiled enigmatically. "Come along with me tomorrow to her club; she would like most awfully to see you, I know."

"May I, Charles? An excellent idea, I still have a day or two's sick leave. It will be most exciting seeing Ida again. Another snort? I'm going to. Waiter!"

A half-hour later the two friends stood in one of London's largest stores, the brown paper parcel still held by Mark, rather carefully, against his left-hand breast pocket. The thick and sluggish stream of shop-gazing charladies, finding an obstruction, bumped it and rolled around it. For Mark and Charles stood together muttering in the middle of the MEN'S SHIRTS. They examined attentively a batch of shirts of most attractive soft check, conspicuously displayed.

"Sixty shillings," said Charles pleasantly, "of which fifty per cent, I expect, is purchase tax. You bought two. So you paid Cripps sixty shillings when you fell for this pretty checkwork."

"Try not to talk like the *Daily Express,*" Mark observed.

"Oh, well, you love Cripps so much you probably feel patriotic about it."

Mark asked a tall shopman where the manager of the department was to be found.

"I am the assistant manager," he was politely informed. "The manager is away."

A young man came up to him with a bill which he initialed or something. Mark opened his parcel and revealed a shirt identical in all respects with the attractive pale blue checks displayed on the counter. The assistant manager gazed at the shirt and then looked inquiringly at Mark.

"Have you had any complaints about these shirts?" Mark asked him.

"No, sir. None whatever."

"I bought two of these here recently. Have you a room where I can put this shirt on?"

Mark and Charles were conducted to a small room and Mark changed into the shirt he had brought in the parcel. Not only his hand but all his bony wrist and a piece of his hairy forearm protruded from the cuff. "When first I wore this," he told the assistant manager, "it was rather embarrassingly long in the sleeve, the cuffs almost reached my knuckles. This has only been washed *once*. You can see for yourself what has happened to the cuffs. They receded at least four inches, leaving my wrists high and dry."

The A.M. produced a tape measure and adjusted it to the area in dispute. "Yes, sir," he agreed. "Two and a half inches."

"I call it four inches," Mark corrected him.

"We, of course, will give you another shirt." There was to be no unseemly dispute, the A.M. made it clear.

"It was this shirt I bought, though. I do not want just *a shirt*. I was not short of a shirt."

"Of course not, sir, I quite appreciate that. No shirt today as I dare say you know, sir, is 100 per cent safe, most unfortunately. The trouble is in the factory. In the weaving of the fabric if they do not weave it close . . . well, there is a space between the threads. Naturally, sir, when you *wash* this cloth the space between the threads tends to close up. The cloth *shrinks,* in other words. It is the work people. They will not work as they used to. Since the war it is terrible. Not that we don't insist, sir, that goods we buy are *tested*. Oh, yes. As an instance, in the Swiss factory where these shirts come from everything is thoroughly washed before it is made up."

"These cuffs must have extended well over the fingertips, mustn't they, before *that* wash!"

The A.M. tittered politely. "That's right, sir. That's what puzzles me."

"Are people, customers, still too timid to complain?" Charles asked him. "If they take home an article of this sort have they not the spirit to bring it back and raise hell? Do they think *anything* is good enough for them? Because they are merely English?"

"A year ago they were, well, a little like what you say, but they do complain now. There are people bringing back things all the time. But I wish they *would* complain more!" protested the assistant manager. "You would be surprised the kind of goods we get sometimes. A consignment of thin vests arrived this summer. We opened up one vest and there was a blooming great hole the size of a half-crown right in the middle of the back. We opened up a few more and I'm blessed if there wasn't a hole in every blooming one! All had to be condemned, of course, but I'm bothered if I can explain this Swiss shirt."

He affected to muse for a moment. "It is just possible, of course, that these shirts come from here."

"What!" Mark was indignantly alert. "From England?"

Charles lay back in his chair and laughed. "*Never* from this land of competence and integrity! What are you saying!"

"I don't say it *is* so," the A.M. corrected. "It is possible, that is all."

"Do you mean that *material* was sold by us to some Swiss factory," Mark demanded, "which that factory proceeded to make up into shirts: and that when the first of these shirts began to be sold to the Swiss they duly shriveled up (like this one) in the wash? As you see, I cannot even *button* this collar. And did the Swiss—is that your theory—then send the whole consignment over here?"

"To sell them to the poor boobs of English—that sort of thing?" Charles added.

"Well it's you that put it like that, you know, sir! I know nothing about it at all, I only think that perhaps the shirts themselves were made here for export to Switzerland. The Swiss are fond of checks you see— the way we like stripes. But" (catching sight of the displeasure which Mark did not seek to hide) "remember I know no more than *you* do. I am only trying to put two and two together." The cloud on Mark's face made the man nervous. Could he, he wondered, be a shirt manufacturer?

"Your explanation seems to me an exceedingly plausible one," Charles told him. "You are to be congratulated on your brutal frankness."

Mark was silent. Thoughtfully he took off the shirt. "Will you please let me see what you propose I should take in exchange."

Back at the counter the assistant manager muttered obviously confidential instructions to the young man serving at that counter. At last two shirts were produced from some secret recess and laid side by side for Mark to make his choice. One was of exceptionally cheap and garish blue, coarsely striped, the other white.

Charles said in Mark's ear, "They keep these for such occasions. You would look well in that *blue* one!" Mark shortly left, his shirt beneath his arm, informing the assistant manager that he would write to the management. "It is disgraceful!" he added, in a rather official voice. As they marched away Charles affected to be concealing a smile which Mark affected to ignore. When they reached the street Mark said his head was aching badly, which indeed was the case, and that he thought he would go back to the flat if his friend didn't mind. In an offensively "understanding" voice Charles advised him to rest up for a while. They arranged to meet at a downtown restaurant for dinner and Charles took a cab to keep an appointment with an eye doctor. This had been the main purpose of his visit to London.

The eye specialist, who was one of the leading consultants in this specialty, possessed a large, brilliantly lighted residence, eloquent of wealth, health, and a beaconlike eyesight. Within, it was sumptuous. The young woman who answered the door (one of the doors of Death, after all) breathed an expensive friendliness. The strains of "Cosi Fan Tutte" came down from halcyon regions above, also brilliantly lighted, at the summit of a vast staircase. "How fortunate it is," thought Charles —as he passed into the costly and cosy waiting room (which was actually *warm*) and took up a copy of *Life*—"how fortunate it is that I only suffer from astigmatism."

This was one of the many eminent specialists who had refused to take service under the State. "Cosi Fan Tutte," Charles approvingly reflected, "does not belong to the same dimension as the Welfare State!" But when he found himself in the presence of the large preoccupied man, with a shock of white hair, he received no response to the first of his disparaging remarks about socialized medicine. The man he had come to consult went down in Charles' estimation. "Whatever did Williams want to send me to this old fool for?" he grumbled internally.

His was a routine eye test, "no thrills," as they say in Harley Street when no pain is to be inflicted. The massive and clumsy frame used for tests was stuck upon his nose. The big anguished-looking red-faced man then delicately placed lenses out of a box in the empty sockets of the frame. He dropped one of these, which later was discovered in the cuff of Charles' trousers. The lenses of course were revolved and Charles was asked what he could see. There was sometimes an embarrassing absence of *rapport* between what Charles saw and what the doctor thought he ought to see.

The doctor, twisting the lens slowly towards him would comment, "Now that is better like that, isn't it?" Charles would answer, "I'm afraid not." "Not?" the doctor would ask with surprise. He then would place another lens in one of the sockets and say confidently, "Now *that* is clearer, isn't it?" When Charles would answer "No, that is worse" the doctor would observe gruffly, "No, it can't be *worse*. Let us try again. Now I will put back the one that was there before. Remember what it looks like through this. Now"—and snatching one out and placing the disputed one once more in position (and it was during one of these lightning exchanges that a lens flew out of the doctor's hand and nestled in the trouser cuff)—"now is that not better? You can see better with that, can't you?" "No, sir, I am afraid not. I cannot see so well." This happened more than once. Charles naturally concluded that the great specialist was no magician. The doctor, on his side, decided that Charles was one of those insufferable patients who always try to put the doctor in the wrong. At the end of the test he was even less talkative than before.

When Charles said, "I suppose I shall have to wait months for these bifocals," the doctor said: "Probably. That, however, is not my affair." "You could not," Charles asked, "use on my behalf, sir, one of the priorities they give you?" But the only answer he got to that was: "It is dispensing opticians who are the people to talk to about that, not doctors." Meanwhile the specialist was making out the prescription for the spectacles. "Do you mind where you go?" he asked Charles. "You don't mind where it is?" A curious question. However, Charles declared himself indifferent, and the specialist said, "Then go to Davis and Merks. You have on this envelope their address." And Charles saw that the name "Davis and Merks" was printed on the envelope. (The old devil gets a rake-off, mused Charles.) "I will telephone them and see what I can do."

Charles would, of course, have preferred one of the spacious and dignified Wigmore Street Opticians' saloons, where a staff of impeccably mannered male mannequins still fit spectacles upon one's nose as though it were a historic nose and as if Debrett were their bible. But he sat in Davis and Merks' modest premises in an insignificant side street for a long time before he realized the sort of place he had been sent to—before it dawned upon him that the treacherous old eye doctor (obviously playing a dirty game, with one foot in both camps, but his *left* foot having precedence over his *right* foot) had sent him to a National Health Service shop.

When he first went in he sat beside a woman in a fur coat with a well-dressed youngster. They seemed to him quite nice people until the fur coat *spoke*. He was deeply shocked to hear the accents of the Harrow Road. There were a couple of bald men who looked like clerks in his father's office. Although deploring the presence of what Mr. Orwell called "Proles," and wishing that the eye doctor had better taste in opticians, he was still a long way from understanding the dirty trick that had been played on him. The eight tables, at which client and shopman sat face to face gazing into one another's eyes, were huddled together, and at each were two figures, their intent faces a foot or two apart. Charles became increasingly fascinated in the problems of a young charlady having her spectacles adjusted at the nearby table. Charles watched the expressions in the assistant's face and studied the extraordinarily expressive fat little back of the youthful charlady.

A mirror stood upon the table, placed there that she might gaze into it. As she studied the revolution her personality must endure, the addition of a pair of ultra-gay spectacles doing strange things to her face, alarm and doubt were expressed by her back muscles. As the quizzical eye of Mr. Charles Dyat was trained upon this bauble, this festively colored nose-toy, he reflected, "That's what gets their silly votes! God, why did those dratted fools of Tories never think of *spectacles*—colored like sugar-sticks? Thirty million pairs of cheap specs would have won for them a hundred seats!" But now came the buxom young char's leisurely (everything luxuriously leisurely) terminating of the proceedings. Time was made for slaves and slaveys—and Britons were *no longer* slaves. She poked several short black neck curls back under her bulbous tammyish cap. And oh with what delicate restraint the assistant advised her: "Always clean them with water—with—well, tapwater."

The little shy respectful hesitation before actually referring to anything so plebeian as a *tap*—and then the little laugh of comradely complicity. "Why *not*, after all?" he might almost have said. "A little lady like yourself is broad-minded enough not to mind my mentioning the tap over the sink!"

At the street door there was another leisurely palaver, shopman all smiling charm, as he deferentially, yet a little flirtatiously, held the door open. Charles heard him reassuring her. They would, she would find, *quieten down* with use. Yes, the canary-yellow would no longer, er, be quite so painfully canary (no longer scream at you, my dear, *"I'm cheap!"* —Charles supplemented these adieux under his breath).

The shop was emptying and refilling all the time and Charles missed his turn twice because of his absorption in the *tapwater* episode. It was now that he began to say to himself that *there was something wrong about this place*—something terribly wrong! After all, there were *too many people* in it, to start with.

A dark baldish individual, Charles noticed, was sitting alone at a table. He walked over and sat down in front of him. Charles did not like the face of this man, nor did Charles' face appeal to the assistant—who made no pretense that he was a "younger son" who had gone into trade, who obviously would *say tapwater* without a modest pause beforehand. But he was not uncivil. It was a skimpy table, it was close quarters; Charles silently handed him the "Davis and Merks" envelope.

"Bifocals," said the assistant, staring at the prescription.

"Yes. Bifocals," Charles repeated.

"You know, don't you, sir, that the earliest you can expect these, or any bifocals with as large a reading segment as this, is three months?"

"Three months!" Charles scowled.

"That is the earliest."

"Oh, dear." Charles looked disagreeable. "What is the *smaller* reading segment you spoke of?"

He was shown a bifocal with a round spy-hole for reading at the bottom, of about the diameter of a lead pencil.

"Why does it take so long to get these glasses?" he asked angrily. "Is it a result of the National Health Act chaos?"

A tough look came into the spectacled eyes opposite his own. "It is nothing whatever to do with the National Health Service."

"Oh, you deny that!" Charles said disagreeably.

"I don't deny anything. I tell you what the situation is regarding bifocals. It always has taken a long time."

Charles reached over and took the prescription from the assistant's hand—not without a certain difficulty.

"This is mine—excuse me!" He pulled.

"You cannot get them made quicker anywhere else."

Charles and the assistant darted a nasty look at one another, and Charles left the shop. He made his way as quickly as possible to Wigmore Street, and entered the first luxurious optician's he encountered, Craxton and Dawson, Opticians to H.M. the King of the Hellenes. It was five times the size of Davis and Merks, discreetly lighted—and completely empty.

"No blasted National Health Service *here!*" Charles told himself with satisfaction.

A tall distinguished grey-haired gentleman (he turned out to be the manager in person) approached. They took to one another at once. Both suggested by their demeanor that they had been born in a Palladian palace in a vast park, in which deer drifted from tree to tree: and naturally Marlborough and Magdalen in the clothes of Savile Row defeated with great ease the Secondary School and an Austin Reed suiting.

There was complete harmony—but alas, the reality of popular government in its ultimate totalitarian phase imposed its ugly presence, inasmuch as the manager was sorrowfully obliged to confess that he had no influence whatever with the factory that makes bifocals. That factory is the only one doing bifocals: it has literally tens of thousands of orders to be executed before it can deal with any new order. Nothing any shop says makes the slightest impression. Such was the gist of the manager's information. Asked whether the National Health Service was responsible for these conditions, the manager answered, a little surprised, that of course that and nothing else was the cause.

"Why does not the Government set up a *second* factory?" Charles inquired idly.

"Why does it not do a great many things!" the manager countered.

These two supporters of the old order parted on the best of terms. "Not a gentleman, but a damned sound feller!" was Charles' mental comment. The manager, without realizing what he was doing, wrote "Major Charles Dyat, Tadicombe Priory" against the order though Charles had laid no claim to military rank.

— 4 —

Since their return from the cinema in an attempted snowstorm—a fiasco resulting in very dirty soft hail—the two friends had sat in front of the gas fire. A French existentialist film they had gone to see after dinner—"Time the Tiger" was the English title—had predisposed Mark, in the brief halt before re-entering his unmade bed, to a deeper discouragement than he had known for some time. The past fifteen hours pressed on him in this relaxed moment, in the way a crowd presses on you as soon as you stand still. Mark's mind was now accessible to the day's frictions, against which it had been shut firmly all day, in spite of Charles' propaganda. The 'flu, he told himself, still lurked in his bloodstream, and perhaps some further toxins, as the doctor suspected. He grilled his feet before the red-hot elements superstitiously.

Charles sat at his side, gazing at the stream rising from the water placed in front of the fire. He thought of what "the actor-feller" had said: "Time is not passive—it is like a tiger devouring its prey." Its prey is *us*. But its prey is temporal, like Time itself, for we are merely time-stuff, existential ephemera. It is not something timeless it devours (how could Time do that?) nor is it something timeless devouring something temporal. It is Time devouring itself, time eating up time indeed. But *is* there in reality any devouring? Is not everything we see just something fizzling away like a firework, which we call *time*? This verbalism has misled us, we create an abstract entity.

Arguments of this sort had been going on in the film and were now prolonged lazily in his mind. He excogitated dimly an objection to Time seen as a Tiger. Our existence is more like the water, he thought, in that bowl—a small and limited quantity. The active principle is like that fire, which slowly disperses the little body of liquid placed in front of it, until there is nothing left.

Mark at all times was liable to be visited by the discontents which—both because of inherited stoicism, and of a repressive ideology lately acquired—he daily smothered. This was a very severe attack, not unique. But day's discontents came not singly, as disagreeable memories—for he would not have admitted them into his memory any more than he had done at the time: they came as an anonymous *cafard,* an exquisite depression. On the other hand Charles was subject to no attacks of this sort: he was more analytical to start with and a truculent perfectionist. For Charles, life was a silly wrangle over a shrunken shirt: life as he saw it was waiting months for spectacles—so life becomes a struggle *to see* (which ought not to be the case in the twentieth century): was a struggle *to eat*—as if we were paleolithic: he thought of life as charged with toxins no blood test could isolate—he saw life as a struggle not to be poisoned by all the *ideas* that were injected as antitoxins into it by malignant quacks: he saw life as a hysterical chemist obsessed by problems of antisepsis. But he never had the rough philosophy or the detachment to say "what is one man's meat, etc." The man who was being poisoned was *himself*, that was sufficient. But at least he *knew* he was being poisoned, he knew what was poison for him.

At Oxford they had sometimes sat like this, Mark and Charles, at the end of the day: and as their discussions used to start then, so now one started rather suddenly, with Charles looking up and saying:

"Do you think Time is a tiger, a ferocious beast of prey?"

It was an undergraduate opening, how people talk when they are young.

Mark shook his head.

"No," he said magisterially, "nothing forcible and palpable like that. More like the bacteria of a disease."

"It is rather a fierce malady!"

Mark shook his head again. "I don't think so. I know you do."

"At least," Charles said, "it moves at an accelerated tempo at present. Perhaps Time has contracted a fever."

Mark looked up, his handsome eyes of a mildly stern big dog losing their lethargic droop.

"A *fever*. Perhaps." Mark passed his fingers through coarse dark hair. "Time has certainly shown itself in the tiger class during this century. The immense explosion of technical creativeness has torn the world of two millennia apart."

"You call that tiger *Time*. You are sure the tiger is not Man?" Charles asked.

"There were men there in the eighteenth, the seventeenth, the sixteenth century and so on. No, I prefer to say *Time*. In 1900 the bee was in the clover. God was in His Heaven, all was well with the world. Fifty years ago the scene was amazingly different. The radio, the automobile, the airship and airplane, the telephone, television, the cinema—these revolutionary techniques did not come one at a time with decent intervals in between. Four decades absorbed this stupendous cataract."

"The advent of energies out of scale with man, as if a race of giants had been born the size of skyscrapers." Charles shook his head; "1900: a blessed time."

"In some ways, yes," Mark agreed. "Though neither of us was born yet. We are like the cinema and the telephone in that respect."

"I am neither like a telephone nor like the flicks." And they both laughed. "Tonight," Charles proceeded, "we have been to a movie play. Forty years ago it would have been living, sweating actors. Much better!"

"I too prefer the mime in the flesh: as I prefer a concert hall to a radio," Mark again agreed. "However, the cinema has its uses and beauties. You would not deny that? At present it is *mis*used in the most disgusting way by Hollywood."

"And don't forget what is done over here."

"All right. But once the profit motive is banished—as it will be in a socialist society, then there will be nothing but an intelligent standard of movie. If nothing else, its educative power will be enormous. Today it miseducates and corrupts. *Then* it will. . . ."

"No it won't," shouted Charles, "not if you have that pack of vulgar nobodies still there! By *education*, which you stress, they would mean *propaganda*. And as for *art!* In the company of some film magnate they lap up the vulgarest rubbish the cinema can produce. No Hollywood horror would be too stupid for *them*. One would say that they identify *socialism* with *philistinism*."

Mark laughed nervously. "You have got that all wrong too, Charlie. That is not bad taste, the minister involved is a man of sensitive culture. Alfred Munnings and he, for instance. . . ."

"Yes, yes, and Augustus John!" Charles laughed boisterously.

"Augustus John?" A rather grave look came into Mark's face. "I don't know about Augustus John," he said slowly, "but the responsible officials are not philistines whatever else they may be. No. It is DOLLARS."

"Nothing but dollars," echoed Charles. "You believe that on the sly these great ministers of state slip out to see films of the type we have been to this evening? Who knows, that fat man at my side may have been Bevan."

"Highly probable," snapped Mark. "I know Bevan likes good films."

"Don't speak to me of *vermin!* There are vermin in *all* movie houses."

"Poor Nye."

"You will really have to get a new type of politician, Mark, for your brave new world. Do be serious about it if you must go in for it! . . . But I have been thinking about what you said—the last forty or fifty years you know and Time going berserk."

"Well?"

"Well," said Charles, "I of course agree that Time has packed a millennium into a half-century. But what should interest us most, purely as citizens, is not the terrific stepping up of man's power over nature but the fantastic power conferred upon the politicos in this new era of radio, automatic weapons, atomic bombs, and so on: of man's power over man. The power of a Sultan or a Mogul was absurdly limited in comparison with that of present-day Iron Curtain rulers. And the fact that they rule *for the rulees' good* (so they say) does not make it a more attractive proposition. Upon what they might think was *for my good* we should violently disagree, were I a Pole or Romanian."

Mark groaned and placed his hand affectionately on that of his friend. "Charles—chum. . . ."

"Please!" Charles looked up with alarm.

"All right!" Mark laughed, "I thought you'd rise to that. But we *are* very old and very great friends."

"Yes, indeed," Charles responded gravely.

"I was not born a socialist—quite the contrary."

"Anything but!"

"Well, Charles, what I suggest you remember is that I have *made* myself a socialist—just as you might do."

"No thank you!" Charles told him. "When you see me in a 'Liberty Cap' you will know I am on my way to Colney Hatch."

"I understand perfectly. It was not at all easy at first in my own case. I felt just like you. *Inside* I still feel in many ways as you do. Habits acquired in one's young days . . . oh, of eating, dressing, and of thinking: don't I know their power! They form an unbreakable framework— I can never be a socialist like Bevan. . . ."

"I hope not."

"But cannot you see, old Charles, that all the molds are being broken *for* one? Do you feel intact yourself? I feel sometimes like an oyster without a shell" (hastily). "I know you will *say* you do. There is nothing left of the world we both grew up in. We have been forcibly, violently, reborn. I am not a *convert* to socialism: I have been reborn a socialist."

Charles blew, to denote disgust. "Well, I *haven't*," he said, and put a match to a new cigarette.

"You're a pig-headed blighter, Charles. But force your mind open a fraction. Consider! The right word for what you hate is not 'socialism,' in fact. It is not a theory of the state I have been reborn to. It is a set of *quite novel conditions*. But, for those conditions, like it or not, socialism is the necessary political philosophy. The society that was here in 1900 is as utterly of the past as the England of the Wars of the Roses. You have omitted to be reborn or have escaped rebirth, that is all."

"Thank God."

"All right, Charles, but you move about in this world like a ghost. You are, my dear Charles, a ghost from my past life. You are not a creature of flesh and blood!"

Mark laughed heartily, gazing affectionately at his friend.

"No?" said Charles. "I am not of flesh and blood?" At the same time he administered a pinch of considerable force. Mark started and caught

Charles' wrist. "Such demonstrations," he observed, "prove nothing. A poltergeist is still a ghost."

"What you *say* proves nothing either, for it has no logical support."

"You think not."

"No. First of all, the word 'socialism' needs to be defined of course. What you mean is Marxism. Its prophet flourished a century ago. Marx's 'class war' is the sociological complement of Darwin's lethal biological vision."

"Is life not a nightmare battle of organisms to survive? But go on."

"Marxist socialism comes to us from the past as a sacred text. It has been imposed upon this age by means of a ceaseless propaganda. As to Marxism being the only doctrine that is compatible with the air age and the ether age, that is rubbish. It is arbitrary and irrelevant. It is just as archaic as those other things which continue to be foisted on us such as the credit system, the Texas hoard of gold, Cabinet rule masquerading as parliamentary democracy—there is a long list of these obsolete institutions and techniques deliberately preserved. It is a very eccentric theory that television, rocket bombs, radio, and X-ray oblige us to accept Marxism."

Mark lay back and yawned nervously. "If," he said, "you find yourself unable to accept my solution of your difficulties. . . ."

"What difficulties?" Charles interrupted.

"Wait a year or two, Charles, and you will find out. But here is something else. Socialism is so solidly entrenched that no Blimp crusade is likely to dislodge it."

"So you think."

"So I know. Its leaders are *de facto* rulers of England."

"What if the Tories come out on top at the general election?" Charles asked.

"If they were the strongest party? They could hardly secure a working majority. But if they did—if they do—they could not rule. There would be a general strike, a violent one. Should the Tory Government succeed, for argument's sake, in breaking the general strike, that would not be the end. In suppressing it there would be bloodshed. A nascent class war would be on. There would be great bitterness, nation-wide plotting and agitating, half the country permanently strike-bound. Do not delude yourself: the old party-system seesaw is at an end in this country. Not to adjust yourself, Charles, to this new situation is hopelessly romantic. Are you impressed with Lord Woolton by any chance? Are you an admirer of Mr. Anthony Eden? Or are you go-ahead, and a hot Butlerite?"

Charles laughed as he got up and stretched himself. "Now you are on sounder ground," he said. "The winning-side argument—the best I know of in dealing with the intelligent."

"That's good."

"No, it isn't. Because I am not ambitious."

"Nor am I," Mark pointed out. "Ambition has nothing to do with it. It is just in order to live on the side of the law."

"You mean," Charles told him, as he went back and sat down, "you mean to *starve safely*. To go on saying *Yes* ever after—unmolested, in a shabby corner. For *without ambition* that is all that you can mean. Well, Mark, that may be a prospect to tempt some people with. You might find that they would come and join you with alacrity. But to employ such arguments with *me* . . . ! I am off to bed and to dream of my own little millennium."

"Pleasant dreams then—full of free enterprise, free speech for the upper classes, and a little freebooting thrown in. Good night, mad rebel!"

— 5 —

Mark's dreams that night were colored by anticipation of the next day's lunch with Ida. Memory led off with an album of dream-pictures of Ida as the most lovely schoolgirl that ever shook a golden curl—seventeen, a year younger than he was then. She poked fun at him, in the dream, and finally gave him a huge pinch, hooting with schoolgirlish mischief. The pain of the pinch woke Mark up. When in a few seconds he was again asleep, it appeared that he was on his way to visit his wealthy aunt who lived at York. Soon he had reached his destination, and as he had been fancying she might be dead he pressed the bell, making ready to say how sad it was and he did hope she had not suffered at the last. However, she was not dead: he saw her crossing the cavernous drawing room quite skittishly as he entered. "How down-in-the-mouth you look, Mark? Has anything happened!" she was exclaiming, her white teeth flashing in the gloom, holding out briskly a shriveled hand. And then he perceived it was Ida smiling at him ironically: only an Ida of what would probably be called "a young seventy." The face changed sometimes into that of his aunt Susan (Robins), and then his aunt began to masquerade as Ida, in a really horrible fashion. They were looking into a very large glass bowl containing goldfish when his aunt made a sickly little soft gasping sound. He found himself supporting her in his arms. She was quite heavy, he placed her with difficulty on a sofa, on the way tripping over a rug and almost falling to the floor with her. It was obvious to him that she was dead, and he looked at her face most unwillingly. It was that of Ida, a waxen white, deeply lined, the scalp disagreeably grizzled. Turning away violently he cannoned into a parlormaid who had arrived there behind him without noise. "She passed away quite peacefully," he told her and she smiled. He smiled too. Then he laughed.

When next day at her club Mark found himself in the presence of the

real Ida, for a moment he was incredulous. He smiled at her emptily
with his teeth, as if to show he was not taken in. But he soon warmed
up, for she was no apparition.

Ida looked—oh, around twenty-five. The lazy laughing lips of Rossetti's
Jenny ("fond of a kiss and fond of a guinea") were as roseate and indolent as ever: her eyes were steady, an almost imperceptible dance, as
well, giving them a remote glitter of gaiety.

As if it were *a top,* humming and spinning on without changing position, perhaps she would go on being like this until suddenly time as-
serted itself and she stopped dead. Such images of precarious fixity were
frankly admitted to his consciousness by the otherwise infatuated Mark:
but he was not altogether innocent of cosmetics. He was aware that the
illusionist's name might be Rubinstein, but what did that matter? It
could not be *all* Rubinstein. A divine mental sloth, it occurred to him,
played a major part. She would have agreed actually: she knew more
about herself than the fish does regarding its marvellous iridescence, or
the hummingbird its aerial spinning. Any marvels she could account
for.

The quality was still dreamlike and introspective, certainly, only
Mark felt confident that this time she was not going to turn into a
wealthy aunt.

"Your labors at the Ministry have greyed you, Mark, a little," Ida said
at once (no doubt reading his thoughts and diverting attention from her
face to his). "Otherwise much the same."

"Yes, I have altered, but *you,* my dear Ida, are *just* the same—and if
there is art, its causes are not found."

She shook her 'twenties curls with a nervous and defensive mirth. "A
little vanishing cream, combined with an empty mind, is quite enough,"
she laughed. So he and the woman he had always been in love with—and
had not married any other because she was always there in his imagination—eyed one another benignly. He exposed his haunted vacuum, and
she automatically entered and warmed it to the temperature of paradise.

They were a party heated by the suns of the past: they were three
people in the nineteen-twenties who entered the Ivy Restaurant. The
restaurant personnel, stolidly Italian, were cold and hard in nineteen-
forty-nine. Mark, Ida, and Charles talked of old 'twenties books and
dishes and jokes, their politics were only those that may be found in a
Gilbert and Sullivan Opera where everyone present is a little liber*al* or
a little conserva*tive*—except for a moment in the small entrance lobby.
An authentically proletarian youth, attempting to look dramatic and
sinister, was heard to ask the doorman-vestiaire, "Is Mr. Zilliacus here
yet?" Charles said "I hope not" to the ceiling, but the comment was intercepted by the doorman-vestiaire, who looked curiously at Charles and
Charles returned his gaze.

Ideology, otherwise, was wiped off this trio who had that *clean* sensation the nonpolitical have. Mark had actually put the question to himself. Why had he not married Charles' sister? He supposed it was Charles. It would have been too like homosexuality, which was an absurd sensation. She had not married, herself, until nearly thirty, and in a couple of years that marriage was terminated by the death of her husband in the hunting field. He had been no horseman, poor chap. She insisted on his learning to ride in a Bayswater riding school, however, and she whisked him off to week-end hunts with a stockbroker outfit in East Anglia. Since his death she had divided her time between Tadicombe Priory and Withers Norton, the other parklet which had materialized on her wedding day and which she had so far been able to retain.

Three theatre queues outside had an Italian minstrel in attendance; with a most piercing pathos locked up in his sinuses, the high notes of heart-throb of a gutter-Pagliacci penetrated the lunch-time roar of the ever full Ivy, and provided a musical sugar-stick background as the three old friends rolled again in memory in the Swiss snows at Wengen—or drifted, talking very youngly along "The High" on their way to Blackwell's to buy Lawrence's *Sons and Lovers*. And Mark reflected as they talked that one never knew, one *might* some day (if one did not come to the point with Ida) get married at this late date and to the wrong woman. Horrifying thought! He had a premonition of the form the wrongness would take.

But the cocktails and the Sylvaner were taking effect. What happened arrived with great suddenness. At one moment they were blissfully gay as they revisited the landscapes of their youth—as if by common consent refusing to admit anything to their consciousness later than 1929 (that as a rather dangerous limit). Next moment almost, it seemed, they were all three glaring at one another. Ida—an Ida at least twenty years older—was denouncing the socialist government: she had asked why he, Mark, had not immediately handed in his resignation after the "vermin" speech of "that filthy little man Bevan, who ought to be horsewhipped!" "Ida!" Mark had protested, half-rising. But "why not!" had shouted Charles, half-rising, too, "is he not the lowest and dirtiest. . . ." "I am not going to listen to this nonsense!" Mark protested still more strongly. "If Ida is drunk, that is one thing. You, Charles, should have a stronger head! I see you should take water even with your wine!"

The change of climate, however, had been so abrupt and so absolute, and Mark prior to that had been so completely transported into the neutral fairyland of the past, that—though he attempted to silence public abuse of a powerful minister, and of one personally admired by him as well—he was for a short time dull and bewildered, groping his way about between two worlds.

But the *Navy League* side of Ida, aroused with so alarming a suddenness, tore on into battle, her face distorted with partisan rage. "They have cut down the reserve of officers!" spat those lips so recently models of a charmed aloofness. "The last R.N.V.R. cadets are now in training. There are to be no more. Who are to replace officer casualties? The lower deck, I suppose! Only half the Fleet is in commission. Fine fighting units are rotting in port—soon we shall have the navy of a South American republic. We could be defeated in battle by Brazil!"

Her eyes flashed as, in indignant fancy, she saw the flagship of the Home Fleet cock up its stern, explode, and sink, the victim of a Brazilian torpedo.

"Ida, do stop talking such dreadful nonsense," Mark expostulated.

"She is not talking nonsense, but very good sense," Charles objected. "Ida has her facts from a pretty reliable source. Admiral Darrell is a neighbor of hers at Withers Norton."

"Wars are decided in the air—surface craft are militarily obsolete," Mark said with cross indifference. "Darrell is gaga anyway."

"Say what you like," Ida broke in again. "England is defenseless. The gang of ex-dock-laborers, Asiatics, and corporation lawyers who push us around from Whitehall are traitors. They should be hanged from the yardarm!" She pointed fiercely out of the window at a convenient lamp-post.

At a neighboring table a man who had been reading put down his paper and signaled angrily the *maître d'hôtel*. He was recognized by Mark as a socialist member of parliament. He was complaining about them to the *maître d'hôtel*, who studied Mark with attention but apparent lack of interest.

Ida by no means desisted—she became personal.

"You, who are of our class, deliberately helping that rabble to enslave England! It does not make sense. Can't you make an equally good living in some more honest way?"

"By engaging in a bit of black marketing?" he inquired dryly.

"Yes, Mark, yes! That would be a damn sight straighter than what you are doing."

"I'm sorry, Ida, but you see I am a socialist."

"So you say!" Charles smiled with good-natured skepticism.

Mark closed his eyes to shut out Charles' smile. He felt very foolish, and his choler was unabated. To the springtime regions where the great sex issues are normally decided he had returned—the greatly retarded mating was in process of consummation when his love transformed herself with nightmare suddenness into a Tory soapboxer. He had consented to play Romeo, and Juliet, at the critical moment, had acquired the mask of Col. Blimp, haranguing him from the moonlit balcony. An irrational resentment towards the brother and sister he was sitting with possessed him. He was in no mood to see in it an illustration of Time's tigerish leaping. He had been *tricked,* was what he really felt, by Charles and Ida; they had made a regular fool of him. This was a matter of feelings only, though, for he did not suspect a *plot.*

Mark looked across the table coldly at the vindictive female mask. A woman he had a few minutes before theoretically united himself with! He understood that it would be impossible for her to behave otherwise: that even from 1939 to now was a great time-leap for her—from a life of petty pomp to one of straitened anxiety—dismissal of gardener, disposal of a horse or horses, acuteness of the dress problem, and a prospect, as she saw it, should this election go the wrong way, tantamount to *murder.* Murder just as truly by Cripps as would have been murder by Crippen. What was the difference between a man who killed you with taxes or one who killed you with a revolver bullet or a dose of arsenic? None: except that the *taxer* takes longer over it—and is not tried for homicide!

A long silence was broken by Charles' laugh.

"Three old friends," he croaked, "who stopped to look *forward* at the Sodom and Gomorrah of the Future—and they all three are turned to salt!"

Charles was unable, however, to turn them back into flesh and blood; and when not long afterwards these three old friends left the restaurant all three knew that they would never lunch together again, that they were friends no longer. Charles, singly, would have been able to postpone, for some time at least, this break. But Ida had been decisive. The Brazilian Navy had sent to the bottom the good ship Friendship, built in the palmy days of pre-World War I.

Charles had taken his bag away about five—both were a little stiff at the last. That evening a loneliness attacked Mark in quite new places, even interfering, he found, with housework. He had had no time to make any arrangements for the evening, so there he was cleaning up after Charles, and afraid to sit down—for he had already tried to read and found he could not. The expulsion of Ida from her place in his imagination was responsible. These were the final pangs of Mark's rebirth into a novel age, as well as the death throes of Ida's image. But he did not identify his pangs: he did not analyze. He went to his desk, took out a piece of notepaper and wrote "My dear Wendy." Wendy Richardson was a good party woman, with a pretty face. He asked her if she thought Time was a tiger or a pussycat. He had been thinking a lot about Time lately, he told her. He thought himself it was a pussycat that had grown overnight into a tiger. Anyway, would she go with him to see the French film "Time the Tiger." "It is," he concluded, "a film with a kick in it. Excuse the Americanism."

EPILOGUE

*Post-General Election exchange of notes between
Mark Robins and Charles Dyat*

3 March, 1950

MY DEAR MARK,

Your "Pick the winning side" argument is only effective if the side you support is at the moment winning. With a majority of merely seven in the House of Commons you have to find a new argument, don't you? What is it?

CHARLES

DEAR CHARLES,

Like most Tories, you seem to forget that the Election was won by the Socialist Party. You will yet be disagreeably surprised by what can be done with a majority of seven. But you seem to mistake me for a recruiting sergeant. If I were one, however, I should not be interested in you as a recruit. I should tell you to go and join some other army. Meanwhile I suggest you find some other correspondent.

MARK

Allan Seager (1906–   )

THE UNICORN

Like that of "Time the Tiger," this story's tragedy is generated on the frontier between two versions of the world; in its final paragraph it very nearly becomes an explicit parable. The story's piquant detail is all located in its evocations of Tony's past; Ellen's present contains neither suicide nor romance. Try to state the theme of the story.

He had begun to talk. First she had served tea and anchovy toast and he had lain silently in the armchair staring into the fire with the flames glinting off his beautiful shoes. When he had finished his tea, she had brought out the decanter and a siphon as usual. He had made himself three big warm drinks one after the other and his face had brightened. He had noticed her. He began to talk. It was a kind of reminiscent chant done more or less for her pleasure but he never took his eyes off the fire.

". . . and a battle quietens down eventually, you know. I had a bathe and a feed and one evening I went out to walk about a little. Quite cool there after the sun goes down. I came to the officer's cage. . . ."

"Cage?" she asked.

"Misnomer. It's not a cage at all, really; barbed-wire pen for the prisoners. They were a sad lot. Damned poor show for them, peeping through the wire. Not peeping curiously, though, at us or anyone, not they. They were seeing vistas, *Deutschland*, home, and glory, that sort of thing. Stared right through me into Germany. I had just about seen enough when someone called out 'Antony!' and there stood old Gussy surrounded by what was left of his staff."

"Gussy?" she said punctually.

"Gussy von Stolp. Colonel-General Baron Gustav von Stolp," he said in German. "Their commander."

"You knew him?" It made her seem stupid to ask but even now he was incredible.

"Oh, rather. He was at Sandhurst when I was and once upon a time he and I were at a cram school together at Westgate-on-Sea. Had a wen or pimple on his foot. Got it infected somehow and he spent a fortnight in some awful nursing home—nothing to do; the doctors suspicious of the Teuton; the sisters all plain-faced and surly. And the food, one's gorge simply soars at the food in a nursing home. He wrote me plaintive little post cards, whimpering little post cards about the food. He was discharged at last, foot perfectly O.K., and we went out for some golf. He felt something softish in the bottom of his golf bag, reached in and came out with a boiled lobster. 'Good God, Gussy, what a revolting thing to carry about with you,' I said. He cracked the shell on a rock and sat down to eat it. 'How old is that dreadful creature?' I asked. 'I cannot tell you. I haf him only since four days,' he said. 'I bought him when I leave the nursing home and I forgot him until now. All the time I am lying in bed I am dreaming about lobsters. Now I eat.' And he ate up every bit." He stopped. It was one of his little courtesies to stop before the climax of a story so that she might ask a question.

She had learned to be equally courteous and never to ask the question he expected. "Why had he put it in his golf bag?"

"It was wrapped in paper."

"But. . . ."

"Gussy was already a German officer on leave from his command." He paused. "Officers are not seen carrying parcels."

"Oh," she said. "What did you say to the Baron when you saw him behind the wire?" There had never been a baron in this house or within fifty miles of it. It gave her a pleasure she recognized as faintly snobbish to ask the question as if the ghosts of her mother and grandmother were behind the plum-colored window drapes to hear.

"Say? Oh, 'How are you? How've you been?' What does one say to a friend?"

"But wasn't he a Nazi?"

"Gussy?" He barked once contemptuously. "He was a Pomeranian," he said as if that explained everything.

"I'm sorry. They're just fluffy little dogs to me."

"Really, Ellen, you don't know the very simplest things, do you? Pomerania is Prussia, don't you see?" He turned now to look at her, his face motionless, but the very fact that he had made the effort, had turned his head, expressing his mute fury, not at her, not at this strange country, rather at his own stupidity for allowing himself to be drawn into situations where he had to expound the things one took for granted as naturally as earth or sky. When he saw that she didn't see, he said, "Oh, damn it, Ellen. They were an old family. Knights. Soldiers. Served the

country, the land. You follow me?" He sighed, swallowed half a drink
and spoke with a gentle condescension. "The von Stolps lived in an
actual castle, full of towers and steeples, moat with a drawbridge, a great
moldy old pile. I saw it once. As a matter of fact, the family of their
Jäger, the chief huntsman, had served them for four hundred years. Any
government, Hitler's or Friedrich der Grosse's, simply doesn't matter. A
government is only temporary." He looked back into the fire. He was not
particularly anxious that she understand; he was merely willing to
explain.

She was charmed and irritated by this elegant figure lying almost on
the back of its neck in her chair by her hearth. It was as if she alone on
this middle western plain had snared some strange heraldic beast like a
unicorn. From him she had learned that there was more to conversation
with a man than the feints and sleights preliminary to an attack. Since
he was a man, he began always with himself but, encouraging her with
the foreign inflections of his voice and the beckonings of his long, bony,
graceful hands, he led her unwittingly into an empire she had hurried
over as a tourist or glanced at in forgotten history books and there
pointed out hundreds of fascinating things she had never heard of.

He dressed well, too. She had seen English clothes before, but she
had never studied them. When he saw her a little surprised at the handkerchief up his sleeve, he remarked coldly that officers kept it there. He
wore a black homburg cocked on the side of his head in a town where no
one wore such a hat and an old dark blue Guards overcoat with long
leather-lined pockets, "for carrying whisky in," he said. It pleased her to
see how conspicuous he looked among the solid lawyers, bankers, and
factory owners the rare times he took her out.

Although she had noticed it briefly in other Englishmen, his confident rudeness annoyed her. No one had ever treated her like that before and she was shrewd enough to know why: she was too rich, and,
although the decision before the mirror took a shade longer now that
she was thirty-six, she was at the very least too handsome, perhaps too
beautiful. In the right light, certainly too beautiful. He had been dropping in two or three times a week for months and she had just begun to
comprehend, startled, a little dejected, that he was indifferent to her in
the flesh and to her money; at least he treated it casually enough. She
was beginning to be nervous about him because she did not know what
he wanted.

". . . hell's own time finding one. No fishing much then because of
the bombardment. I had half the Wogs in Bizerte looking for one."

"One what?"

He sighed and drank again. "A lobster."

"Oh."

"But at last I got a beauty. Broiled it. Wangled butter. Sent my batman down to the cage in a jeep with it on a covered tray. 'Major Braithwaite's compliments to General Baron von Stolp.' Absolutely wizard show. God, how I laughed."

"Did he like it?"

"Did he not! Sent a note back."

"What became of him?"

"I haven't the vaguest," he said coldly. "Dead, very likely."

She was shocked by his callousness and was about to tell him so when she heard the maid's heels in the hall. "Dinner is served," the maid said.

"You'll stay, won't you, Tony?"

"Yes, thanks," he said, boosting himself erect out of the chair.

She was alert. She had learned not only the composition of an English menu from his stories but also its peculiar *mystique*. They began with a clear soup and a glass of sherry. This was followed by what passed for fillet of sole at the local fish market. Then she had ordered a joint of beef with the blood running out of it, some riced potatoes, and a dismal little dish of Brussels sprouts. Bread lay on the table but no butter. For a sweet, they had a "trifle." She had superintended the making of it herself. It was a cake soaked in Jamaica rum and as frosting it had a layer of whipped cream ornamented with bits of colored sugar. (She had sent all the way to New York for the sugar.) She thought it loathsome to taste but he ate it up, every bit, as Gussy ate the lobster, and said to her quite warmly as he finished, "English food," which she knew she was to take as a compliment.

They returned to the living room for port and coffee. He began a tale of rock-climbing in Wales when he had watched George Mallory ascend an overhanging cliff face without a rope, without *pitons*, with his bare hands.

"I was below on a ledge. The climb was impossible. The law of gravity forbade it."

"Did he fall?"

"No bloody fear. Went up like a cat. I had known George all my life, but in places where the ground was flat. Never understood why people talked him up so. I did then, though. Understood it very well, indeed."

"Was he famous?"

"George? Oh," he let his voice fall as an acknowledgment that she did not know who he was at all. "He died on Mt. Everest in the 1934 expedition. Got to within a hundred feet of the top when a flurry of snow blotted him out. Never saw him again. May have made it, at that, though."

Her impatience, curiosity, anger at last burst out. "Tony, why don't you ever talk about yourself?" she said. By which she partly meant, "Why don't you ever talk about me?" but not entirely. She wanted to be better friends with him, to pierce his reserve somehow, and men had usually begun by talking about themselves or about her but never about third parties, however courageous.

"Why? Because here I am. One talks about what is past, what is elsewhere. Bloody embarrassing to talk about one's self when here, in fact, one veritably is." Then his invariable courtesy showed itself. "But I'm boring you."

"Oh, no, you're not—but I sometimes wonder why you bother to come to see me." It was true he never bored her. He was handsome in a conventional English way—she had seen men who resembled him at Cannes and Miami—but he suppressed some force or emotion, rage or disgust perhaps, that gave his talk its scintillating energy and let it out only in his sudden glances or the abrupt and graceful gestures of his long brown hands.

"Must all the men who come to see you talk about themselves? Do you exact it as a tribute?"

"*All* the men," she thought wryly. "They usually do," she said.

"Surely you ought to know why I come to see you. Can't you suspect?"

"Why do you?"

For just a second his face seemed to open, almost smiling, as if he were about to say something pleasant and sincere. Then, with hardly any change of plane or feature, it closed. He said, "Because you are a very lovely woman, as you well know. Because this is the one place I can get a proper English meal. And because you give me money."

He startled her. He had told the obvious truth, and the candor that should have lacerated him only made his statements seem dull and final.

"Have you ever thought of going back to England?" She did not know whether she "loved" him or not. She wanted to force him into a kind of emotional allegiance to her that she could recognize, and, in her exasperation, she was using the gambits of a schoolgirl: she wanted to trap him into saying, in a trembling voice, if possible, "I can't go back because I can't leave you."

What he did say was, "We're not fighting anyone now."

"Have some more port," she said in a fury.

"No, thanks."

"Can't you stay the evening?" He had never stayed the evening.

"I'm sorry. Playing poker with some chaps. Can you give me a hundred dollars?"

As she had planned the dinner, she had foreseen his question. Before he had arrived, she had gone to the kitchen when the cook was laying out the coffee tray and laid a hundred-dollar bill under the sugar bowl. Calmly, watching his face for the least twitching of shame, she lifted the bowl and handed him the money. "Will this be enough, Tony?"

He was absolutely impregnable. "Oh, quite. Thanks awfully, Ellen. Marvelous dinner." He did not pause. "Good night."

"Good night, Tony."

She heard him let himself out. She took a big gulp of port. She set the glass down and said aloud, "Now how many kinds of a damned fool am I?"

She took pride in recognizing, because no one else in the town could recognize, Tony as an almost flawless specimen of a type she had met in her interminable reading and a few times in her travels, the Englishmen of good family who had gone bad somehow. Like Tony, they wore their clothes well. They were or had been handsome in a lean way. They had mustaches. They said rude things, especially about America, with a smile. Some, like Tony, had been officers in good regiments, or said they had. And for various shady reasons at which they were willing to hint portentously but never to explain, they were living very well but they were not working. Tony was unique in one respect: he never hinted at anything.

Someone had told her of his first appearance in the town. Apparently by instinct he had gone to the bar of the Shawnee Club. She wondered at the aplomb that could support a man before a bartender when, as a stranger, he was not permitted to buy drinks, yet Tony had not budged and when the bartender said, "Something?" he had answered, "I'm waiting for a friend." At that moment he knew no one in the whole town, but when the bar filled up a little, a combination of brass and charm led him into acquaintanceship and ultimately into a poker game. He had won twelve dollars.

Perhaps she could have left Tony in the pigeonhole if he had been a good gambler, if he had shown the deftness of long practice, but she had seen him with cards. He could deal without turning them wrong side up but that was about all. And, although he played poker constantly, the word had come to her that he lost as often as he won. It seemed to be a pastime, not a living.

He did not employ another resource of the floating Englishman, opening a riding school. Not many people were wealthy enough to ride. Show riding contended with Western riding for their money. The local horse show, given late in the summer at the county fair grounds, turned out half a dozen in hard hats on English saddles and about as many on palominos jingling with silver. Watching them from her box, Tony had thought them a sad lot and said so. She had borrowed a horse from Sally Shaw, a big chestnut brute over sixteen hands high that Sally was going to get rid of. She dared Tony to ride it. He had appeared in a tweed cap, a turtle-neck sweater, a jacket with two vents in the back, and a pair of magnificent old, old boots. Of course, as she had feared, he rode beautifully. He was calm and relaxed and Sally, who talked more horse than she rode, excitedly pointed to his hands as Tony was racking the chestnut past them and screamed, "Look! You could balance a glass of water on them."

So he was not a gambler or a riding instructor. She was not so blind as not to see that he was living very well off her nevertheless, but, since he was not making love to her or anything like it, she knew her allowance to him was a whim she could abolish at any moment. It gave her a hold over him, not that she wanted one, but it did not explain why he had come to the town in the first place. A last romantic possibility occurred to her: he might be a secret agent, but she could not for the life of her find a reason why the British or any other government should want information about her home town although she had to admit the notion that they might enhanced the town's weak importance in her eyes. However, she was a stockholder in all of the four factories. She knew what they made, springs for automobile seats, paper boxes and containers, canned soup, and gents' suspenders. None of these products could have any crucial weight with Downing Street, the Kremlin, or whatever. Tony was not a spy. But what was he? Why was he there?

She had asked him one day why he could bring himself to accept money from her. She hoped to embarrass him and make him reveal something. He had been telling a story about being hauled before an Italian magistrate for running over a pig in his car. He was very amusing about it. The point of the story was that the magistrate, a big, cynical, fat man, hated the British and was inclined to throw Tony in jail and Tony was a guest at a house party at Ventimiglia and could hardly absent himself because he was the extra man. The friend with Tony, Michael Somebody, had tried to frighten the court by alleging that Tony was a noble lord, a cousin of the King's and. . . .

"You're not, are you, Tony?" she had broken in.

"God, no. I'm only a Right Honourable. . . ."

The long evenings with the mound of pillows at her back, the novel on her knees, and the Nembutal at her elbow helped her out. She knew that Right Honourables were younger children of earls and marquesses. "How does it come, then, that with noble blood in. . . ."

"Pip, pip, pip," he interrupted. "Only Father. He's the bloody earl, not me."

"How does it come, then, that you, an aristocrat, can accept money from me?"

He raised his head in sincere astonishment. "Why, you've got packets, haven't you?"

"And all you have to do is ask?"

"Of a friend, yes," he said as if it were obvious. There was something open and childlike about him as he said it.

Hurrying it a little because she had at last forced him into a corner, eager to have the immense satisfaction of saying something both apropos and cutting she had thought of beforehand, she said, "You sound like a peasant asking help with the plowing."

"Of course. Lords and peasants are born to it. They know who they are. Only the middle class has to have manners."

He had won again. Her wince did not show and what he said sounded vaguely true, or rather, it was a statement that once had been filled with truth but now the truth had almost all leaked out of it but not entirely. She never included herself as a member of the middle class but she knew she was in Tony's eyes and when she thought about it later, she was in her own. All she had to remember was her grandfather who chewed plug tobacco. Or her father.

Her vast brick house, built by her grandfather, still bearing the complicated wooden scrollwork of his period, was surrounded by trees, gigantic maples, whose crusted boles rose thirty or forty feet before they branched, a grove. And, as a child, she thought it was a grove for hiding in, safe from the world. Later the house and yard had changed. They became a dreadful little arena where her mother, a thrifty, kind, neighborly, small-town woman who had been stiffened and corrupted at the discovery of how much money there was, tried to make her better than other people, teaching her tricks out of the etiquette books, dressing her from pictures in the magazines, grinding into her the legend of her own superiority to the children she had known in grade school, and all with a dry, untender determination she called love.

Partly because she had been prepared in this fashion and partly because she was stifled by the preparation, she raced away from the town the first chance she got: into a second-rate Eastern school because it was the only one her mother had heard of and later into a first-rate Eastern college. She thought she wanted excitement, and aloof, now beautiful, almost consecrated to the search since she in her turn had discovered how much money there was, she nearly found it at Princeton and New Haven.

In her senior year at college she married a tall, quiet young man from Dartmouth because she had seen him at a Winter Carnival soaring a hundred feet in the air, flapping his mittened wings above all the admiring faces, and his flight seemed as daring and luminous as her hopes. Pleased to find her rich as well as beautiful, he had taken her first to the Telemark in Norway, next to Garmisch and Saint-Moritz. They skiied. And using her money like a dowser, she divined something of the richness and complexity of Europe's old life. She persuaded her husband to return in the warm weather, and after the initial disappointment every traveler suffers disembarking at Le Bourget or the Gare du Nord, she discovered Paris, *couture* and *cuisine*. Just before the war, she found she was quite happy. She had matured, only a little disappointed in her clean, single-minded, muscular husband, and the goal that had shimmered first as mere excitement, then as sophistication, at last defined itself. She felt she had been promised a vividness of life, a proof that the world did not end under the big trees of her front lawn, a trophy she could shake before the eyes of her dead mother in pride and defiance, and, staring past her tanned knees through a row of cypresses at the Mediterranean, where, far in the distance like a wound-up toy, her husband was aquaplaning, she was sure she almost had it.

But the war came and her husband, sullenly raging because he was too old to fly, got himself heroically killed on a destroyer in the Philippine Sea. They sent her the Silver Star and she kept it faithfully on her dressing table. She was living at home alone in the big house. She wore black its due season, redecorated the house, and flew off to South America, where she found the beaches of Copacabana and Mar del Plata not so very different from those at Antibes. She returned home again.

There were people there she had always "known" because, although it was growing, the town was still a small town where you knew "everybody." These people asked her to dinner, one after the other, with a cateress in the kitchen and maids hired for the occasion creeping about in the lengthening silences. She had lost touch with them. She was sure they were decent, upright, hard-working people, but they were dull. She had nothing to say to them, really, except accounts of her travels, and they listened so hard it was embarrassing.

So she tried Italy another summer. She found herself giving large sums to all the charities and she seemed to attract suave Italians of fifty, tall, often with blue eyes, who wanted as they had wanted for two hundred years to sell paintings by Mantegna and Perugino, "quite genuine." She noted with surprise that, except for the poor, she was much alone. She was chic, handsome, driven by her avidity for something, some person who would be flashing, wild, and beautiful, but unfortunately there were many other women like her at the Ritz Hotel level where she lived. It was then that she began to read in her bedrooms. Treasonably, she admitted Italy was unsatisfactory and she went home again.

The dust covers were hardly off the furniture when a man telephoned her and asked if he might come to see her that evening. She said yes. She remembered him from her two years in high school before she went East. She had cheered him the length of a football field as he had plunged down it, haggard and battered, six or seven yards at a time. Even over the phone she recalled an aura of heroism about him and she rather looked forward to the evening. When he came into the room she saw his hair had gone and he was wearing rimless glasses. He had primed himself with a drink or two which she could smell as he actually and awkwardly bent over her hand and kissed it. With a straight face, she began to laugh and she laughed for an hour while the fake Continental graces he had devised to impress her melted into a proud, straightforward account of the money he was making and at last into a groveling whine, "What do you do with yourself? Aren't you lonely? Can't I come to see you?" before she got rid of him.

That night as she was reading her dilemma emerged more clearly: she did not want to go away again, because they had changed the countries on her somehow; she did not want to stay here, because she could not stand the people. She had been taught to despise them and it did not occur to her—how could it?—that these were the people she wanted to impress. She had not learned that her life was rich only as theirs was stupid and monotonous, by contrast. They provided the dark background for her to shine against. In Europe she was not unusual. Here, she was, and only one or two old ladies in the town, wealthy and shrewd, born out on farms in the country like her own grandmother, suspected the truth, that Ellen Catesby was a small-town girl.

Quite naturally, when Tony showed up, she welcomed him.

In spite of the stagnancy of their relationship, her impatience and curiosity about Tony and a long string of novels wore out the winter. She was growing more uneasy. She was still young, youngish, and she could read about things and be told about things when she was seventy. To be already stuck at one remove from life seemed a waste.

She tried very hard to break down Tony's diffidence, shyness, reserve —she did not even know what it was she was assailing—but nothing came of it. She did not dare send him away for good. She did not want to send him away at all, and during the winter she reached the point where she would not dare because then she would be utterly alone. If that was going to be the only bond between them, she knew she would have to accept it.

It was now, however, spring. It had rained a lot. The trees were in full leaf, the grass was a brilliant green, and her garden (walled) was bright with the fragrance of early flowers that had shot up almost overnight. When Tony came she gave him little sandwiches of tomato and watercress with his tea instead of anchovy toast, and he sat decorously sprawled out in a white chair, talking as usual. Nothing had changed.

". . . off Oxford Street. Crown glass in the windows. You opened the door and a little bell tinkled. Mr. Brown was never actually *in* the shop, however. He was down cellar fondling and clucking to the bottles in the gloom, I suspect, and presently you heard his footsteps on the stair. Except for some white patches where he squinched up his eyes, his face was nearly the color of an old saddle, deep and rich. He said, 'Good morning, sir. Care for a glass of sherry?' And he would bring out two old-fashioned cut-glass sherry glasses. He filled them. But before you could touch a drop, he said sternly, 'Have you smoked this morning?' and he thrust a packet of what you call crackers at you and commanded, 'Eat a biscuit.' You meekly ate and only then did drink." He paused. "Incredible little place. Burnt to ashes in the fire raids." He paused again. "I say, Ellen. You are lovely." He stood up swiftly, bent over, kissed her, and did not let her go at once. It was the first time.

"Why, Antony, what came over you?" she said lightly.

"Oh, I'm terribly sorry, Ellen." There seemed to be a real regret in his voice. "I didn't mean anything by it."

"Go ahead, Tony. Mean something for once."

He seemed flustered. "Well, I mean to say, you *are* a beautiful woman. The curve of your cheek—it took my eye. And, oh, spring, perhaps. The pretty birds do sing. Flowers." He threw out his hand helplessly.

"But nothing serious, eh, Tony? Merely some vague seasonal stirring of the blood?"

"Oh, now, damn it all, Ellen. Don't try to put me in the wrong. I'm not an absolute swine, you know." He was walking up and down now, apparently with some agitation.

"But it's not serious, is it, Tony?"

He walked toward her and stood looking down with an absolutely new expression on his face. She could call it tender inquiry. "You want it to be quite serious?"

"Oh, quayte," she said. She could not resist the impulse to devil him. He had to pay something for the long hard winter.

"Marry me, then."

She was so absorbed in remarking his change of manner that at first he did not seem to be speaking to her at all and she could say only, "Really?"

"Oh, I know there's damn all to recommend me. Be a bloody bad benedick, I daresay, but"—here his face broke into a broad smile—"we could have a couple of kids. I mean, not so young ourselves, but still. Just a couple, you know. Perhaps a piece of land. Some of these tractors for the corn. Cattle. A little shooting. Room for the children to grow. I should think I could manage the place. . . ."

"An estate," she murmured not loudly enough to break his flow.

"That's it. Wonderful prospect, really." He looked down from the sky over her shoulder. "I'm sorry. Actually, I mean you're a damned fine woman, Ellen. Awfully good and kind. It could be marvelous."

"I think so, too, Tony."

"Oh, good girl. I'm frightfully happy about it." He pulled her to her feet, kissed her mouth and throat, and muttered inexplicably into her shoulder. "Near thing, Ellen. You don't know. Very near thing."

For the next few minutes she found him almost pathetically endearing. Then she said, "Where in England would you want to buy?"

His face stiffened. "England? No. Not there. Definitely."

"But I assumed, naturally. . . ." She saw she had said something really wrong.

"No!" he shouted as if he were in uniform. "England's *kaput*. Too many queues, too many things to sign. Man's not a man in England any more. He's an ugly little photo on an ugly little card. His dossier's more important than he is. No. No, no. Here."

"All right. Here. Any place you say, Tony."

She planned a small June garden wedding. She had a wonderful time giggling over the list of guests because she guessed what everyone in town had been saying about her and her pet limey. She was preparing a big reception after the ceremony with floods of champagne and she wished she could hear every single thing that would be said. When she finished all the minor arrangements, she flew to New York to buy a second trousseau. Tony saw her off and as they walked across the windy pavement of the airport, she said, "Take one of the cars while I'm gone, and go out into the country and pick out your plot of ground, will you, Tony?"

Hat and gloves in one hand, the wind ruffling his hair, he said, "Yes, darling," and except for his farewell, that was the last thing he ever said to her.

For when she returned from New York he was not at the airport, and when she opened the front door of her house, the maid came running up, her eyes big, and said hoarsely, "There's a woman wants to see you, Mrs. Catesby. In there," and she pointed to the larger drawing room.

Ellen thought, "Oh, God," and she stopped to do her mouth very carefully before the mirror in the hall.

The woman was American, about sixty years old, bareheaded and shabby. She wore a black winter coat with a ratty brown fur collar thrown over a blue gingham dress. She came limping and shuffling across the floor, greatly excited. "Mrs. Catesby? Don't sit down. Don't even take off your coat and hat. You got to come with me. Right away. You. . . ."

"Why must I?"

"Major Braithwaite's dead." Her voice soared up to a high wheeze and she began to pant. "Shot himself right through the forehead and. . . ."

"Tony?" The old woman was hustling her toward the front door. "How do you know? Who are you?"

"He boarded with me. My name's Williams. He had my front room, the one with the fireplace." By this time they were down the front steps.

"But what happened? How did he do it? Are you sure he's. . . ."

"You'll see. You'll see."

Ellen drove very slowly and fussily, the old woman telling her the way because she had never known where Tony lived; she had never even asked. She knew why she felt weak and cold—that was shock. The pounding headache that began was shock also, and the pepper that seemed to burn inside her nose. She did not know why all the big green maples in the streets should start to fall inward upon her, lunging at the car and barely missing it, or why flashes of sunlight on windows and windshields should stab her eyes like a pin. She heard Mrs. Williams' rapturous garrulity in spurts and flashes, such a handsome man, kind of like that Ronald Colman in the movies, a real gentleman, him behindhand? No, sir, always on the dot, ever notice his hands, really beautiful long thin hands, a third cousin in South Bend ran a photograph gallery, hands just like his. . . .

It seemed unimportant, merely a blemish like a birthmark, the small neat dark-red hole in his forehead. He had lain down on his bed and the revolver had not slipped from his stiff hand. A coronal of dark blood stained the pillow around his head. A piece of note paper lay folded on his chest.

"That's for you," Mrs. Williams said. "I read about you and him in the papers. That's how I knew you was Ellen."

Ellen unfolded it and read, *I'm sorry, Ellen.* It was the first time she had ever seen his handwriting, small, spiny letters, almost unreadable.

She came back to his room once more before the funeral to see if she could find the name and address of anyone she should notify, friend or kin, but she found nothing. At least fifteen members of the Shawnee Club volunteered as pallbearers, and there were more flowers than she expected, all from men he had played poker with. She buried him just outside her own family plot, and when she ordered a headstone, a plain slab of gray granite, she wrote out the name, *Antony Braithwaite,* on a card for the stonecutter.

He said, "Year of birth?"

She had to guess. That was the first time she cried and they called her house for the maid and chauffeur to take her home from the monument works because no one knew who her friends were.

The summer was a horror. It did not rain and she could hear like the faint swish of a whip the automatic sprinklers turning on her lawn to keep the grass from shriveling. The heat seeped in through the thick walls, under the high ceilings of her house, and she carried an old palm-leaf fan she found one day in the attic.

Her usual consignments of books arrived but she could not read them, a few pages and the type would blur and she would get up and start to walk again. She walked slowly up and down through all the darkened rooms of her house, wearing only a negligee, her naked feet thrust into high-heeled mules that sometimes caught on the carpets, and, when they did, she stepped out of them absently and walked barefooted, fanning herself languidly. A dozen times a day she passed the massive sideboard in her dining room. There were the decanters, heavy, cut-glass, with little silver plaques hanging from chains around their necks, Scotch, Bourbon, Rye, Irish. She sometimes stopped and looked at them speculatively, picked them up and jiggled the liquor around inside, and once or twice she drew the stopper and smelled of it, but she shuddered and put it back in its row. She took quite a lot of Nembutal, not that it was less vicious but that it was less traditional, and she could tell herself she did have to sleep a little after all—the heat—but sometimes she woke up at night just the same.

The worst time came in August. The heat was drier and worse. She could hear the streets were nearly empty in the middle of the day and she could not shut out the scraping cheep of the cicadas in the trees around the house. Although she did not walk so much any more, she was thinner. She lay on one sofa or another or on her bed, smoking, her legs crossed, in her negligee, her blank gaze stopped by the ornate moldings around the ceiling, and when she inhaled, the cage of her ribs shone dully beneath her breasts.

In August the women started coming to call. She had the maid turn the first two away with "Mrs. Catesby is ill" but when they kept coming, she decided to let them in. She did not value their condolences but she wanted to see somebody, anybody because she was beginning to be frightened. She had read about grief. When her husband had been killed, she thought she had suffered it but she had, as she saw it now, blandly endured a little sadness, some regret. Nothing in her life, the life she wanted so intense and vivid, had prepared her for a shock like the blow of a club which erased all memory of Tony as if her skull had been broken, left her weak and listless as if she had lost blood. All day and most of the night her head ached and the joints of her wrists, knees, shoulders, and elbows were sore. She could touch the places with her fingers. And it did not get any better. That was what frightened her.

She dressed and received her callers, with her head on one hand, barely listening. Slowly she spotted the false innocence of their questions. They wondered too many times why Major Braithwaite should have made away with himself, and their smiles were not sympathetic but openly snotty and triumphant. When old Mrs. Danvers came, a woman she had known all her life who used to give her cinnamon cookies as a little girl, and asked the same question with a concern too sorrowful not to be genuine, Ellen shut up the house again and ordered any others turned away. They had all been talking about her and she had not thought about it once.

That night she did not take any Nembutal. She lay on her bed with the light out, two long hot bars of moonlight striping her body. She tried to make herself sleepy by planning a trip but she found it hard to imagine going anywhere, and she deliberately turned to the past as a more trustworthy period—but she found her memories sparse and color-less, as if someone had photographed paintings in black and white. Yet it passed the time better than any contemplation of the future, because the future was nothing at all.

After a while she switched on the light by the bed and picked up the Nembutal. She shook one capsule out in her hand, then she tipped up the bottle. She looked at the little heap of yellow capsules. She was holding her death in her hand. "Why not?" she thought.

At some moment or other, Tony had picked up the gun and he must have thought the same thing. Was it because an empty future might as well be extinguished neatly as wandered into? A chill ran down her spine and she shuddered. For the first time she seemed to be near an answer to the questions that had throbbed so long like the ache in her head, perhaps were the ache in her head, "Why had he come? Why had he killed himself?"

Like her, he believed only the images of the past to be proof of life. The present was something merely to be got through until the silliness of the process grew obvious and you ended it. Now that she thought of it, he had never mentioned anyone who was not dead. The places and the times he had been happy were elsewhere and long ago. When she had searched his room for a relative's name, she had gone through the pockets of his suits. There were only three of them; they were all made in Savile Row but they were threadbare, almost worn out. The shoes she had always admired she had never seen up close. Held in her hand they were neatly treed up and shining but cracked into a myriad of tiny lines.

The pigeonholes of a rather nice little escritoire had contained a Dis-tinguished Service Order in a leather case, an ordnance map of Glouces-tershire, and one symbol of the present, the box of bullets for the gun he had shot himself with. As if he had forgotten or broken with every-one, there were no letters.

One wall of his room was covered with photographs: Tony in flannels and a striped blazer with a group captioned *The Oxford University Tennis Club;* a polo team, Tony with a mallet under one arm, a splen-did silver cup on the ground before them, and syces in turbans holding the ponies at the rear. There was a muscular Tony in a black clout lying beside the pool at Eden Roc talking to Marlene Dietrich. There were several groups of British officers standing in mud and in sand and Tony was in every one. One picture showed only a vast unidentified explosion. The most interesting was a family group on a broad lawn in front of a country house. Tony was in the center, young, thin, almost in the act of ducking his head with shyness. On a table in front of him shone an ornate silver service and in a clump at the side stood the servants, butler, footman, first maid, second maid, and all. Across one corner of the picture Tony had scrawled "Twenty-firster." It was his coming-of-age party, and the servants had just presented him with the silver. Tony's father looked hard-bit and military with what Tony had once distinguished as a colonel's mustache, a drooper, and his mother was a handsome tall woman with one of those brick-red outdoor complexions, a shapeless print dress, and flat-heeled shoes with a strap across the arch. Whether the other young people were his brothers or sisters, she could not tell.

There it all was, the only world intelligible, the happy past he had moved in so easily, with such grace and courage, carrying with him lightly the freight of so much history, and now all worn away, blown up in vast unidentified explosions.

Now she could see what had killed him, since she felt something like it working in herself. It was exhaustion. He had been worn out. She had a vision of him landing in New York, suave, correct, and gentle, his box full of his old shoes and threadbare clothes, and the stack of photographs. Perhaps he cherished then unrotted some bare fragment of hope and it had led him to this town, a strange and unfamiliar place, which he had attacked with the only means he knew, by making friends. He might even have loved her a long time before he asked her to marry him. Certainly his proposal was the last dying flicker of his strength and, once accepted, he could not make the effort to begin again to gain the archaic riches of family and estate, because he was by then too weak to take one single step into a future, however sure.

"Poor Tony," she thought.

She looked down at the capsules in her hand. She was too young for them. The republic was not old enough. Her grandfather had plowed with oxen, tramping in his own furrow, while Tony's had sat drinking brandy at the Café Anglais in the red tunic of a military observer attached to the French Army during the siege of Paris. And if she and Tony had reached the same point, she was not as tired as he. She dumped the capsules back into the bottle, turned out the light, and went to sleep.